Contents

Introduction

GCSE Single Award Science for CCEA has been specially written to cover the specification for CCEA GCSE Science (Single Award). The course contains six Modules – two for each of Biology, Chemistry and Physics, and the 20 chapters in the book are arranged similarly, closely following the sections within the Modules. Content that is required only at Higher Tier is identified by a coloured stripe down the edge of the text (see pages 3–4).

Each chapter begins with a clear list of the main learning objectives, those at Higher Tier marked out by a coloured background and different type.

The Single Award Science course is an innovative GCSE course that aims to equip students with the knowledge and skills they need to understand the key scientific issues that affect their everyday lives.

The content of the course reflects recent advances in science, with the emphasis on areas such as drug development, cloning, gene therapy, food processing, DNA profiling, global warming, waste recycling and nuclear power – issues that are seldom out of the news today. These issues are covered in a readable style in the book, with local examples used where possible.

This course, as other new GCSE Science courses, places significant emphasis on the process of 'How Science Works'. The main idea is that students develop an understanding of the factors that affect the reliability of experimental results and scientific data, and an understanding of how scientific theories are developed. While these areas have been covered in previous science courses, there is now a greater emphasis on them. Additionally, students need to appreciate the role of science in society, and to understand and discuss the ethical issues that are raised.

In this book the 'How Science Works' requirements are integrated with the other more 'traditional' content throughout. Activities and questions have been specially designed with these in mind, and will help to equip students with the knowledge and skills required. Ethical issues associated with scientific knowledge and advances are presented for debate or discussion as the topics arise.

There are questions throughout each chapter to test students' learning and understanding. Those on Higher topics have a coloured background. There are longer examination-type questions at the end of each chapter. Many of these have been written specifically for the new specification, and some are from current specimen papers; others have been chosen from past examination papers to match the new requirements. High-demand questions (that would only appear on a Higher Tier paper) have a coloured stripe at the left-hand side. Answers to all questions are available on the website: www.hoddernorthernireland.co.uk

Not only has the content of Single Award Science changed, but there is an increased emphasis on the use of ICT in the new qualification. The inclusion in this book of activities that involve the use of ICT and useful websites for further research will encourage and enable students to integrate ICT into their learning.

GCSE Single Award Science for CCEA provides the essential information and develops the understanding and skills required for students to fulfil their potential and successfully complete this innovative Single Award Science course. Additionally, this book will help students become aware of, and contribute to, the great scientific debates and dilemmas of our modern age.

James Napier

GCSE single award
SCIENCE
for CCEA

Theo Laverty **James Napier** **Roy White**
Editor: James Napier

Rewarding Learning

Hodder Murray
A MEMBER OF THE HODDER HEADLINE GROUP

Orders: please contact Bookpoint Ltd, 130 Milton Park, Abingdon, Oxon OX14 4SB. Telephone: (44) 01235 827720. Fax: (44) 01235 400454. Lines are open from 9.00 to 6.00, Monday to Saturday, with a 24 hour message answering service. Visit our website at www.hoddereducation.co.uk

First published in 2006 by
Hodder Murray, an imprint of Hodder Education,
a member of the Hodder Headline Group
338 Euston Road
London NW1 3BH

Impression number   5 4 3 2 1
Year   2010 2009 2008 2007 2006

Cover photo Paal Hermansen/NHPA
Illustrations by Oxford Designers & Illustrators
Typeset in 11/13pt Century ITC by Tech-Set Ltd, Gateshead
Printed in Italy

A catalogue record for this title is available from the British Library

ISBN-10 0340 926007
ISBN-13 978 0340 926000

Chapter 1

Food and energy

By the end of this chapter you should know and understand:

➤ The word equation for photosynthesis
➤ The starch test, and investigations which show that light and chlorophyll are needed for photosynthesis and that oxygen is produced
➤ The chloroplast as the site of photosynthesis
➤ The word equation for respiration
➤ The essential components of the diet
➤ The relationship between diet and health
➤ Causes of heart disease and strokes, and preventative measures
➤ The effect of exercise on the heart

All living things must have energy to live. Energy comes from food. We know that animals use plant or animal material (living or dead) as food. However, plants are able to use light energy to make their food. This is one of the most important differences between plants and animals.

Using light energy to make food in plants

How do plants make food? Plants do this by converting the raw materials of carbon dioxide and water to plant food (starch). This process is called **photosynthesis** and it takes place in the green parts of plants, particularly in the leaves. The green pigment **chlorophyll** is an essential part of photosynthesis, as it is the chlorophyll that traps the light energy from the sun that is required for the process. Oxygen is produced as a (very useful) waste product from photosynthesis. The process can be summarised by the equation:

$$\textbf{carbon dioxide + water} \xrightarrow[\textit{by chlorophyll}]{\textit{light energy trapped}} \textbf{starch + oxygen}$$

If we think of photosynthesis in terms of energy change, light energy from the sun is converted into chemical energy (food). Photosynthesis is important for animals, as well as plants, as it provides a source of food for them and it releases oxygen back into the air. Without photosynthesis it is unlikely that much life could survive on Earth.

Photosynthesis experiments

It is possible to carry out investigations to show that photosynthesis is taking place, or that a particular raw material or materials are needed for the process.

The starch test

The starch test can be used to show that starch is produced during the process of photosynthesis. The starch test consists of a series of steps:

1 Remove a leaf from a plant that has been placed in bright light.
2 Place the leaf in boiling water for at least 30 seconds. This will kill the leaf and will also weaken the cell structure, allowing iodine to come into contact with the cell contents in step 5.
3 Place the leaf in boiling ethanol (alcohol). This will remove the chlorophyll (green colouring) from the leaf. This procedure must take place using a water bath as ethanol is flammable and must not be exposed to a direct flame.
4 Dip the leaf in boiling water again. This will make the leaf soft again, as the ethanol makes the leaf very brittle.
5 Spread the leaf on a tile and add iodine to the leaf.
6 If starch is present the iodine will turn the starch blue–black. If there is no starch present the leaf will remain a yellow–red colour (the colour of the iodine – iodine can vary in colour quite a lot but is usually yellow or red).

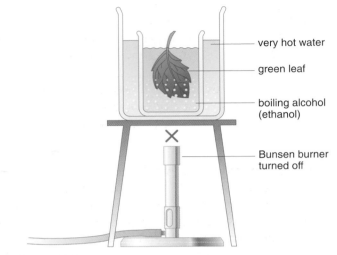

Figure 1.1a

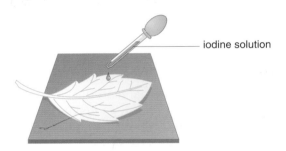

Figure 1.1b

Investigations to show that light and chlorophyll are necessary for photosynthesis and that oxygen is produced

To show that light and/or chlorophyll are essential for photosynthesis it is important to remove any starch that is already in the leaves first. Leaves can be **destarched** by leaving the plant in the dark for at least two days continually. This will make sure that any starch already in the leaves will be used by the plant during this period.

> 1 Suggest why it is important to destarch the leaves before carrying out the experiment.

Showing that light is necessary
A leaf is partially covered with opaque paper or with light-proof foil as shown in Figure 1.2. The plant is kept in bright light and after a period of time the leaf is tested for starch, as described above.

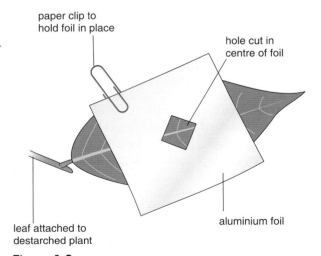

Figure 1.2

> **2** What would happen if the leaves had not been destarched first?

Showing that chlorophyll is necessary

To show that chlorophyll is necessary it is important to use plants with leaves that are part green and part white. These leaves are described as being **variegated**, and one type is shown in Figure 1.3.

> **3** If chlorophyll is essential for photosynthesis, what results would you expect when a variegated leaf shown in the photo is tested for starch? Suggest why very few plants have variegated leaves in nature.

Figure 1.3
Variegated leaves

Showing that oxygen is produced

Using apparatus similar to that shown in Figure 1.4, it is possible to demonstrate that oxygen is produced in photosynthesis. The rate of photosynthesis will affect the rate at which the bubbles of oxygen will be given off, and this can be used to compare photosynthesis rates in different conditions. For example, by moving the position of the lamp it is possible to investigate the effect of light intensity on photosynthesis.

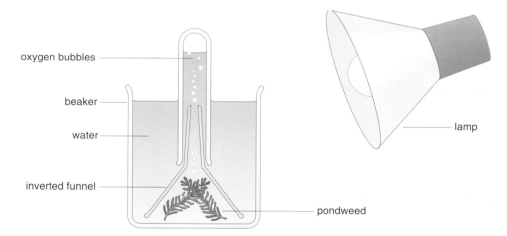

Figure 1.4 Measuring the rate of photosynthesis

The rate of photosynthesis can be more accurately calculated by measuring the volume of oxygen produced in a certain time.

> **4** Suggest why it is more accurate to measure the volume of oxygen collected than to count the number of bubbles.

The chloroplast: the site of photosynthesis

Most photosynthesis takes place in plant leaves. Leaves are adapted for photosynthesis in a number of ways, including being specialised for allowing as much carbon dioxide to enter as possible and for trapping as much light as possible. However, the main adaptation is the presence of small sub-cellular structures called **chloroplasts**.

The chloroplasts contain pigments that can trap light energy and convert it into chemical energy during the process of photosynthesis. In green plants the most common pigment for trapping light is chlorophyll and it is this pigment that gives the plant its green colour. The chlorophyll appears green because it reflects the green part of the visible spectrum and absorbs the red and blue parts. Usually chloroplasts also contain other pigments, which absorb slightly different wavelengths of light. In this way as much of the available light energy as possible can be absorbed with relatively little light reflected or passing through the chloroplast.

Figure 1.5 summarises the energy changes that take place in the chloroplast.

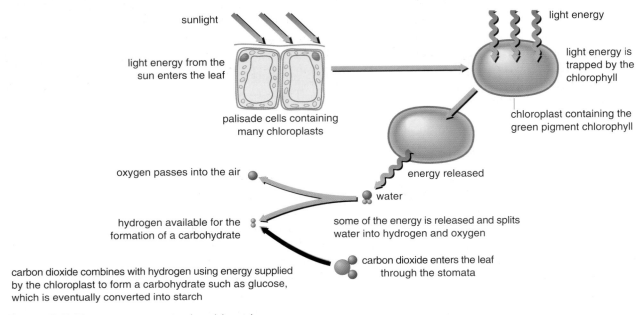

Figure 1.5 Trapping energy in the chloroplast

ACTIVITY

Examine a cross-section of a leaf through a microscope. You will notice that most of the chloroplasts are concentrated in a specialised row, or rows, of cells (the palisade layer) near the top of the leaf. This helps explain why the upper side of a leaf is usually a darker green than the lower side.

5 Remembering that leaves need chlorophyll, light and carbon dioxide (as well as water) for photosynthesis and that each of these materials must reach the chloroplasts in the leaf, list the ways in which the leaf you are examining is adapted for photosynthesis.

Using the food: respiration in animals and plants

Animals do not make their own food as plants do. The food that animals eat, and that plants make by photosynthesis, is a source of chemical energy that can be used in energy-requiring activities such as growth or movement in animals.

This making of energy from food takes place during the process of **respiration**. Respiration can be summarised by the following equation:

glucose + oxygen → carbon dioxide + water + energy

Both plants and animals respire to produce energy. Animals are always taking in oxygen and giving out carbon dioxide, a process called **gas exchange**, during the process of respiration. At night plants take in oxygen through their leaves and give out carbon dioxide, as a result of respiration.

The process of gas exchange is more complicated in plants during the daytime. When it is light, plants will photosynthesise as well as respire. If there is a lot of light, the rate of photosynthesis will be much greater than the rate of respiration and so a plant will be taking in carbon dioxide (due to photosynthesis) at a faster rate than it is giving it out (due to respiration). Similarly, in bright light, more oxygen will be given out (due to photosynthesis) than is taken in (due to respiration).

Food and diet in humans

In humans the main types of food that are used in respiration to provide energy are carbohydrates and fats. **Carbohydrates** include simple sugars, such as glucose, and the more complex starch. Sugars provide us with a quick source of energy, as they do not need to be broken down before being used in respiration. Starch does need to be broken down before it can be used and is therefore referred to as a slow-release carbohydrate. **Fats** or **lipids** are even better energy providers than carbohydrates. However, too much fat in the diet will cause us to become overweight, and too much of some types, called saturated fats, can contribute to circulatory problems (see page 10).

Protein is used for the growth and repair of body cells, but it is also an energy source if we have a lot of it in our diet or if we do not take in enough carbohydrate or fat.

Figure 1.6a Foods rich in carbohydrate

Figure 1.6b Foods rich in fat: all saturated fats apart from *Flora* and olive oil

Figure 1.6c Foods rich in protein

Carry out food tests for starch, sugars, protein and fat on a range of foods. (See Table 1.1 and Figure 1.7a–c.) It is often necessary to break the food up using a pestle and mortar and to add a small quantity of water to make it into a solution before carrying out the test.

Design a table or spreadsheet to record your results clearly.

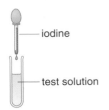

Figure 1.7a Starch test

Table 1.1 Food tests

Food	Name of test	Method	Positive result
starch	starch test	Add iodine to the food	The iodine turns from yellow–red to blue–black
sugar	Benedict's test	Add Benedict's solution to the food. Heat in a water bath	Turns from blue to green, then to orange or brick red depending on how much sugar is present
protein	biuret test	Add sodium hydroxide to the food solution. Then add copper sulphate. Shake	Turns from blue to purple
fat	emulsion test	Shake the fat with alcohol in a boiling tube. Add an equal volume of water	A cloudy white precipitate is formed

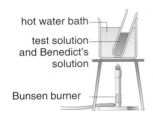

Figure 1.7b Sugar test

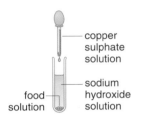

Figure 1.7c Protein test

These tests are qualitative and not quantitative, which means they can tell us whether a food type is present but not how much is present (note the Benedict's test is a partial exception in that the final colour gives some indication of the amount of sugar present).

Obviously different foods will have very different energy contents – ask anyone who is watching their weight! We can easily compare the energy content of a range of different foods in the laboratory by carrying out the following practical activity.

Set up the apparatus as shown in Figure 1.8 and use a range of food types such as crisps, dried pasta, and so on. Ignite each type in turn and measure the increase in temperature of the water for each food used.

The energy released from each food, measured in joules (J), can be calculated using the following equation:

energy released from food (J) = mass of water (g) × rise in temperature (°C) × 4.2

You could use a spreadsheet to perform the calculations.

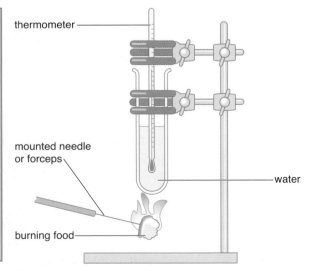

Figure 1.8 Measuring the energy content of food

6 a Although the experiment in the previous activity can be used to compare the energy value of different foods, it is unlikely to give accurate measurements of the amount of energy in each food. Explain why this is so.

b List some of the factors (variables) you would have to keep the same in this experiment for each food you use, to make a fair comparison.

How much energy do we need?

Each of us requires different amounts of energy to keep us living. Each person also requires varying amounts of energy, depending on their stage of life and also depending on how active they are. Figure 1.9 shows how the body's energy requirement varies in some different situations.

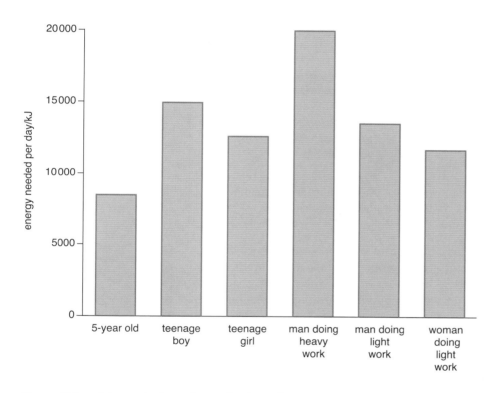

Figure 1.9
Energy needed per day by different people in different situations

You will be able to deduce from the bar chart that there are three main factors that affect our energy requirement. These can be grouped as:

- age
- gender (male or female)
- activity.

Of course the effects of these factors often overlap. A very young baby will not be as active as a teenager and some men may need more energy than women because they have more physically demanding jobs.

What else do we need in our food?

We wouldn't remain healthy for long if our diet included only carbohydrate, fat and protein. We also need **vitamins**, **minerals**, **water** and **fibre**. We will look at these in turn.

Vitamins and minerals

Vitamins and minerals are needed for the healthy functioning of our bodies. We only need to take relatively small amounts of each of these in our diet but if they are missing the symptoms (signs) of deficiency (shortage) become apparent. Thankfully most people in western societies have access to sufficient quantities of each of the essential vitamins and minerals. However, it is all too clear that many people in underdeveloped parts of the world, such as many areas of Africa, suffer from a deficiency in vitamins or minerals and in some areas simply do not have enough food of any type.

> 7 Do you know the difference between starvation and malnutrition? If not, find out.

Two of the essential vitamins, their sources and their roles in the body are displayed in Table 1.2.

Table 1.2 Vitamins

Vitamin	Good sources	Role in the body
C	citrus fruits (oranges, lemons, limes, etc.), and some vegetables such as broccoli and peppers	Keeps the cells of the body in good working order, particularly teeth and gums. Keeps blood vessels strong
D	fish liver oil, liver, eggs and milk (Can also be made by the skin when sunlight shines on it)	Essential for normal growth – helps in the development of bones and teeth

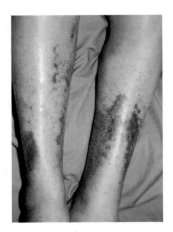

Figure 1.10
One symptom of scurvy

Scurvy is a condition caused by a lack of vitamin C. People with scurvy often have bleeding gums and a number of other symptoms including bleeding around the bones (see Figure 1.10).

Up until a few centuries ago, scurvy was a very big problem for sailors on long voyages. On some long journeys (often lasting months) most of the sailors may have died from this condition. Probably the first serious nutritional experiment was conducted in 1747 at sea by Dr James Lind who noticed that a number of the sailors on his boat were ill, with what we now know as scurvy.

Dr Lind thought that there was something missing from the diet of all the sailors who were ill, but he did not know what. He divided the sick sailors into groups and gave each group different foods and drinks over a period of time. For example:

- One group drank cider each day.
- One group drank sea water.
- One group drank barley water.
- One group ate oranges and lemons.

After a few days the only group to show an improvement was the group who had been given oranges and lemons. Dr Lind had discovered the foods that provided the missing nutrient. After the work of James Lind the Royal Navy made sure that sailors had good supplies of lemons or limes when they were at sea for long periods. Over the two and a half centuries since then, a greater understanding of the link between diet and health has gradually developed.

Minerals such as calcium and iron are essential for healthy living. The sources and functions of these minerals are shown in Table 1.3.

Table 1.3 Minerals

Mineral	Good sources	Role in the body
calcium	milk, cheese, cereals, vegetables	Essential for bone and teeth development, nerve and muscle action, blood clotting
iron	liver, red meat, spinach	Needed for making haemoglobin in red blood cells. The haemoglobin transports oxygen around the body in the blood

> 8 Suggest what would happen if we had a shortage of iron in our diet.

Water

Water is another essential component of the diet. It is needed because much of the body is water and it is necessary as a solvent and as a transport medium. Reactions could not take place in the body's cells without water.

Fibre

Fibre is a complex carbohydrate found in the cell walls of plants. It is essential in the diet for the efficient functioning of the digestive system. Constipation is likely to result if there is not enough fibre in the diet. High levels of fibre in the diet are also believed to reduce the risk of developing bowel cancer.

Figure 1.11 Foods rich in fibre

The link between health and diet: are we what we eat?

The previous section outlined some problems that may be caused by a poor diet, such as not having enough minerals or vitamins. However, there are many other ways in which our diet can be poor. You may have read in a newspaper or heard on television something along the lines of:

'for the first time in history a significant number of today's young people will have a shorter lifespan than their parents'

What do you think it is that prompts such a statement? Is it that so many young people today are leading unhealthy lifestyles? One of the factors that makes health professionals very concerned is the link between poor diet and obesity and the link between obesity and poor health.

Seriously overweight people are termed **obese**. We know that obesity in children is a major problem in the USA, and evidence suggests that it is becoming an increasingly greater problem in the UK. A recent survey suggested that there may be up to one million obese children in the UK.

Although there will be exceptions, the current preference for 'fast' or 'convenience' food means that many people now are likely to take in more fat and salt than people of earlier generations. In addition, we are these days much more likely to snack or 'graze' than before, and today's children probably eat more food overall than earlier generations.

This change in dietary habit leads to more people becoming overweight or obese. Being overweight or obese increases the risk of developing heart disease (see below), or other circulatory problems (see page 11), or Type 2 diabetes (see page 38).

How and why do heart attacks happen?

Cholesterol is a fatty substance made by the body and found in the blood. The amount of cholesterol in the body depends on the diet but also is affected to some extent by genetic factors.

Cholesterol (and other fatty substances) can be present in such high amounts that it is deposited on the walls of the arteries. These patches of fat are referred to as **atheromas** and the process is called **atherosclerosis**. Over time this leads to a narrowing of the arteries, making it more difficult for blood to flow through them. This is particularly likely to happen in the **coronary arteries** – the small arteries that supply the heart. This is the cause of a type of heart disease called **coronary heart disease** (**CHD**).

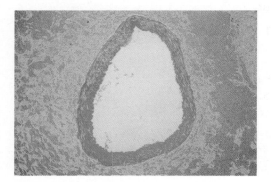

Figure 1.12a A healthy coronary artery

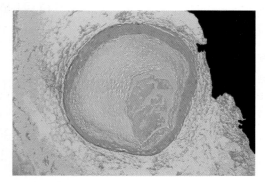

Figure 1.12b A coronary artery that has become blocked by cholesterol (orange)

Eventually an artery may narrow so much that a blockage forms. A blood clot forms and stops the blood flowing any further in this particular artery. This prevents the heart muscle that this artery serves from receiving oxygen and glucose. Respiration can no longer take place in these heart cells and they die, causing the heart to stop beating. This is a heart attack.

Heart attacks and heart disease in general are major causes of premature death in the UK. As noted above, dietary factors can contribute to heart disease but there are many other factors as well. **Lifestyle** is important. Smoking and heavy drinking increase the chances of developing heart disease, as can high levels of stress. There is evidence that genetic factors may also have a part to play.

Clearly many factors can contribute to the development of heart disease and it is usually difficult to pinpoint which factor has been most important when someone has a heart attack. Usually several factors interact to cause it. What is clear, however, is that it is possible to reduce the risk of having a heart attack by following a number of guidelines. These guidelines are regularly promoted by the National Health Service and other health-promoting agencies, and include:

- **reducing saturated fat, cholesterol and salt intake**. There is evidence that a diet high in saturated fat (see page 5) increases blood cholesterol levels but some evidence also that 'polyunsaturated' fats in the diet may actually *reduce* blood cholesterol levels. High salt levels in the diet can cause high blood pressure, which is a contributory factor in heart disease.
- **stopping smoking**. Smoking makes the blood clot more easily and raises blood pressure.
- **drinking alcohol only in moderation**. Too much alcohol can damage heart muscle and cause high blood pressure.
- **reducing stress levels** where possible.
- **increasing exercise**. This helps to control weight and blood pressure and reduce stress.
- **having regular health checks** to check cholesterol levels, blood pressure and so on.

> 9   The incidence of coronary heart disease is higher in Northern Ireland, Scotland and the north of England than in the south of England. Suggest some of the reasons that might explain this. Why do you think many people fail to adapt their lifestyle to reduce some of the factors that can lead to heart disease?

Figure 1.13
A health-promoting leaflet encouraging smokers to stop

Other circulatory problems

Poor diet and the other factors discussed above can damage the circulatory system in other parts of the body as well as the heart. If the build up of fat and subsequent blockage is in blood vessels in the brain, a **stroke** can result. Again the cells deprived of oxygen and glucose die, and this means the affected part of the brain stops functioning properly. This often causes paralysis of parts of the body, and difficulty with speech and memory.

Although the links between diet, obesity and health are well established, it is important not to assume that if someone is not obese his or her heart and blood vessels will be in good condition. Some people have a very poor diet but are not obese, possibly because they do not overeat or possibly because they have a fast metabolic rate that 'burns off' the energy quickly. However, if they do not have enough of all the essential dietary components, or too much saturated fat, cholesterol or salt, serious illness linked to poor diet can still result.

The costs to society of circulatory diseases

The treatment and rehabilitation of people who survive heart attacks and strokes is very expensive. This is partly due to the fact that these patients are usually very seriously ill and need constant medical attention and treatment for a period of time. In addition, patients recovering from a heart attack or a stroke often remain in hospital for long periods of time for long-term care, monitoring and rehabilitation.

It is important to be aware that the costs associated with circulatory disease are not only the monetary costs involved in the treatment. Family life will be severely affected if a family member has had a stroke or a heart attack. Business, too, will be affected. In Northern Ireland alone, thousands of days in employment each year are lost due to employees being ill with circulatory disease.

ACTIVITY

Plan a presentation for your class or group. How could you convince them of the importance of taking steps to reduce the risks of having heart disease or a stroke?

Other medical conditions associated with diet

Anorexia, bulimia and compulsive eating are all types of eating disorder.

Anorexia nervosa, sometimes called 'slimmers disease', is a condition most commonly seen in young females. In this condition the individual is able to suppress the appetite to the extent that she/he will become well below the optimum body weight. These individuals have an intense dread of gaining weight, even though they are underweight, and they appear unable to understand that they are too thin. The exact reasons that cause this condition are difficult to determine but it is clearly linked to a psychological fear of being overweight. It is perhaps not surprising that models and dancers are more likely to have this condition than the general population.

Bulimia is also more common in young females. In this condition 'binge eating' is often followed by self-induced vomiting or taking laxatives. Again there is a psychological fear of gaining weight with this condition. Sometimes there is no clear distinction between anorexia and bulimia, and one condition can merge into the other.

A third eating disorder is **compulsive eating disorder**. With this there is a psychological need to eat extremely large meals on a regular basis or a need to continually snack. Individuals affected are likely to become overweight or obese and often have very low self-esteem.

Improving our health: the benefits of exercise

It is often said that we as a society do not exercise as much as we did even a few years ago. This may be due to the greater demands of modern life or the many other leisure activities that take up our time. Computers, more TV stations and the ever-increasing number of electronic games that are available often get the blame. But how important is exercise for health?

Figure 1.14 Which activity do you think is the healthier?

Investigate the effect of exercise on heart beat and recovery rate. To do this you first need to calculate your heart rate at rest, by measuring your pulse rate (usually easiest at the neck or wrist). Do some vigorous exercise for a short period of time, for example 25 step-ups as fast as possible. Following the exercise, measure your pulse rate immediately you stop and then at intervals, for example every 2 minutes, until it returns to the normal resting rate. The time taken for the pulse rate to return to normal is referred to as the recovery time. Compare the results with other members of your class.

You also need to work out some way of estimating your level of fitness. This is very difficult to measure accurately but a rough estimate could be worked out by using the length of time it takes to complete the vigorous exercise done in the practical activity.

You should be able to use your results to discuss the following points.

- Is there a link between level of fitness and heart rate?
- Is there a link between level of fitness and recovery time?
- If each individual became fitter over time, how would this affect his or her recovery time?

10   Do you know what causes your pulse? If not, find out.

How regular exercise affects the circulatory system

The amount of blood that the heart pumps round the body per minute is referred to as the **cardiac output**. The amount of blood pumped depends on how much blood is pumped each time it beats (the **stroke volume**) and the number of heart beats per minute (the **heart rate**).

$$\text{cardiac output} = \text{stroke volume} \times \text{heart rate}$$

You are probably aware that your cardiac output is much greater during exercise than when at rest. You will almost certainly have found that your heart rate increases considerably during vigorous exercise. This on its own will increase the cardiac output. However, the stroke volume will also increase during exercise. You can tell this by the fact that the pulse is much stronger (and obviously easier to feel) immediately after exercise.

Why do we have an increased cardiac output during exercise? The muscles involved in exercise use considerably more energy during exercise compared to when at rest. The energy comes from the process of aerobic respiration, which requires the raw materials of oxygen and glucose (see page 5). These will have to be delivered to the muscles at a fast enough rate and in sufficient quantity to enable the muscles to respire more quickly and produce more energy.

Why being fit helps

Regular exercise strengthens heart muscle over a period of time and the stroke volume becomes greater even at rest. This means that a fit person will pump more blood with each heart beat than someone who is unfit. Someone who is less fit will need an increased heart rate in order to pump the same amount of blood around the body in the same time.

A strong heart built up by exercise will therefore be more efficient – its greater output ensures that sufficient blood is pumped round the body under normal resting circumstances. In addition, during exercise it will be under less strain as it increases cardiac output more easily.

It is not surprising that many health professionals are delighted that the Olympics are coming to London in 2012. The hope is that this will encourage more people in the UK to become involved in athletics and sport in general. The benefits of increased exercise on the nation's health are all too obvious.

websites

www.bbc.co.uk/health/
easy links to sections on nutrition, fitness and heart disease

www.healthpromotionagency.org.uk
publications archive contains useful information

www.patient.co.uk/showdoc/23068754/
summary of heart disease and the risk factors

http://nhlbisupport.com/chd1/chdexp.htm
information about cholesterol and heart disease

www.bhf.org.uk
British Heart Foundation site

http://askabiologist.asu.edu/research/scurvy/
further information on Dr Lind's work with scurvy

Questions

1 This experiment was set up to estimate the energy in a peanut.

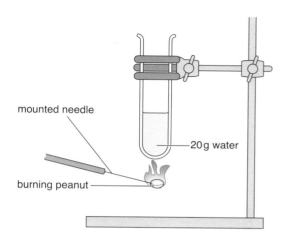

mounted needle

20 g water

burning peanut

The heat from the burning peanut heated the water in the boiling tube.

Temperature of water at start (°C)	21
Temperature of water when peanut stopped burning (°C)	34

$$\text{Energy released from the peanut (J)} = \text{mass of water (g)} \times \text{rise in temperature (°C)} \times 4.2$$

a Using the information provided, calculate the energy value of the peanut in this experiment. *(1 mark)*

b Suggest why your calculated value is an underestimate of the energy value of the peanut. *(1 mark)*

c The energy values for three foods (bread, meat and butter) are given in the table.

Food	Energy (J/g)
A	17 000
B	39 000
C	10 000

Which of the three foods (A, B or C) is butter? Explain your answer. *(2 marks)*

CCEA GCSE Science: Double Award (Modular)
Foundation Tier Nov. 2004

2 An experiment was set up to investigate gas exchange in living organisms.

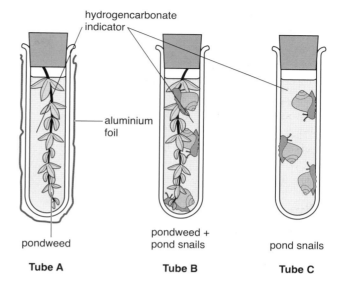

hydrogencarbonate indicator

aluminium foil

pondweed
Tube A

pondweed + pond snails
Tube B

pond snails
Tube C

$$\text{purple} \xleftarrow[\text{CO}_2]{\text{decreased}} \text{bright red} \xrightarrow[\text{CO}_2]{\text{increased}} \text{yellow}$$

hydrogencarbonate indicator

Tube	Colour of hydrogencarbonate indicator at start of experiment	Colour of hydrogencarbonate indicator at end of experiment
A	bright red	
B	bright red	purple
C	bright red	

a Complete the table to show the colour of the hydrogencarbonate indicator at the end of the experiment for tubes A and C. *(2 marks)*

b Explain the colour change for tube B. *(3 marks)*

CCEA GCSE Science: Double Award (Modular)
Higher Tier March 2005

3 In 1747 Dr James Lind noticed that many sailors on long voyages became ill with what we now know as scurvy. At that time no one knew what caused the condition.

Lind carried out a very important experiment. He divided the sailors into a number of groups, and each group was given different things to eat or drink.

One group was given cider	One group was given sea water	One group was given oranges and lemons
↓	↓	↓
No improvement	No improvement	Health improved after a few days

a Does the experiment suggest that sea water and cider cause scurvy? Explain your answer. *(2 marks)*

b Suggest what Lind's recommendation was to the Navy to improve the health of sailors in the future. (*1 mark*)

c Suggest what the oranges and lemons contained that made the sailors better. (*1 mark*)

4 The diagram shows a section through a normal coronary artery and one narrowed by fatty deposits.

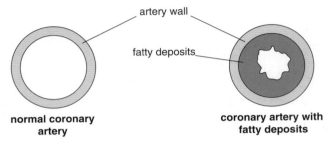

artery wall

fatty deposits

normal coronary artery

coronary artery with fatty deposits

a Explain how fatty deposits on the wall of the coronary artery could cause a heart attack. (*2 marks*)

b State **three** changes in lifestyle which would reduce the risk of a heart attack. (*3 marks*)

5 The bar chart shows the pulse rates of four students before and after vigorous exercise.

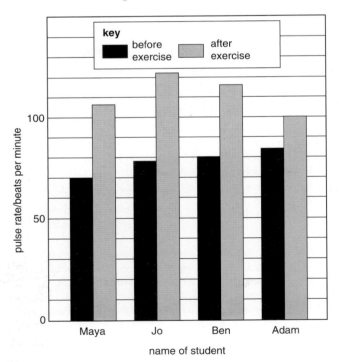

a Describe the effect of exercise on pulse rate. (*1 mark*)

b Whose pulse rate changed the most? (*1 mark*)

c Explain why the pulse rate needs to increase during vigorous exercise. (*3 marks*)

6 The graph shows the relationship between the length of exercise taken by a group of pupils and their recovery rate.

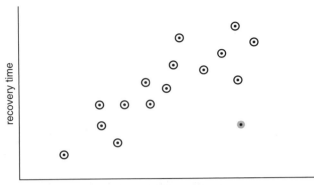

a What is the relationship between the length of exercise taken and the recovery time? (*1 mark*)

b One pupil thought that the shaded result was a mistake. Using evidence from the graph do you think he was correct to think this? Explain your answer. (*2 marks*)

c Suggest how you would design an experiment to identify if boys had a faster recovery rate than girls. (*3 marks*)

Chapter 2

DNA, genetics and ethical issues

Learning objectives

By the end of this chapter you should know and understand:

➤ The structure and function of DNA, genes and chromosomes
➤ How DNA controls protein synthesis
➤ How to interpret and complete simple genetic diagrams
➤ How to use pedigree diagrams
➤ Genetic screening and gene therapy and the ethical issues involved
➤ The issues involved in cloning
➤ The advantages and disadvantages of GM crops

Chromosomes and DNA

The nucleus of a cell is often referred to as the control centre of the cell. It is the **chromosomes** in the nucleus that control the activities of the cell and, in turn, the characteristics of the whole organism. As humans we have 46 chromosomes in our cells (organised as 23 pairs) but the number varies from one type of organism to another.

But what are chromosomes made of and how do they work? Around 50 years ago one of the most important scientific discoveries of the last century was made. The molecule that makes chromosomes work was discovered. This molecule is **deoxyribose nucleic acid** or **DNA**. A chromosome consists of a long strand of the DNA molecule running from end to end.

Each chromosome is made up of a number of smaller sections or blocks called **genes** that carry out a particular function or role. In humans, there are genes that control eye colour, the ability to tongue roll, and thousands of other characteristics. The genes act like codes to control the characteristics. Each individual chromosome may have hundreds of genes along its length.

The DNA molecule is constructed very much like a ladder. If we imagine the ladder to be flexible and it is twisted round on itself, it gives a structure called a **double helix**. See Figure 2.1.

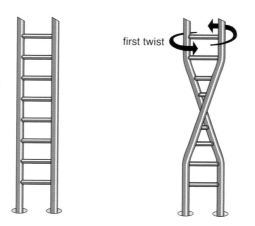
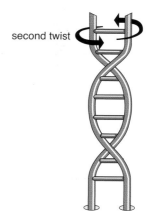

Figure 2.1 A model of the DNA double helix

The structure of DNA

DNA consists of three sub-units that are regularly repeated throughout the length of the molecule. These sub-units are **deoxyribose sugar**, **phosphate** and **bases**. There are four different types of base: **adenine**, **guanine**, **cytosine** and **thymine**. In the double helix the rungs of the 'ladder' are the bases and the sides are alternating units of deoxyribose sugar and phosphate.

Each repeating unit of DNA that consists of a phosphate, sugar and a base is called a **nucleotide**. Figure 2.2 shows that bases link the two sides of the molecule together in such a way that only adenine combines with thymine and only guanine combines with cytosine. This arrangement is known as **base pairing**. The arrangement of the bases along the length of the DNA is what determines how a gene works.

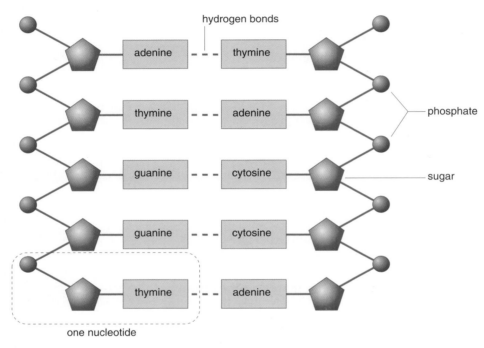

Figure 2.2 Base pairing in DNA

If we map the arrangement of bases along each individual's chromosomes, we will find that, while there will be similarities between different individuals, no two people will have the same sequence of bases along the entire length of all of their chromosomes (except for identical twins – this will be explained later).

How does DNA work?

The DNA works by providing a code to allow the cell to make the proteins that it needs. The DNA determines which proteins and, in particular, which enzymes are made. Enzymes are extremely important proteins that control the cell's reactions. Therefore by controlling the enzymes, the DNA controls the development of the cell and, in turn, the entire organism.

The bases along one side of the DNA molecule (the coding strand) form the genetic code. Each sequence of three bases, called a **base triplet**, along this coding strand codes for a particular amino acid. Amino acids are the building blocks of proteins. As a protein consists of many amino acids linked together, it is important that the correct base triplets are arranged in the correct sequence along the coding strand. Figure 2.3 shows how base triplets code for particular amino acids. You can see that the first and fourth base triplets have the same code; this means that the first and fourth amino acids are the same. The model only shows a small section of a gene and a small section of a protein that it produces.

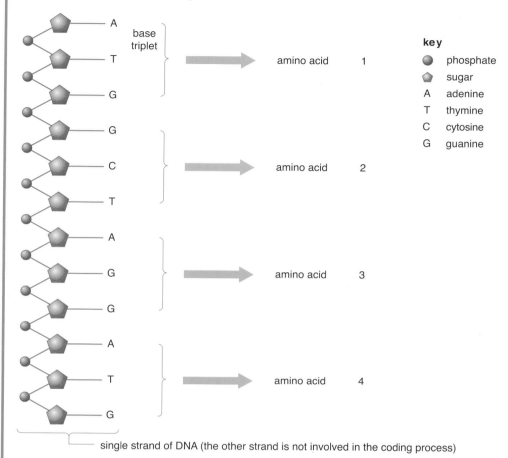

Figure 2.3 How base triplets code for amino acids

Building the theory: working out the structure of DNA

As you can see from the diagrams so far, DNA is a very complex molecule and a lot of expertise and hard work was required in working out its structure. By 1950 scientists had worked out that DNA was the molecule that determined how organisms developed, but they knew nothing of its structure.

Then in 1950 the Austrian chemist **Erwin Chargaff** discovered that although the arrangement of bases in DNA varied, there was always an equal amount of adenine and thymine. Similarly, there was always an equal amount of guanine and cytosine.

1   Explain Erwin Chargaff's observation.

The next part of the DNA jigsaw was soon put in place by **Rosalind Franklin** and **Maurice Wilkins**, who were research scientists working at King's College, London. They used a process called X-ray diffraction. They fired beams of X-rays into molecules of DNA, and from the ways in which the

DNA scattered the X-rays they obtained information about its three-dimensional structure. Franklin and Wilkins were able to work out the overall shape of DNA but they were not able to confirm exactly how the sub-units were linked together.

The last part of the puzzle was solved by **James Watson** and **Francis Crick** at Cambridge University in 1953. They were able to build on the earlier work of the other scientists to deduce how the bases were arranged and also to conclude that the molecule is arranged as a double helix.

The discovery of the structure of DNA is typical of many scientific discoveries, in that theories are often built up in stages, with many scientists laying the foundations before the final details are worked out. Another common characteristic of scientific discoveries can be seen here – the scientists who put the finishing touches to the theory get most of the credit!

Figure 2.4 Watson and Crick with their model of DNA

The genetic basis of inheritance

Genetics is the study of inheritance. Genetics explains the way in which chromosomes, genes and DNA are passed from generation to generation.

Gregor Mendel: the founder of genetics

Much of our understanding of genetics is based on the work carried out by **Gregor Mendel**. Mendel was born in Austria in 1822 and as a young man became a monk. At the monastery he developed an interest in the breeding of garden peas, plants that were common in the monastery garden. Mendel noticed that the garden pea had many characteristics that varied from plant to plant. These characteristics included pea shape and pea colour. The peas in the garden were either green or yellow and they could be round or wrinkled. Mendel carried out a range of breeding experiments in which he **crossed** (mated) plants carrying particular characteristics that he was interested in. By careful observation of the offspring produced, he was able to draw conclusions about the nature of inheritance.

Figure 2.5
Gregor Mendel

One characteristic of pea plants that Mendel was interested in was plant height. Pea plants occur in their normal tall form or in a much shorter dwarf variety. One breeding cross that Mendel carried out was a cross between tall and dwarf plants. Before he carried out this cross he allowed the tall plants to breed with each other for a period of time to ensure they always produced tall plants. He did the same with the dwarf plants. The parent plants he used were then referred to as **pure breeding**.

When Mendel crossed the tall plants with the dwarf plants (the **parental generation**), he found that all the plants in the first, or **F1** generation (the offspring) were tall. However, when he crossed these F1 plants with other F1 plants, their offspring (the second or **F2** generation) were a mixture of tall and dwarf plants. Furthermore, as he carried out many crosses that produced hundreds of F2 plants, he worked out that approximately 75% of these were tall and 25% were dwarf. See Figure 2.6.

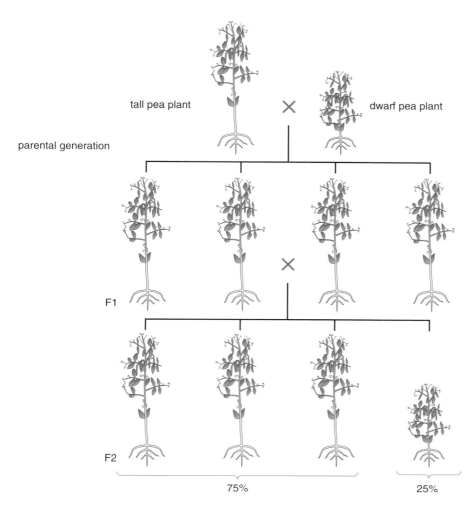

tall pea plant   ✕   dwarf pea plant

parental generation

F1

✕

F2

75%   25%

Figure 2.6
Mendel's results

Explanation of Mendel's cross with peas

Mendel decided to assign symbols to the characteristics he was observing. He used the symbol T for the tall plants and the symbol t for the dwarf plants. He used a capital for the tall state, as it appeared to dominate the dwarf condition. Mendel suggested that there was some factor for tallness in the tall plants and an alternative factor for the dwarf condition in the short plants. We now know that Mendel's factors are genes and they are carried on the chromosomes. As chromosomes occur in pairs, the genes also occur in pairs, as shown in Figure 2.7. The two contrasting forms of a gene, in this case T and t, are called **alleles**. Alleles are different forms of the same gene. Alleles occur in the same position on the chromosome. As the parental plants were pure breeding, Mendel suggested that the tall parent plants carried only the tall factors (genes) and the dwarf parent plants carried only dwarf factors. These plants containing only one type of allele are called **homozygous** (TT or tt). When both types of alleles are present the individual is **heterozygous** (Tt).

The paired symbols used in genetics are referred to as the **genotype**, and the outward appearance (tall or short) is the **phenotype**.

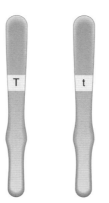

T   t

In this example the two alleles of the gene are different. The individual is heterozygous for the characteristic concerned.

Figure 2.7 A pair of chromosomes showing the position of the alleles of a particular gene

21

Mendel also deduced that when **gametes** or **sex cells** are produced, only one factor from each parent passes on to the offspring. Only one chromosome, and therefore one allele, of each pair can pass into a gamete.

The F1 plants in our cross must have received one T allele from their tall parent and one t allele from the dwarf parent. The F1 plants were therefore Tt (heterozygous). Although all these plants contained both the T and the t allele they were all tall. This can be explained by considering the T allele **dominant** over the **recessive** t allele. The recessive condition will only be expressed, or visible, in the phenotype when only recessive alleles are present in the genotype, e.g. tt.

Figure 2.8 explains Mendel's results that when the F1 plants were interbred, a ratio of 3 : 1 (tall : dwarf) was produced. This ratio is achieved because the two alleles (T and t) of one parent will produce T and t gametes in equal numbers, and they each have an equal chance of combining with the T or the t gamete produced by the other parent during fertilisation.

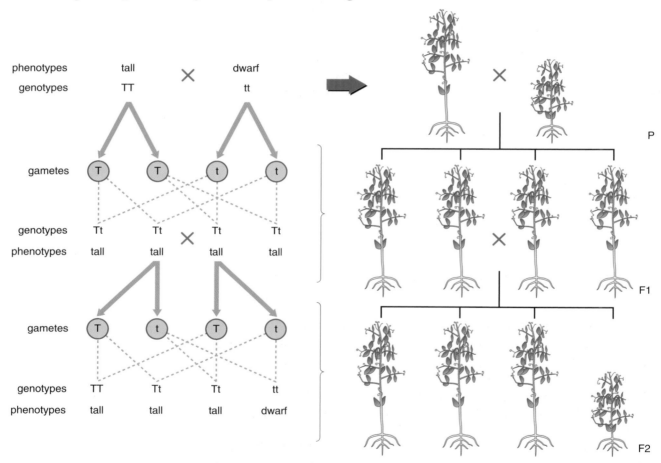

Figure 2.8 Explaining Mendel's results

Mendel completed his work without being aware of the existence of chromosomes or genes. He published his work in 1866 but it did not get the credit it deserved and remained largely ignored. It was only at the start of the 20th century when chromosomes were discovered under the microscope that the significance of his findings was appreciated. Although additional research and knowledge has increased our understanding of genetics in recent times, it is important to note that this has built on Mendel's findings and not in any way contradicted them.

Inheritance of human characteristics

Although the inheritance of most human characteristics is complex, often involving many genes, and even several chromosomes, for a single characteristic, some human features do show the single gene inheritance described above. An example includes the ability to roll the tongue.

When working out inherited genotypes, it is helpful to use a genetic diagram called a **Punnett square**. Figure 2.10 uses a Punnett square to show the inheritance of tongue rolling in humans.

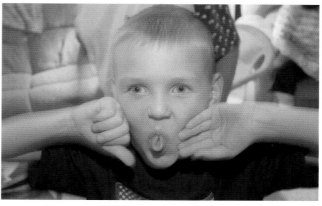

Figure 2.9 The ability to roll the tongue is an inherited characteristic

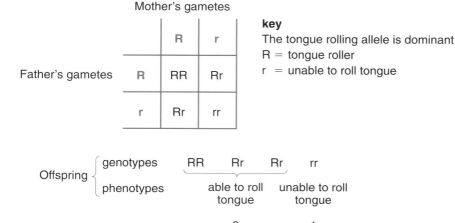

Figure 2.10 Punnett square showing the result of a cross between two parents heterozygous for tongue rolling

Some important points about genetic crosses

- It is common practice to use the same letter for both the dominant and recessive alleles, with the dominant allele being the capital and the recessive allele written in lower case.
- Ratios will only be accurate when large numbers of offspring are produced. This is because it is totally random which gametes, and therefore which alleles, join during fertilisation.
- If a 3 : 1 ratio is present in the offspring of a particular cross, both of the parents involved will be heterozygous for the character being considered.
- If a 1 : 1 offspring ratio is produced in a cross, one parent will be heterozygous and the other will be homozygous recessive.

Inherited diseases

The passing on of genes from parent to child can have harmful results, as some diseases are inherited. Examples in humans include **cystic fibrosis** and **Down's syndrome**. The way in which each of these conditions is inherited will be discussed in turn.

Cystic fibrosis

Individuals with cystic fibrosis have a genetic condition that causes problems with breathing and also with the digestion of food. The cystic fibrosis allele is recessive. Therefore, children who are born with cystic fibrosis must have two recessive alleles. Almost always, the parents of children with cystic fibrosis do not actually have the condition but are heterozygous. They are **carriers** in that they carry the cystic fibrosis allele but do not show the condition themselves.

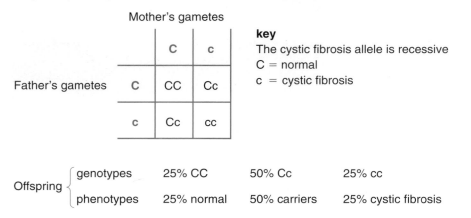

Mother's gametes

	C	c
Father's gametes		
C	CC	Cc
c	Cc	cc

key
The cystic fibrosis allele is recessive
C = normal
c = cystic fibrosis

Offspring
- genotypes: 25% CC, 50% Cc, 25% cc
- phenotypes: 25% normal, 50% carriers, 25% cystic fibrosis

Figure 2.11 The inheritance of cystic fibrosis. The Punnett square shows a cross between parents who do not have cystic fibrosis but who carry the allele

Down's syndrome

Down's syndrome is also an inherited human condition. It is not caused by a recessive allele but is caused by an error in the formation of gametes. In humans, gametes (sperm and eggs) normally have 23 chromosomes (one from each of the 23 pairs of chromosomes). Occasionally gametes are formed with 24 chromosomes. If the affected gamete is involved in fertilisation, resulting in pregnancy, the new individual will have 47 chromosomes in all his or her cells instead of the normal 46.

Other genetic conditions

There are a large number of conditions or diseases that are either caused directly by the chromosomes and genes that an individual possesses, as in the examples above, or for which there is a strong genetic component. Several of the conditions that are discussed in this book are thought to have genetic factors. These include diabetes and heart disease. As our knowledge of inheritance and genetics increases, it is hoped that we will eventually be able to reduce the occurrence of genetic disease in the population in the years to come. Ways of reducing the occurrence or the effects of genetic conditions include genetic screening and gene therapy, both of which will be discussed later in this chapter.

ACTIVITY

Discuss the issues that arise when it is discovered that a pregnant woman is carrying a fetus with severe abnormalities. You will probably want to discuss issues such as:

- the value of finding out early in pregnancy whether a fetus has any serious medical condition
- whether in such a case a termination of pregnancy should be considered.

Pedigree diagrams

A **pedigree diagram** shows the way in which a genetic condition is inherited in a family or a group of biologically related people. Figure 2.12 shows an example.

Figure 2.12 shows, by the change of colour from blue to green, that one of the children has cystic fibrosis. It is possible to use the information provided to work out the probability of other children having the condition. Genetic counsellors often construct pedigree diagrams and use this information to advise parents who may be carriers or have a genetic condition.

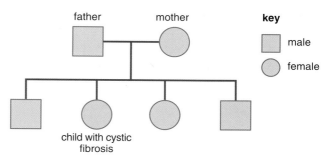

Figure 2.12 A pedigree diagram

> 2 Use the diagram above and your knowledge to answer the following.
>   a What is the genotype of the child with cystic fibrosis? Use the symbol c to represent the cystic fibrosis allele.
>   b What are the possible genotypes for the other children in the family? Explain your answer.
>   c What is the probability that the next child of these parents will have cystic fibrosis?
>   d Approximately 1 in 25 people are carriers for cystic fibrosis. Use this information to work out the proportion of people in the population who have cystic fibrosis.

Pedigree diagrams can be used in any type of genetic cross but they are obviously very valuable in tracing and predicting harmful genetic conditions.

Some genetic conditions such as Down's syndrome cannot be predicted by the use of pedigree diagrams. In these cases other ways of assessing the chances of a child being born with this disorder are used. For example, the likelihood is much greater for older mothers.

Genetic screening

In an attempt to reduce the incidence of genetic conditions, **genetic screening** may be used. This is testing people for the presence of a particular allele or genetic condition. Whole populations can be tested, or targeted groups where the probability of having (or passing on) a particular condition is high.

Genetic screening has been available for a long time for Down's syndrome. In one screening process, cells are taken from the liquid surrounding the baby in the womb and then allowed to multiply in laboratory conditions. This is called an **amniocentesis test** (see Figure 2.13 on the next page). The chromosomes in the cells are then examined to see if the developing fetus has the condition. This genetic screening for Down's syndrome is offered to all pregnant mothers in Britain but is only strongly advised for older mothers. There is a 1% risk of miscarriage with the test.

Genetic screening is also available for cystic fibrosis.

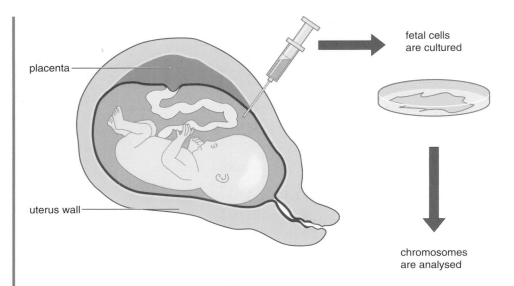

placenta

fetal cells
are cultured

uterus wall

chromosomes
are analysed

Figure 2.13 An amniocentesis test

The ethical issues

What are the options if genetic screening shows that a fetus has a condition such as Down's syndrome? Should the mother have an abortion? The results of genetic screening, and even of being a carrier of a serious genetic condition, can create considerable dilemmas for the individuals involved.

ACTIVITY

Have a class debate about the ethics of genetic screening. The types of issues you may wish to debate could include:

- the ethics of abortion for medical reasons
- is there an acceptable risk associated with genetic screening?
- the costs of screening compared with the costs of treating individuals with a genetic condition – should cost be a factor?
- should parents be allowed free choice of whether to screen or not?
- should genetic screening be extended to more than just serious genetic conditions? What if it could predict life expectancy?
- should screening for the sex of a child be allowed? What if it is not what the parents want?

It will soon be possible to screen everyone (whether before birth, in childhood or as an adult) for many different alleles. The information obtained is referred to as a **genetic profile**. Should this information be available to life insurance companies and employers?

How does life insurance work? Many people take out life insurance for a fixed term, e.g. 20 years, and pay an amount each month, called a premium, to the company involved. If the person insured dies during the term insured, the insurance company pays a guaranteed sum of money to the dependents of the insured person. Life insurance is very important as it often is needed to provide for the children or non-working partner in a family unit when the main income earner dies. Some insurance policies also provide a sum of money should the insured develop a 'critical' illness – one that would mean giving up work.

Obviously these insurance companies would like to have genetic profiles of individuals requesting insurance – they would like to know the risk involved before calculating premiums, or even whether or not to provide insurance. Should insurance companies be able to insist on genetic screening for potential clients?

The links between genetic screening and insurance companies or employers is yet another ethical dilemma. It is becoming an increasingly important issue as the technologies needed to carry out mass genetic screening are being continually developed. The legal position is currently under review.

Gene therapy: the benefits and problems

One way of reducing the effects of a genetic disorder is to 'correct' the harmful allele. This altering of genes, called **gene therapy**, is a controversial area but it does offer many potential benefits. There are two forms of gene therapy:

- Somatic gene therapy involves introducing the normal form of the allele or gene into targeted cells in the patient. This has the effect of treating the patient and reducing the effects of the symptoms in the targeted area.
- Germline gene therapy involves modifying the genes in egg or sperm cells. In this situation all the cells that will develop in the new individual (and any gametes that he/she will produce) will have the normal form of the gene.

Most research is concentrating on somatic gene therapy. Germline gene therapy is much more technically difficult and presents greater ethical challenges involving so-called 'designer babies'. Somatic gene therapy is being used in the treatment of cystic fibrosis.

One of the main symptoms of cystic fibrosis is overproduction of mucus in the lungs. This fills up in the lungs and makes the individual vulnerable to infection.

Gene therapy specifically targets the lungs and the principle is to get the normal allele into the lung cells. One way of doing this is to use aerosols that contain the normal gene together with viruses that are used as 'vectors' to help the gene gain entry to the cells. When the process works well the affected individual will have normal lung function.

However, there are difficulties with the process that have yet to be fully resolved. The problems include:

- the viruses used to introduce the gene can affect other body cells
- the defences of the lung can resist the introduction of the new gene
- benefits can be short lived, because new cells with the cystic fibrosis allele are continually being produced
- the cystic fibrosis allele can still be passed on to the next generation.

Although progress in gene therapy may be slow, it does offer real hope to individuals affected by genetic disorders.

Controlling genetic characteristics

Sexual and asexual reproduction

Most animals that we are familiar with reproduce sexually. **Sexual reproduction** involves the production of gametes (sex cells). When we looked at the production of gametes in genetics earlier in this chapter, we saw that only half the chromosomes and therefore half the genes or alleles in a parent pass into each gamete. In addition, the gametes produced from each parent can have different alleles present. This process has two main effects:

- Because gametes contain only half the number of chromosomes (and alleles) from the parent, this ensures that when male and female gametes combine during fertilisation the new individual produced has the same number of chromosomes as the parent.
- Because each parent can produce gametes with different alleles, variation can be produced in the offspring.

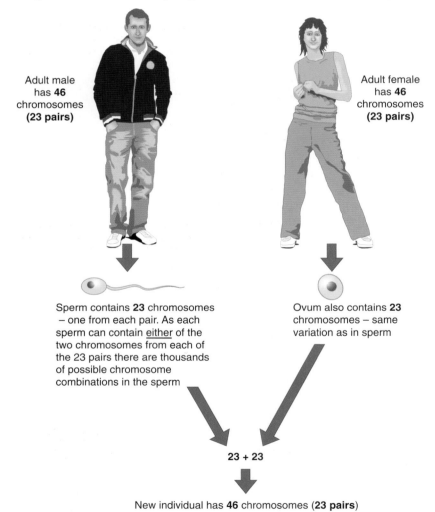

Adult male has **46** chromosomes (**23 pairs**)

Adult female has **46** chromosomes (**23 pairs**)

Sperm contains **23** chromosomes – one from each pair. As each sperm can contain <u>either</u> of the two chromosomes from each of the 23 pairs there are thousands of possible chromosome combinations in the sperm

Ovum also contains **23** chromosomes – same variation as in sperm

23 + 23

New individual has **46** chromosomes (**23 pairs**)

Figure 2.14 Chromosomes in human reproduction

Asexual reproduction, common in plants, produces identical offspring. This is because gametes are not involved; the cells from the adult simply reproduce identical copies of themselves when forming a new individual. Examples in nature include daffodils forming daughter bulbs, and strawberry runners producing new plants. As the new plants are identical genetically to their parent, they are referred to as **clones** and the process is called **cloning**. The advantage to the organism of asexual reproduction is that only one parent is needed.

Cloning in plants

Although asexual reproduction or cloning of plants occurs in nature, sometimes there is an advantage to deliberately cloning particular plants to make sure that they develop with the characteristics we want. Taking cuttings of plants is a form of cloning that has been taking place for a very long time. It is a popular way for gardeners to grow and propagate favourite plants. **Cuttings** are small parts that are removed from a parent plant. These can be parts of the stem or even as little as part of a leaf. Cuttings can develop new roots and grow into a fully developed plant genetically identical to the parent, usually in a relatively short time. Sometimes gardeners can improve the development of cuttings by applying hormones that encourage root development. One parent plant can produce many offspring in this way.

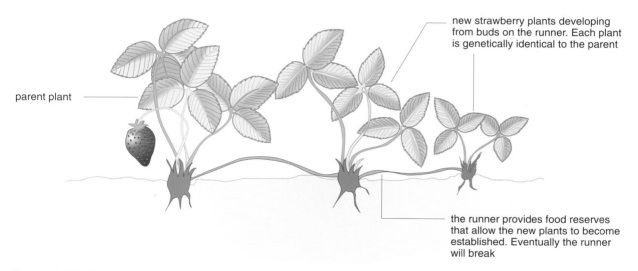

new strawberry plants developing from buds on the runner. Each plant is genetically identical to the parent

parent plant

the runner provides food reserves that allow the new plants to become established. Eventually the runner will break

Figure 2.15 Natural cloning in strawberries

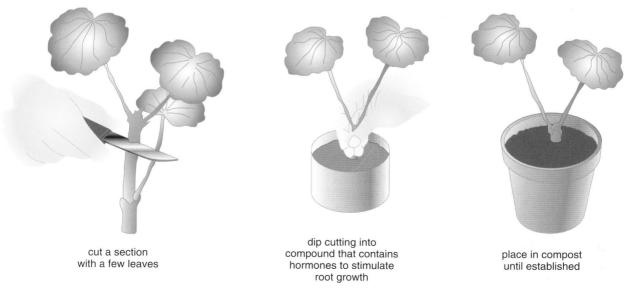

cut a section with a few leaves

dip cutting into compound that contains hormones to stimulate root growth

place in compost until established

Figure 2.16 Taking cuttings

> **3 a** Use the information on the previous page to list three advantages of cloning plants.
>
> **b** It is often beneficial to keep cuttings in a moist environment until they are established. Suggest why this is necessary.

A more sophisticated form of cloning plants is **tissue culture**. This involves taking very many sections of the parent plant and treating them with hormones in very strictly regulated laboratory conditions.

Cloning in animals

While cloning has been widely used in plant breeding, its use in animal breeding has been more limited. It has been demonstrated for over a decade that cloning of an animal is possible (a good early example was 'Dolly', the famously first cloned sheep), but some aspects of animal cloning, and in particular human cloning, raise many ethical concerns.

The process of dividing embryos to produce identical offspring has been successfully used in the breeding of high-quality cattle. This particular cloning procedure is seen by many people as being of little ethical concern. It is similar to what happens naturally when identical twins are formed.

The cloning of human tissue, such as liver tissue, for transplant purposes is seen as acceptable by many people, but the cloning of an entire human being is seen by the vast majority as wholly unacceptable.

As with many potential scientific or medical advances, the ethical issues with cloning animals and human tissues is not clear-cut. The Government is keeping up to date with scientific developments, and on-going legislation in this area is likely to balance the potential for medical research with public opinion.

ACTIVITY

Produce a table listing the benefits and disadvantages of cloning in animals and humans. Do you think your attitude would be (or is) influenced by being close to someone with a medical condition that could be helped by cloning?

More advances in gene technology: GM crops

The process of combining the DNA in an organism with the DNA from another organism is referred to as **recombinant DNA technology** or **genetic engineering**. This process has been in use for a considerable period of time with clear benefits. An example is the use of genetically engineered bacteria to produce human insulin for the treatment of diabetes.

However, the development of **genetically modified** (**GM**) crops has produced much more opposition from the general public. Plants that have been genetically modified include maize plants that are more resistant to drought than normal maize plants, and disease-resistant potato plants. These modifications produce plants that give higher yields or that can grow in a wider range of environments.

Benefits of GM crops include improved resistance to herbicides (weedkiller), disease and pests. They also include increased tolerance to environmental conditions such as drought, and the production of better yields.

Concerns include the possibility of genetically modified pollen or seeds being carried away from the GM area and affecting 'normal' crops. If the genetic modification involves resistance to herbicide and this gets transferred to weeds, 'superweeds' might result that are difficult to control. As with any form of genetic modification, people are concerned that problems might arise in the future that we have no awareness of at the present time.

The role of science, society and the Government in regulating scientific advances

With the genetic advances associated with genetic screening, gene therapy, cloning and GM crops, it is important that the proper safeguards are in place to ensure that safety and ethical issues are fully researched and debated in tandem with the scientific advances. While the scientists develop the technology it is the responsibility of the Government to create the laws that determine what can and cannot be done. The Government has scientific advisors to evaluate the benefits and risks of new technologies, as well as advisors on the ethical aspects, and is also influenced by public opinion.

websites

www.ba-education.demon.co.uk/for/science/dnamain.html
summary of the key stages in working out the structure of DNA

www.bbc.co.uk/education/asguru/biology/04genesgenetics/
animation showing the structure of DNA

www.sonic.net/~nbs/projects/anthro201/disc/
good explanation of Mendel's work

www.biotopics.co.uk/genes/pedigr.html
examples of pedigree diagrams

www.biotopics.co.uk/genes/clones.html
examples of cloning

www.globalchange.com/clonenews.htm
useful links on recent cloning issues

Questions

1 a List the base pairs which make up the genetic
code of DNA. *(2 marks)*

b Explain how Rosalind Franklin investigated
the structure of DNA. *(2 marks)*

c Name **two** other scientists who investigated
the structure of DNA. *(2 marks)*

CCEA GCSE Science: Biology (Higher Tier) 2004

2 The diagram shows part of a DNA molecule.

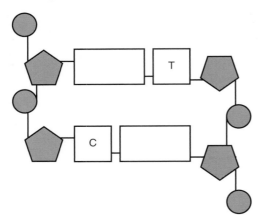

a i Copy and complete the diagram by filling
in the letters missing from the boxes. *(2 marks)*

ii Name the three-dimensional shape of the
DNA molecule. *(1 mark)*

b One strand of the DNA molecule carries the codes for
particular amino acids.

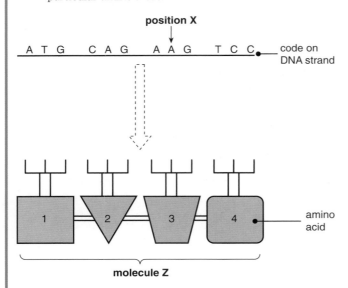

Use the diagram to help answer the following questions.

i Suggest how many bases code for one
amino acid. *(1 mark)*

ii Name molecule Z. *(1 mark)*

CCEA GCSE Science: Biology (Higher Tier) 2005
(part question)

3 The plumage of rock doves usually shows two distinct
wing bars. Occasionally rock doves with no wing bars will
occur in the population.

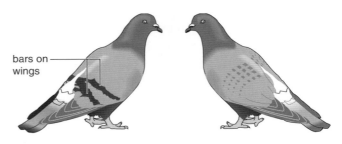

The gene (allele) for wing bars is dominant to the gene
(allele) for no wing bars.

Let B = gene (allele) for wing bars
Let b = gene (allele) for no wing bars

a Use a Punnett square to show how rock
doves with no wing bars may be produced
from parents with wing bars. *(4 marks)*

b Explain why it is not possible to tell the genotype
of a rock dove which is homozygous dominant
for wing bars from a rock dove which is heterozygous.
(1 mark)

4 In guinea pigs black coat (B) is dominant to white (b).
A homozygous black male guinea pig was bred with a
white female.

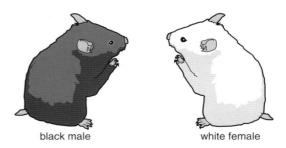

black male   white female

a Complete the Punnett square of this cross. *(2 marks)*

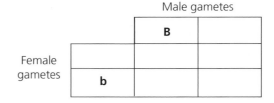

Male gametes

		B	
Female gametes			
	b		

b What proportion of the offspring are black? *(1 mark)*

CCEA GCSE Science: Biology (Higher Tier) 2005
(part question)

Chapter 3

The nervous system and hormones

By the end of this chapter you should know and understand:

➤ The basic structure and function of the nervous system
➤ How a reflex action occurs
➤ How hormones work and the main difference between hormones and nervous action
➤ Hormones and male and female secondary sexual characteristics
➤ The role of insulin in controlling blood sugar levels
➤ The causes and treatment of diabetes

The nervous system

A major difference between plants and animals is that animals can respond to the environment in a more rapid and complex way. A change in the environment is called a **stimulus** and each stimulus often produces a specific **response**.

In animals each type of stimulus will be recognised by a **receptor** in the body. There are many types of receptor, each capable of identifying a particular type of stimulus. For example, in our hand and fingers we have receptors sensitive to touch, pressure and temperature. If a receptor is stimulated it may cause an **effector**, such as a muscle, to produce a response.

This system of responding to the environment requires a **coordinator** to link between the receptor and the muscle. In complex animals such as humans the coordinator is either the **brain** or the **spinal cord**. Together these two structures make up the **central nervous system** (**CNS**). Figure 3.1 gives some examples of the link between stimulus and response.

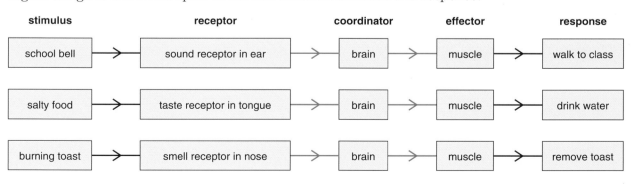

stimulus	receptor	coordinator	effector	response
school bell	sound receptor in ear	brain	muscle	walk to class
salty food	taste receptor in tongue	brain	muscle	drink water
burning toast	smell receptor in nose	brain	muscle	remove toast

⟶ = nerve impulse pathways

Figure 3.1 How we respond to a stimulus

Nerve cells or **neurones** link the receptors and the effectors to the coordinator. A neurone carries information in the form of small electrical charges called nerve impulses. **Sensory neurones** connect receptors to the coordinator, and **effector** or **motor neurones** link the coordinator to the effectors.

Sensory and motor neurones do not make direct contact with each other in the brain or spinal cord. There is a small gap or junction between neurones across which the impulse jumps. These gaps are called **synapses**. These allow a lot of connections to be made, rather like in a telephone exchange. Millions of sensory and motor cells end and originate in the brain.

The coordinator can control whether or not a response should be made to a particular stimulus and, if so, what the response should be. When the brain controls the response it is referred to as a **voluntary** response.

Occasionally we need to make very fast responses without involving active thought. This type of very rapid response is called a **reflex action**.

Reflex actions

If we accidentally touch a very hot object we respond immediately by rapidly withdrawing our hand away from the danger area. The advantage of this is that we move the hand away before it can get burned too badly. This type of action does not involve any 'thinking' time, because the time taken to consider a response would cause unnecessary damage to the body. All reflex actions have several characteristics in common:

- they occur very rapidly
- they do not involve conscious thought
- they are automatic and rigid in that they always occur in the same way.

What makes a reflex action so rapid? In a reflex pathway the total length of nerve pathway is as short as it possibly can be. In addition, there are relatively few synapses as these are the places where impulses travel relatively slowly.

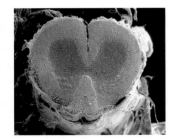

Figure 3.2 Cross-section through the spinal cord

The coordinator in reflex actions is usually the spinal cord rather than the brain. Figure 3.2 shows a photograph of a section through the human spinal cord. The photograph shows the dark central 'grey matter' surrounded by the lighter 'white matter'. The spinal cord runs from the base of the brain to the lower back. At intervals along the spinal cord, nerves (a nerve is a bundle of neurones) leave the spinal cord and link with the rest of the body (see Figure 3.3).

The spinal cord is an extremely important and delicate structure. To give it protection it is enclosed in the vertebral column (the backbone).

Figure 3.3 shows that where nerves leave the spinal cord, there are two entry or exit points on each side of the spinal cord. In the diagram the upper branch is called the dorsal root and the lower branch the ventral root. Different types of neurones are carried in these roots. Figure 3.4 shows a diagram of the spinal cord at the position (the base of the neck) where nerves travelling to the arm are entering and leaving.

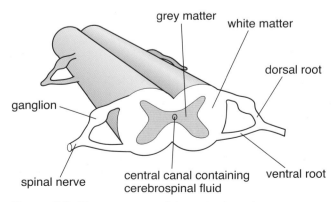

Figure 3.3 The structure of the spinal cord

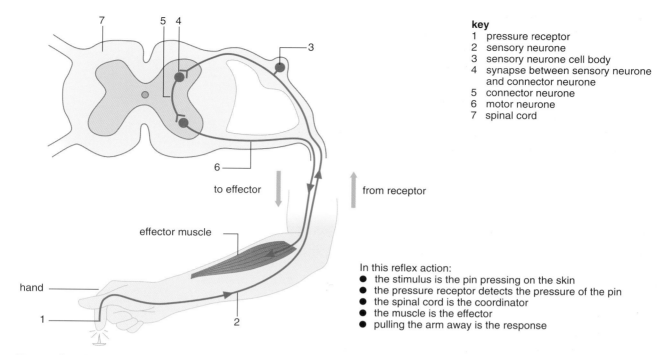

key
1   pressure receptor
2   sensory neurone
3   sensory neurone cell body
4   synapse between sensory neurone
    and connector neurone
5   connector neurone
6   motor neurone
7   spinal cord

to effector   from receptor

effector muscle

hand

In this reflex action:
● the stimulus is the pin pressing on the skin
● the pressure receptor detects the pressure of the pin
● the spinal cord is the coordinator
● the muscle is the effector
● pulling the arm away is the response

Figure 3.4 Section through the spinal cord showing a reflex arc to and from the hand

The diagram shows the nerve pathway involved when the hand touches a sharp object. There are three types of neurone involved in this response:

● the **sensory neurone**. This neurone carries the impulse from the receptors in the hand into the spinal cord. The cell body of the sensory neurone is on a short side branch in a swelling in the dorsal root.
● the **connector (association) neurone**. This neurone joins the sensory neurone to the motor neurone. It occurs wholly within the grey matter.
● the **motor (effector) neurone**. This neurone leaves the spinal cord via the ventral root and continues into the effector (muscle) in the arm.

The diagram shows that both the connector and motor neurones begin with the cell body (the part of the neurone that contains the nucleus). The cell body of the sensory neurone, by contrast, is part way down its length. The diagram also shows that only two synapses are involved in this pathway. This system of structures is called a **reflex arc**.

Figure 3.5 shows some examples of reflex responses. There are many others, including coughing and sneezing.

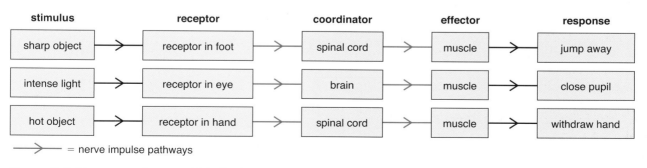

stimulus	receptor	coordinator	effector	response
sharp object	receptor in foot	spinal cord	muscle	jump away
intense light	receptor in eye	brain	muscle	close pupil
hot object	receptor in hand	spinal cord	muscle	withdraw hand

⟶ = nerve impulse pathways

Figure 3.5 How we make a rapid (reflex) response

The speed and effect of the nervous system can be altered by chemicals such as alcohol or caffeine. Caffeine is a stimulant, which means it can make us more alert and has the potential to reduce reaction time. Alcohol has the opposite effect – it slows our reaction times, considerably if too much alcohol is taken. It is not surprising that alcohol limits for driving are strictly enforced.

ACTIVITY

There are many ways in which our reaction times can be measured. Electronic sensors can be used to give accurate measurements but they may not be available in school. Can you design an experiment to measure your reaction time?

Generally, nervous action works rapidly and brings about reasonably rapid responses to a range of stimuli. Another type of messenger system is used by the body to bring about responses, usually in a slower, more long-term way. This second system involves the use of special chemicals called **hormones**.

Hormones

Hormones are produced by special glands that release them into the blood. Although the hormones travel all round the body in the blood, they only affect certain organs called **target organs**. Obviously the target organ(s) differ for each hormone and with some hormones many organs are affected.

Hormones usually act more slowly than the nervous system and act over a longer period of time. Good examples to illustrate these points are the sex hormones: oestrogen and testosterone.

Testosterone and oestrogen and the development of secondary sexual characteristics

Testosterone, produced by the testes in males, and **oestrogen**, produced by the ovaries in females, are important hormones in overall sexual development. One effect they have is the development of the secondary sexual characteristics that are a feature of puberty. The changes that occur in males and females are different but in both sexes they serve to prepare the body for reproduction, both physically and by increasing sexual awareness and drive. Some of the secondary sexual characteristics produced by testosterone in males and oestrogen in females are summarised in Table 3.1.

Table 3.1 Secondary sexual characteristics

Males	Females
Body hair and pubic hair develop	Hair grows in pubic regions and in the armpits
The sexual organs (genitals) enlarge	The sexual organs enlarge and the breasts develop
The body becomes more muscular	The pelvis and hips widen
The voice deepens	Menstruation begins
Sexual awareness and drive increases	Sexual awareness and drive increases

Hormones usually are produced as a result of **internal** changes in the body, for example the quantity of sex hormones produced depends on development.

> 1 Make a table to highlight the major differences between the nervous system and hormone action.

Insulin and diabetes

Insulin is the hormone that prevents blood glucose (sugar) levels from becoming too high. Glucose is constantly needed by all cells for respiration and therefore must always be present in sufficient concentration. However, if there is too much glucose in the blood this will cause problems in the cells of the body. Keeping blood sugar levels constant is an example of **homeostasis** – keeping the body in a steady state.

Insulin is produced by special cells in the **pancreas** in response to increasing or high blood glucose levels. This will usually occur after a meal, especially if the meal is rich in carbohydrates. The insulin will act to reduce blood sugar levels by converting the excess glucose to **glycogen**, which is stored in the liver.

When blood glucose levels are low, less insulin is produced and the above processes (which would decrease levels even further) do not take place, or take place at a slower rate.

Figure 3.6 highlights the relationship between blood glucose level and insulin.

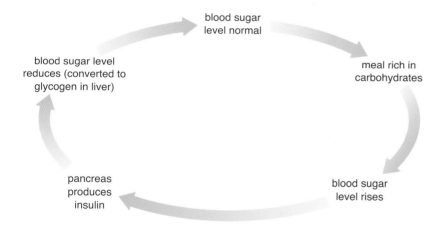

Figure 3.6 Insulin and blood sugar levels

Diabetes is a condition in which the body does not produce enough insulin to keep blood glucose at a controlled level. Individuals who develop diabetes are unable to control their blood glucose levels without treatment, and the following symptoms are often present:

● There is sugar in the urine. This happens because blood glucose levels are so high that some sugar is removed through the kidneys.
● Affected individuals are often thirsty and because they drink so much they need to go to the toilet often.
● Irritability and confusion may result.
● If diagnosis and treatment is delayed by too long, a coma can result.

Diabetes is a fairly common condition in young people, and is increasing in occurrence. It is usually treated by the injection of insulin and by a carefully controlled diet where the intake of carbohydrate is accurately monitored.

Even with the use of insulin injections and a carefully controlled diet, it is difficult for people with diabetes to control blood sugar levels very accurately.

Figure 3.7 A diabetic girl injecting herself with insulin

Problems may arise if too much insulin is taken or if not enough food is taken at regular intervals. If the blood sugar level drops too far, a hypoglycaemic attack (a 'hypo') may occur and unconsciousness will result.

---

2 a Suggest why people with diabetes often take extra glucose (a biscuit or a glucose drink) before they take part in vigorous exercise.

b As part of their regular routine, people with diabetes check their blood glucose levels regularly. What should they do if their blood glucose level is too high when tested?

The type of diabetes normally developed in childhood, and discussed above, is referred to as **Type 1 diabetes**. The diabetes that usually only develops in older people (**Type 2 diabetes**) has a slightly different cause in that insulin is produced but it ceases to work effectively. Type 2 diabetes is often associated with poor diet, obesity and a lack of exercise. Many people with Type 2 diabetes are able to regulate their blood sugar levels by diet alone, without the need for insulin injections.

Long-term effects and future trends

People who have had diabetes for a long period of time (in some cases undiagnosed and unknown) and whose blood sugar level is not tightly controlled are likely to develop serious long-term complications. These include eye damage or even blindness, heart and circulatory system disease and kidney damage. These complications are usually the result of high blood sugar levels damaging the fine blood vessels (the capillaries) that supply the part of the body involved.

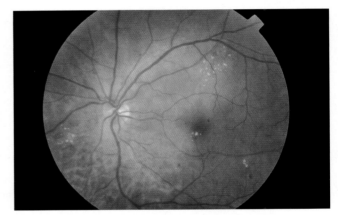

Figure 3.8 Retina of a diabetes sufferer. The areas of small yellow dots, caused by leakage from damaged blood vessels, can cause permanent loss of vision

Recent information suggests that the occurrence of both Type 1 and Type 2 diabetes is increasing. It is unclear why Type 1 diabetes is increasing but it is thought genetic factors are involved and, as it is a condition where the damage to the insulin-producing cells is caused by the body's own immune system, it may be that environmental factors such as pollution are also involved.

The rate of increase of Type 2 diabetes is alarming. In addition, it is now developing in many more young people than previously. With Type 2 the reasons for this increase is much clearer. The failure of insulin to work (as opposed to insulin not being produced, the cause of Type 1 diabetes) is associated with too much sugar intake and obesity, to the extent that the insulin becomes ineffective due to 'overload'. With more people in the population having high-sugar diets and becoming obese, it is not surprising that the number of Type 2 diabetics is increasing. It is thought that as many as 220 million people worldwide may have Type 2 diabetes by 2010.

As the number of people with diabetes is steadily increasing, the cost of treatment is becoming very high – currently almost 10% of the NHS budget. This is largely due to the fact that diabetes is a lifelong condition so treatment is needed for decades. In addition, some of the complications such as kidney damage have significant financial costs.

ACTIVITY

Collect data about the numbers of diabetics in the population. Information can be collected from the internet, from health professionals and from discussion with family members.

Once you have collected your information from a number of sources, describe the factors that influence the validity and reliability of scientific data such as this. If information is **valid** it will be the correct information that you need; if it is **reliable** then other people carrying out the same survey will get the same results.

A greater public awareness of diabetes and the causes of Type 2, together with medical advances, will go some way to reducing the effect of diabetes. Particular medical developments such as the cloning of pancreas cells may eventually provide a cure for many Type 1 diabetics.

websites

www.bbc.co.uk/schools/gcsebitesize/biology/humansasorganisms/4nervoussystemrev4.shtml
animation of reflex arc

www.diabetes.org.uk
many diabetes-related issues

Questions

1 The diagram shows a reflex arc.

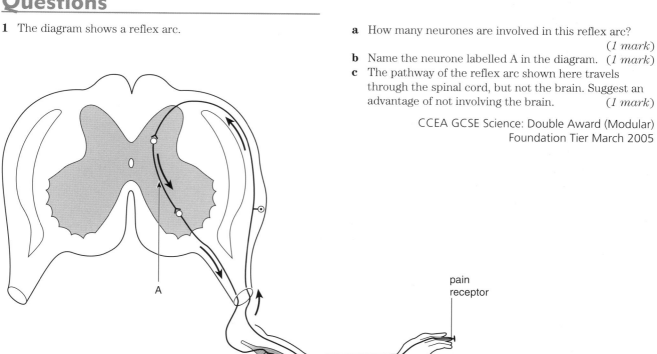

muscle

A

pain receptor

a How many neurones are involved in this reflex arc?
(*1 mark*)

b Name the neurone labelled A in the diagram. (*1 mark*)

c The pathway of the reflex arc shown here travels through the spinal cord, but not the brain. Suggest an advantage of not involving the brain. (*1 mark*)

CCEA GCSE Science: Double Award (Modular) Foundation Tier March 2005

2 A reflex arc consists of several neurones.
  a Name the neurones which carry impulses
    i from a receptor *(1 mark)*
    ii to an effector. *(1 mark)*
  b Copy and complete the diagram to show how these neurones form a reflex arc with an association neurone.

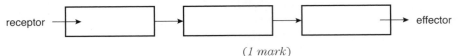

receptor → [→] → [ ] → [ ] → effector

(1 mark)

  c Name the part of the nervous system where association neurones are found. *(1 mark)*
  d Explain how reflex actions can be an advantage over voluntary actions. *(1 mark)*

CCEA GCSE Science: Double Award (Non-modular)
Higher Tier June 2003 (part question)

3 The flow chart shows how high blood glucose levels are controlled by insulin production in the body.

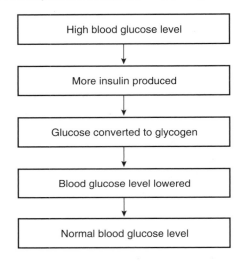

| High blood glucose level |
↓
| More insulin produced |
↓
| Glucose converted to glycogen |
↓
| Blood glucose level lowered |
↓
| Normal blood glucose level |

  a Which organ produces insulin? *(1 mark)*
  b In which organ is glucose converted to glycogen? *(1 mark)*
  c Sarah is diabetic, which means she does not produce her own insulin.

    She gave herself an insulin injection at 8 am. She skipped breakfast and left for school. By break-time, she was feeling very unwell. The school nurse gave her a glucose drink and she quickly felt better.

    Use the flow chart to explain what happened to Sarah's blood glucose level during the morning.

(4 marks)

4 This graph shows changes in blood glucose levels after a meal.

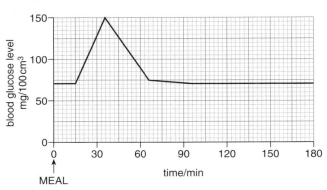

Give a **full** explanation for the shape of the graph.

(4 marks)

CCEA GCSE Science: Double Award (Modular)
Higher Tier May 2005

Chapter 4

Human reproduction and its control

Learning objectives

By the end of this chapter you should know and understand:

➤ The main parts of the male and female reproductive systems and their functions
➤ How a baby develops in the uterus and the process of birth
➤ The importance of a healthy pregnancy and the problems associated with teenage pregnancies
➤ Physical, chemical and surgical methods of contraception
➤ The role of oestrogen and progesterone in the female menstrual cycle

Living organisms need to be able to reproduce otherwise they would no longer be able to exist. Humans, as with most animals, carry out **sexual reproduction**. As noted in Chapter 2, sexual reproduction involves the joining together of two gametes, the sperm and the egg, or ovum. Sexual reproduction produces variation in offspring (see page 50) – this variation is usually easily seen in most families!

Human reproductive systems

Figure 4.1 on the next page shows the female and male reproductive systems.

The functions of the main parts of the reproductive system in females and males are highlighted in Tables 4.1 and 4.2.

Table 4.1 The female reproductive system

Structure	Function
ovaries	Produce eggs
oviducts	Carry the eggs from the ovaries to the uterus. The site of fertilisation
uterus	The structure in which a baby will develop if an egg is fertilised
cervix	The opening of the uterus (closed during pregnancy)
vagina	The opening of the female reproductive system. The male sperm arrives here during sexual intercourse

Table 4.2 The male reproductive system

Structure	Function
testes	The production and development of sperm
sperm tube	Carries the sperm from the testes to the urethra
prostrate gland	Produces a fluid that nourishes and carries the sperm
urethra	The tube that carries the sperm through and out of the penis
penis	Structure that allows the sperm to enter the vagina
scrotum	Structure that holds and protects the testes

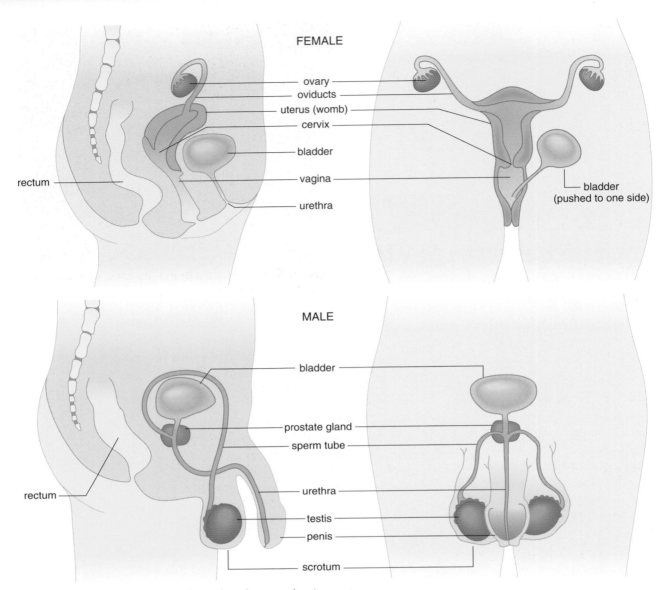

Figure 4.1 The human female and male reproductive systems

Fertilisation, pregnancy and the development of the baby

If a sperm and an ovum meet and fuse (join) in an oviduct, **fertilisation** will result. Following fertilisation, the sperm and egg produce the first cell of the new individual, the **zygote**. This cell then divides and grows into a ball of cells called an **embryo**. The embryo becomes attached (**implanted**) to the wall of the uterus. To enable this to happen the uterus develops a thick lining that holds and nourishes the embryo.

At the point where the embryo begins to develop in the uterus lining, the **placenta** and **umbilical cord** form. A protective membrane, the **amnion**, develops around the embryo and it contains a fluid, the amniotic fluid, within which the growing embryo develops. This fluid cushions the delicate, developing embryo that is referred to as a **fetus** after a few weeks when it begins to become more recognisable as a baby.

Obviously the baby cannot breathe when in the amniotic fluid (its lungs will not be developed well enough, anyway), so during pregnancy useful materials including oxygen pass from the mother to the fetus through the placenta and umbilical cord. Waste materials pass from the fetus back to the mother.

> 1 a Apart from oxygen, name one other essential substance that will pass from the mother to the fetus during pregnancy.
>   b Name one waste material that will pass from the fetus to its mother.

Pregnancy lasts for about nine months in total. The fetus grows a lot in the last two to three months before birth.

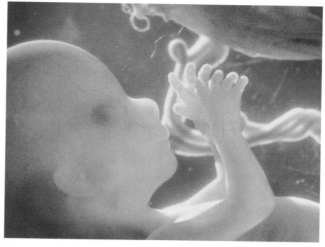

Figure 4.2 Human fetus at four months, showing the umbilical cord and the placenta

Birth

Just before birth the fetus (now called a baby) usually turns upside down in the uterus so that it can be born **head first**. The **uterus muscles begin to contract** and these contractions become more frequent and stronger as birth approaches. In addition, the **cervix widens** (the width of the cervix can help doctors and midwives predict when birth will take place), as it must become wide enough to allow the baby to pass through. The amnion ruptures (the '**breaking of the waters**') and the baby is ready to be born.

The contractions of the uterus force the baby head first through the cervix and out of the vagina. Following birth the umbilical cord is cut and the baby begins to breathe on its own. The placenta ('**after-birth**'), which is now no longer needed, passes out soon after the birth of the baby.

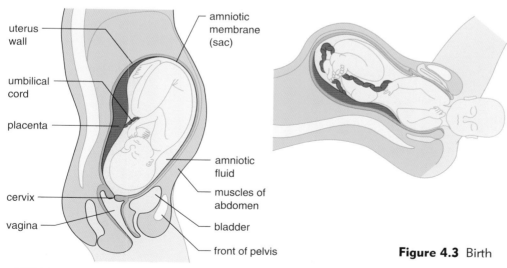

Figure 4.3 Birth

> 2 Give one piece of evidence from the left-hand diagram that suggests that:
>   a birth will soon take place
>   b although it will soon take place, birth is not going to happen immediately.

The healthy pregnancy

There are many factors that contribute to a healthy pregnancy. It is very important that the mother has a good diet during this time. The old phrase 'feeding for two' may be a simple way to describe the importance of a good diet, but it is true that the developing fetus can only get its nutrients from the mother. The mother should have a balanced diet to ensure that the fetus receives all the nutrients required for development.

As the placenta enables the fetus to gain useful materials from the mother's bloodstream, it also allows the fetus to gain harmful substances if any are present in the mother's blood. For this reason it is very important that pregnant mothers do not smoke, take too much alcohol or take harmful drugs during this time. Mothers who smoke tend to produce babies with smaller bodyweights, and alcohol and drugs can harm the development of the baby.

It is also important that the expectant mother has been protected against rubella (German measles), as this can seriously harm the fetus if it is contracted by the mother during pregnancy.

Not surprisingly, expectant mothers should take plenty of rest when pregnant.

Teenage pregnancy

You are probably aware that many school PSHE programmes outline some of the problems that can arise when a young person becomes pregnant. These include:

- teenage pregnancies are usually unplanned
- teenage parents are often in relationships that do not last long-term; consequently many babies born to teenage mothers experience little or no contact with their fathers
- teenage parents often have to disrupt their education/training plans and find employment or become full-time parents
- teenage parents often do not have the life experience and skills to cope effectively with the stresses and strains of having responsibility for a very young child.

Figure 4.4 Teenage pregnancy means a compete change of lifestyle

Even though there are many potential disadvantages with teenage pregnancies, they still occur and in some areas of N. Ireland the rate is quite high compared with some other areas of the UK. Organise a class discussion to suggest some of the reasons why the rate of teenage pregnancies is high, and what can be done to reduce the rates of teenage pregnancies.

Contraception: preventing pregnancy

Often people in a sexual relationship do not want to have a baby at that time. In this situation they use one or more methods of **contraception** – methods that are designed to prevent pregnancy. There are three main types of contraception: **physical**, **chemical** and **surgical** methods. These are each described below.

 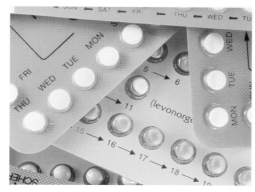

Figure 4.5 Methods of contraception

Some people do not like to use contraceptive methods for a number of reasons including religious or ethical factors. They may try to prevent pregnancy by avoiding sexual intercourse at the time when an ovum is being released. While this **natural method** may reduce the likelihood of pregnancy, it is very unreliable because it is very difficult to know exactly when an ovum is going to be released by an ovary.

Physical methods of contraception

The most commonly used physical, or barrier, method is the **condom**, or sheath. This needs to be fitted over the penis just before sexual intercourse begins. It works by preventing the sperm leaving the male and entering the vagina of the female. Condoms are easily obtained and they are quite effective but not foolproof, as pregnancy can occur due to the condom not being put on properly or being damaged and so allowing sperm to escape.

A big advantage that condoms have over other types of contraceptive is that they help prevent the spread of sexually transmitted diseases such as gonorrhoea and AIDS.

Chemical methods of contraception

Chemical contraception involves the use of a **contraceptive pill**. There are different types of contraceptive pill but the most common form is taken by the female over a set period of days each monthly (menstrual) cycle. It contains female hormones including oestrogen and progesterone. The effect of the pill is to alter hormone levels in the female to prevent the release of an ovum, and therefore pregnancy cannot occur.

The contraceptive pill has clear advantages, including its reliability and the fact that it does not interfere with the process of sexual intercourse. Obviously, though, it will only be effective if the female does not forget to take the pill regularly. There are some health risks and side-effects associated with taking it. For this reason the pill can only be obtained from a doctor or a family planning clinic. Some women taking the contraceptive pill may develop high blood pressure and some may put on weight. Women over 35 are recommended to use other forms of contraception.

Surgical contraception

Surgical contraception is very nearly 100% reliable. This method is really only suitable for those individuals who are absolutely certain that they do not want to have any more children. In males the process is called a **vasectomy** and involves cutting the **sperm tubes** so that sperm cannot enter and leave the penis. In a female it is the **oviducts** that are cut, which prevents ova making contact with any sperm that may be present.

While surgical contraception is very successful as a contraceptive device it is extremely difficult to reverse the process. Consequently, doctors need to be very sure that the people involved will not change their minds after the surgery has taken place.

ACTIVITY

A 35-year-old man goes to his GP asking for a vasectomy. Organise a role play of the discussion that is likely to take place between the GP and the man.

---

3 Why do you think a 25-year-old man who is married with no children is likely to be asked to reconsider his request for a vasectomy?
4 Draw a diagram of the female reproductive system. On it label the ovaries, oviducts, uterus, cervix and vagina, and show where:
   a   ova are released
   b   fertilisation will take place
   c   surgical contraception can take place.
5 Make a table to outline the main advantages and disadvantages of each type of contraception.

Hormones and the menstrual cycle

The process of **menstruation** (having periods) starts in girls at puberty and continues until the end of a woman's reproductive life. Each **menstrual cycle** lasts about 28 days and it is a cyclical event with the release of an ovum, the development of a thick lining on the uterus wall, and the breakdown of this lining (menstruation) occurring in each cycle. The menstrual cycle is controlled by a number of female hormones.

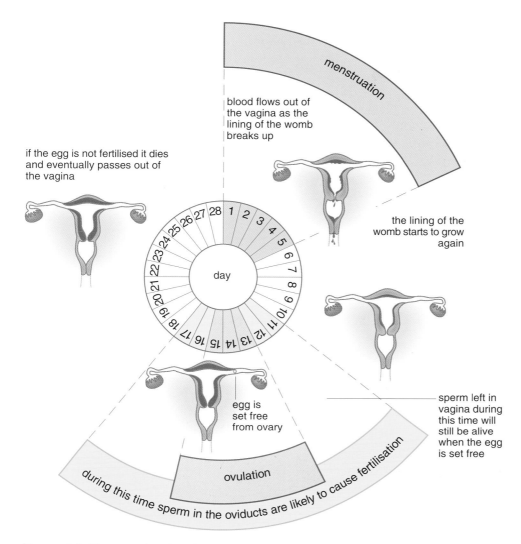

menstruation

blood flows out of the vagina as the lining of the womb breaks up

if the egg is not fertilised it dies and eventually passes out of the vagina

the lining of the womb starts to grow again

day

egg is set free from ovary

sperm left in vagina during this time will still be alive when the egg is set free

ovulation

during this time sperm in the oviducts are likely to cause fertilisation

Figure 4.6 The menstrual cycle

One of the most important female hormones is **oestrogen**. At the start of each menstrual cycle (the onset of bleeding, which we call day 1), the level of oestrogen is low. As the cycle progresses the level of oestrogen rises and peaks in mid-cycle (see Figure 4.7 on the next page), causing the release of the ovum (ovulation).

Another very important hormone is **progesterone**. The level of progesterone is also low at the start of the menstrual cycle and peaks around and in the days following ovulation. The role of progesterone is to build up and maintain the thick uterine lining (and the subsequent development of the placenta and other structures associated with pregnancy), should pregnancy occur. Oestrogen is also important in ensuring that the uterine lining is built up again.

If pregnancy does not occur, the levels of oestrogen and progesterone drop towards the end of the cycle and this causes menstruation to occur. Then the cycle begins again.

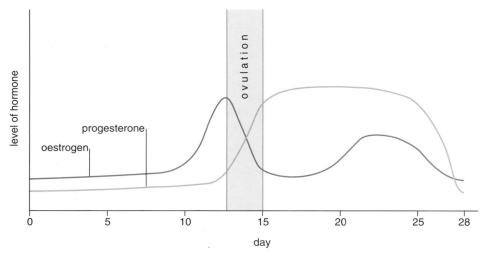

Figure 4.7 Levels of oestrogen and progesterone in a menstrual cycle

6 Suggest why is it important to have a thick lining of the uterus at the time of ovulation.
7 Suggest what happens to the menstrual cycle if pregnancy occurs. Explain your answer.

website

www.fpa.org.uk/about/info/NIteenpreg.htm
useful information about teenage pregnancy in Northern Ireland

Question

1 The diagrams show the male and female reproductive systems.

a Use the labels in the diagrams to identify the structures described below.
Which structure:
   i   produces sperm?
   ii   adds fluid to sperm?
   iii passes sperm out of the male's body?
   iv   releases eggs?
   v   is the place where fertilisation takes place?

(5 marks)

A few days after this, implantation occurs in the uterus and a fetus grows and develops over the next nine months.

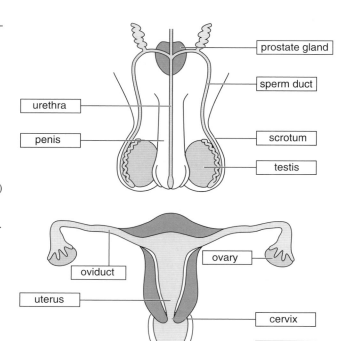

b The diagram shows a fetus in the uterus before it is born.

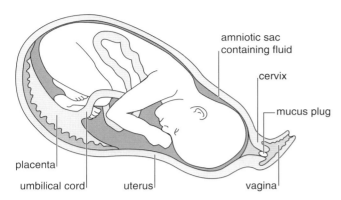

amniotic sac containing fluid

cervix

mucus plug

placenta

umbilical cord   uterus   vagina

i Which structure, shown in the diagram, cushions the fetus in the uterus against knocks and bumps? (*1 mark*)

ii Which structure, shown in the diagram, allows the fetus to get oxygen from its mother? (*1 mark*)

iii Use the labels in the diagram to fill in the blanks in the passage below which describes the process of birth.

One of the first signs of labour is when the muscle wall of the _____ starts to contract. The _____ widens so that the baby can pass into the _____. Soon after this, the baby will be born. (*3 marks*)

c In order to prevent pregnancy, different methods of contraception can be used.

i The table shows some information about four different methods of contraception.
Copy and complete the table to show how condoms and female sterilisation prevent pregnancy.

Method of contraception	How method prevents pregnancy
contraceptive pill	prevents eggs being released
condom	
male sterilisation	prevents sperm from reaching egg
female sterilisation	

(*2 marks*)

ii Which **one** method of contraception, given in the table, can help prevent the spread of sexually transmitted diseases such as AIDS? (*1 mark*)

iii Name **one** method of contraception, given in the table, which is **permanent**. (*1 mark*)

CCEA GCSE Science: Double Award (Modular) Foundation Tier June 2005 (part question)

Chapter 5

Adaptation and variation

Learning objectives

By the end of this chapter you should know and understand:

➤ That variation in living organisms may be caused by genetic and/or environmental factors
➤ That mutations produce genetic variation
➤ That variation and natural selection may lead to evolution
➤ Examples of natural selection in action
➤ Alternatives to natural selection and evolution
➤ The principle of artificial selection and its importance in plant and animal breeding
➤ Factors causing the extinction of species
➤ How to use keys

Variation

There are millions of different types (species) of living organisms in the world today. It is impossible for anyone to learn to recognise more than a tiny fraction of them. Scientists use keys to identify groups of living organisms and even individual species. An example of the use of keys can be found in question 4 at the end of this chapter (page 60).

Even organisms that belong to the same species vary from each other in many ways. This variation is caused by differences in **genetic** makeup and by **environmental** factors. Differences in a particular feature between individuals are usually due to a combination of genetic and environmental factors. A good example is height in humans. A child's genes will determine the potential height that he/she can reach, but he/she will only grow to that height if he/she has a good diet and good overall health. By comparison, eye colour is purely genetic and cannot be affected by any environmental condition. At the other extreme, any differences in the appearance of identical twins must be environmental, because they have identical genetic makeup.

Genetic variation

Sexual reproduction, through a combination of the variation produced in the production of gametes (sex cells) and the random mixing of gametes during fertilisation (you will remember this from Chapter 2), ensures that the genetic makeup of offspring from a particular set of parents will show variation. By contrast, **asexual reproduction** is simply the development of a new individual from a single parent, does not involve gametes, and produces identical offspring, or clones (see Chapter 2).

Environmental variation

This is variation caused by the surrounding environment. Environmental variation is particularly obvious in plants. Plants that are growing in good soils with sufficient supplies of water and minerals will appear very different from plants growing with very poor resources.

Continuous and discontinuous variation

Variation of a particular characteristic can be either continuous or discontinuous. **Continuous variation** is a gradual change in a characteristic across a population. Height is an example of continuous variation in humans. While people can be described as being tall or short, there is not a distinct boundary that separates short and tall people. Figure 5.1 shows a typical set of values for height in human males. The histogram produced shows a 'normal distribution'. A normal distribution is a spread of values with most individual values around the average or mean value and relatively few at either extreme.

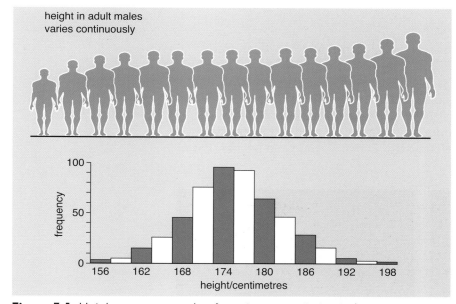

Figure 5.1 Height as an example of continuous variation in humans

When a feature shows **discontinuous variation**, the population can be clearly divided into discrete groups or categories. Examples in humans include the ability, or inability, to roll the tongue (see Figure 5.2) and the presence, or absence, of ear lobes. In each of these examples, individuals will fit into one of two categories – there will be no intermediates. In other examples of discontinuous variation there can be more than two categories, for example blood groups, but again all individuals can clearly be identified as belonging to one particular group.

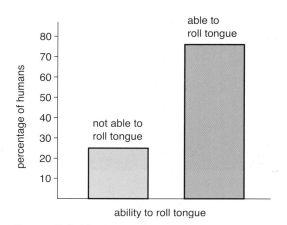

Figure 5.2 Tongue-rolling as an example of discontinuous variation in humans

Collect a number of leaves from two plants/shrubs/trees of the same type. Ideally the two plants you select will be different in some way, for example of different age or growing in different conditions – one might be growing in bright light and one in a more shaded area. Measure some feature of the leaves, for example leaf width or length, for a number of leaves from each of the two plants.

Put your results in a table or a spreadsheet and draw a graph or chart to represent your results.

What type of variation do your results show within each plant? If there are differences in the leaf feature between the two plants, can you explain them?

Are your conclusions reliable and, if so, what did you do when planning your experiment to make sure you achieved reliable results? (Remember that reliable results are results that will be repeated if the experiment is carried out again, even by someone else at another time.)

Mutations

Although variation is a normal feature of sexual reproduction, it can also arise through mistakes in the copying of our chromosomes or genes when new cells are formed. This type of genetic change is called a **mutation**. We have already come across one type of mutation, in Chapter 2: Down's syndrome results from gametes that have one extra chromosome (24 instead of 23) due to a mistake in their production. Figure 5.3 shows a **karyotype** – a chromosome spread – of an individual with Down's syndrome beside that of an individual without the condition.

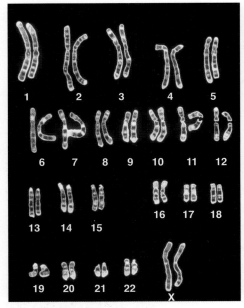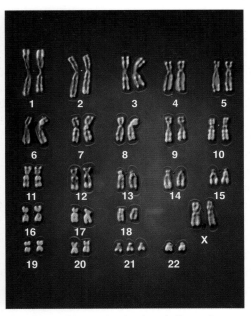

Figure 5.3 Karyotypes of a normal individual (left) and an individual with Down's syndrome (right). Note that with Down's syndrome there is an extra chromosome 21

Many other mutations result in a change in **gene or chromosome structure**, rather than their number.

Mutation is a random process but there are a number of environmental factors that can greatly increase the chances of a mutation occurring. A good example is the link between UV (sun)light and skin cancer.

Cancer is **uncontrolled cell division**, which forms a **tumour** – a growth of new cells that the body does not need. Tumours can cause very serious harm if they develop in the wrong place.

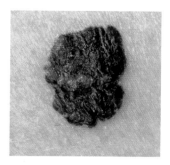

Figure 5.4 Skin cancer

ACTIVITY

Organise a debate to discuss the benefits and disadvantages of getting a tan. Before the discussion you may want to do some research on the internet and from other sources.

1 a Suggest why the incidence (occurrence) of skin cancer in people who live in the British Isles has increased dramatically in recent times.
  b Outline the precautionary measures that can be taken to decrease the likelihood of getting skin cancer.

Variation, selection and evolution

If there is a lot of variation between the animals or plants of the same species (type), it is likely that some of the individuals will be better equipped to prosper or survive in their environment. That is, they are better **adapted**.

Natural selection

In nature, adaptations in living organisms are essential for survival and success in all different habitats. It is not difficult to work out some of the main adaptations in polar bears, for example. These adaptations are even more important when living organisms compete with each other for resources. This **competition** ensures that the best-adapted individuals will survive. For example, the larger seedlings growing in a clump of plants will be able to obtain vital resources such as light, nutrients and water more easily than the smaller seedlings. As a result of this competition the stronger individuals will survive, possibly at the expense of the weaker ones. This competition for survival with the result that the better-equipped individuals survive is the cornerstone of Charles Darwin's theory of **natural selection**.

Charles Darwin (1809–1882) was a naturalist who devoted much of his life to scientific research. As part of his studies he spent five years as a ship's naturalist on the HMS Beagle as it travelled to South America. Darwin was greatly influenced by the variety of life he observed on his travels, in particular the unusual animals of the Galapagos Islands.

Darwin and another scientist, Alfred Wallace, who independently came to the same conclusions as Darwin, jointly presented their theories in a scientific paper titled *On the Origin of Species by Means of Natural Selection* to the Linnean Society in London in 1859.

Darwin's main conclusions can be summarised as follows.

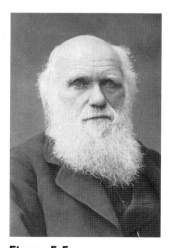

Figure 5.5
Charles Darwin

- Living organisms usually produce more young than can survive. In many species it is the availability of food that limits survival.
- There is variation between the individuals in a population.
- Consequently there is a **struggle for existence**.
- The better-adapted individuals survive this struggle or competition. This leads to **survival of the fittest**.
- The best-adapted individuals are more likely to survive to breed. Consequently they will be the ones that are more likely to pass their characteristics (variations) on to offspring.

It is useful to look at some examples of natural selection 'in action' to highlight the key features of Darwin's theory. The first example below shows how a species can change genetically over a short period of time. The second example is one of the most studied examples of natural selection, the peppered moth.

Antibiotic resistance in bacteria

When bacteria are treated with an antibiotic (see page 68) such as penicillin, most of the bacteria are destroyed. However, a small number (the fittest) may survive, probably because they have a mutation that provides resistance. Very soon the resistant bacteria are the only ones surviving and they reproduce rapidly to produce a large number of bacteria that are all resistant to penicillin.

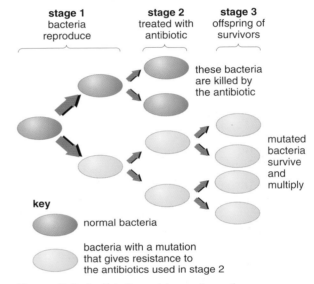

Figure 5.6 Antibiotic resistance in action

> 2 Use the information in Figure 5.6 to suggest how 'superbugs' (bacteria that are resistant to many types of antibiotic) may develop.

The peppered moth

The peppered moth is common in much of the UK. The moth has two very distinct forms. One type has light-coloured (speckled) wings and the other has black wings. A single gene controls the difference in colour, with different alleles of this gene causing the different appearances.

Up until the beginning of the Industrial Revolution, very few of the black form of the moths were seen in the British Isles. This was because the black variety was easily spotted on the lichen-covered trees by predatory birds, and was quickly eaten. The speckled (light-coloured) form of the moth was ideally camouflaged (see Figure 5.7, left) and so was less likely to be eaten.

In 1850, in some areas of the country that were beginning to become industrialised, less than 1% of the peppered moths were black. But within 50 years almost all the moths in these regions were black. This can be explained by the changes that the Industrial Revolution was causing to the environment. The bark of the trees in industrialised areas was becoming blackened due to the large volume of soot in the air. In these areas the black form of moth became the better camouflaged and better adapted, and it was the speckled form that was most easily picked off by birds (Figure 5.7, right).

Figure 5.7 The lighter, speckled moth is well camouflaged on the lichen-covered bark, but is not camouflaged on the blackened bark. The black moth is better camouflaged on this blackened bark

This is an excellent example of natural selection in action. The mutation that produces the black form of moth happens fairly often but in non-industrial areas it obviously disadvantages them and moths with this mutation are quickly eliminated. The mutation became beneficial when the black form was the better camouflaged and therefore the ratio of black to speckled forms increased.

Darwin and evolution

Darwin used his theory of natural selection to explain the process of **evolution**. He suggested that species have changed gradually through time in response to changes in the environment, and that evolution is a **continuing process**. He was not the first to propose that organisms could evolve but his theory was based on much stronger scientific evidence than other earlier versions.

Controversially, Darwin suggested that the theory of evolution applied to all living organisms, including humans. When his theory was first proposed there was considerable opposition to his ideas for a number of reasons. These included:

- It clearly contradicted the teaching of the Church on creation and on the uniqueness of humans.
- There was no explanation as to how variation was caused nor how these variations were passed on to offspring. Darwin then had no knowledge of Mendel and his work on genetics (see page 20).
- He could not demonstrate natural selection in action. Darwin could only observe the process of selection at a given point in time. He did not observe change actually occurring. He was not aware of examples such as the peppered moth and antibiotic resistance in bacteria.

The current position

Following the widespread publication of Mendel's work on genetics, many of the missing parts of the evolution jigsaw were put in place, including the genetic basis of variation and inheritance. Our increased knowledge of how DNA works and the way in which mutations happen helps provide a deeper understanding of the processes of natural selection and evolution.

Darwin's theory is further supported by the extensive fossil record and by other evidence including our greater understanding of living organisms and the relationships between them.

Is evolution the only explanation?

Evolution is not accepted by everyone as being the full, or correct, explanation of how life has developed on Earth. Some people claim that **creationism** – the belief that God created all living organisms as they are today, in the short timescale set out in the Bible – is the correct explanation. Many others believe that a combination of both ideas may be the answer. They accept that the evidence for evolution over a long period of time is so strong it cannot be discounted, but suggest that the theory of evolution cannot explain how life actually began, nor does it preclude the possibility of there being a 'higher being' that is overseeing the development of life on Earth. The belief that a higher being, rather than the random mutations put forward by 'Darwinism', is responsible for evolutionary changes is termed 'intelligent design'.

Irrespective of an individual's beliefs on this issue, it is not difficult to understand why it has taken so long for many to believe in Darwin's theory of evolution and also why there was so much hostility when it was first proposed.

Artificial selection (selective breeding)

For centuries now, people have manipulated the course of natural selection and evolution by deliberately selecting particular characteristics or traits in many plants and animals that are of use to us. This is the process of **artificial selection**. Characteristics that are advantageous include increased crop yield and food value, more attractive produce, better storage properties, hardiness and disease resistance.

Artificial selection in plants

Our manipulation of selection in cereals has been used to create plants that bear very little resemblance to their early ancestors. Typically in cereals the process has been designed to produce plants that give high yield and are less susceptible to disease and harsh weather conditions. Figure 5.8 opposite shows how selective breeding has been used to produce our modern variety of wheat, and Figure 5.9 compares the wheat before and after selection.

The benefits of selective breeding in wheat are easy to identify. There is a greater yield per plant and the short modern plants are less easily damaged by wind. The uniform height means that harvesting is easier and quicker.

Selective breeding in animals

Selective breeding in animals uses the same principles as with plants. Domestic animals have been bred to produce animals with high milk yields, good meat qualities and almost any other characteristic that affects the profitability or value of the animal. The number of varieties that can be produced is almost limitless, as can be seen in the breeding of dogs.

In recent times, selective breeding has become more sophisticated with the use of artificial insemination to more tightly control the variety of genes that will be present in offspring.

The use of cloning, as discussed in Chapter 2 (see page 30), is an extreme example of selective breeding where the exact genetic makeup of all offspring can be controlled.

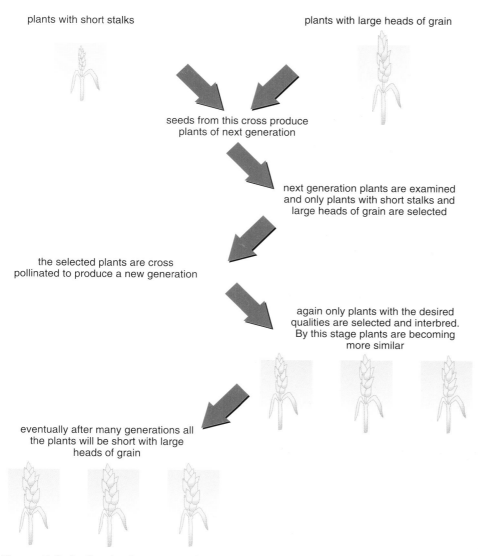

plants with short stalks

plants with large heads of grain

seeds from this cross produce plants of next generation

next generation plants are examined and only plants with short stalks and large heads of grain are selected

the selected plants are cross pollinated to produce a new generation

again only plants with the desired qualities are selected and interbred. By this stage plants are becoming more similar

eventually after many generations all the plants will be short with large heads of grain

Figure 5.8 Artificial selection in wheat

Figure 5.9a Wheat used to consist of stalks of variable size. The number of seeds per head also varied

Figure 5.9b In a field of modern wheat all the stems are of a similar height and the heads contain many seeds

Extinction of species

An organism is described as being **extinct** if there are no living examples of its species left. The fossil record shows that many animals and plants have become extinct through time. The most famous examples include the dinosaurs and mammoths.

Most of the animals and plants that have become extinct have disappeared because they could not evolve fast enough to cope with a changing environment. The fossil record suggests that extinctions have often been associated with climate change. It is possible that other catastrophic events such as meteors striking the Earth could also have disrupted the environment to such an extent to cause the extinction of organisms.

The woolly mammoth (Figure 5.10), a large elephant-like mammal, became extinct at the time of the last Ice Age (10 000–11 000 years ago), probably because of the loss of much of its natural habitat.

Figure 5.10 Woolly mammoths

Although extinctions have always occurred, there is irrefutable evidence that the activities of humans have been directly or indirectly responsible for the extinction or near-extinction of many plants and animals.

This may result from the direct hunting or collection of animals or plants, but the destruction of habitat may have an even more devastating effect. The threat to the giant panda due to the loss of bamboo forests, and the daily extinctions that probably occur as much of the Amazon rainforest is cleared, are now well known. However, there are also many local examples where plants and animals have been driven to the verge of extinction or made extinct by the action of people.

ACTIVITY

Collect information on a number of species that have become extinct since Man has been on Earth. For example, you could research giant flightless birds such as the emu and the dodo. Try to identify the role of humans (if any) in the fate of the species you choose.

Many species are endangered to the extent that their numbers are so low that extinction is a real possibility in the future. Again, factors such as climate change, the loss of habitats and hunting are all contributing.

There is now a greater awareness of our role in the process of population reduction, and attempts are being made to protect the endangered species we have left. Protective measures include:

- **legislation** covering climate-changing emissions, habitat removal and the hunting of endangered species
- improved **education** to make governments around the world and individuals more aware of environmental issues
- **special programmes** such as the setting up of special areas where the threatened species are protected.

While these measures are important, there is much more that could be done. The protective measures listed above (and others) will be discussed in more detail in Chapter 7.

ACTIVITY

Research one or more endangered species such as the giant panda, the orang-utan, or the local corncrake. Find out what is the likely cause of their reduction in numbers, and what attempts are being made to reverse this.

websites

www.bbc.co.uk/education/darwin
useful summaries of natural selection, evolution and extinction

www.nhm.ac.uk
link to Nature Online and then to Evolution

www.wwf.org.uk/core/
links to up-to-date information on endangered species and conservation

Questions

1 The diagram shows the variation in height of a group of men.

a Name the type of variation shown by the height of the group. *(1 mark)*

The factors which cause such variation are genetic and environmental.

b i What is a genetic factor? *(1 mark)*

Food is an environmental factor.

ii Suggest how food may cause variation in height. *(2 marks)*

Tongue rolling is a characteristic which shows a different type of variation.

c Name this type of variation and explain how it differs from that shown by height. *(2 marks)*

CCEA GCSE Science:
Biology (Higher Tier) 2005

2 The number of people suffering from skin cancer has increased in the last sixty years.

a Name the type of radiation in sunlight which can cause skin cancer and explain how it causes cancer.

(2 marks)

b Suggest why skin cancer is becoming more common.

(1 mark)

c If skin cancer is detected early it has a 99% cure rate. Explain why early detection is important *(1 mark)*

The diagram shows some ways to reduce the risk of skin cancer.

Source: www.skincancerfacts.org.uk

d Explain why outdoor workers are advised to wear clothes made from tightly woven fabric. *(1 mark)*

e Suggest why it is safer to stay out of the sun between 11 am and 3 pm. *(1 mark)*

CCEA GCSE Science: Biology (Higher Tier) 2004 (part question)

3 Clover is a plant that is eaten by slugs.
There are two types of clover, Cyanose and Acyanose.

> Cyanose clover – contains cyanide which is poisonous to slugs.
> Acyanose clover – does not contain cyanide and so is **not poisonous** to slugs.

An area was planted with 50 Cyanose and 50 Acyanose clover plants.
Some slugs were introduced into the area.
After six months, there were 76 Cyanose clover plants and 24 Acyanose clover plants in the area.

a What type of selection is shown by the clover plants?

(1 mark)

b Use the information given and your knowledge of selection to explain the increase in the number of Cyanose clover plants. *(3 marks)*

CCEA GCSE Science: Double Award (Modular) Higher Tier June 2004 (part question)

4 Below are pictures of five invertebrates labelled A, B, C, D and E.

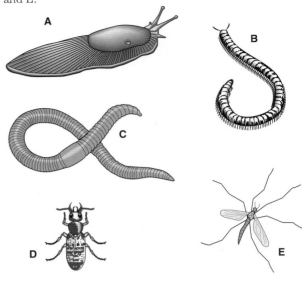

Use the following key to identify these five invertebrates.

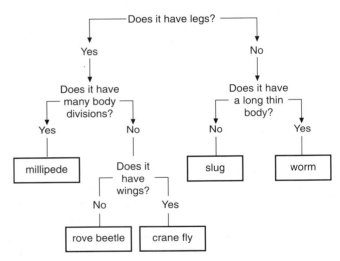

Name each invertebrate A–E. *(5 marks)*

CCEA GCSE Science: Single Award (Modular) May 2003 (part question)

Chapter 6

Defence against disease

By the end of this chapter you should know and understand:

➤ That diseases can be caused by bacteria, viruses and fungi
➤ Details of some common examples of diseases
➤ The action of antibodies, phagocytes, antibiotics and vaccinations in producing immunity
➤ The use of aseptic techniques in culturing microbes
➤ The discovery of penicillin
➤ The stages in the development of medicines and drugs
➤ The use and misuse of drugs

Microbes

It is very easy to take good health for granted, but from time to time we all fall ill. Most illnesses in this part of the world, while often making us feel very poorly, usually only last for a short period of time.

These illnesses are usually caused by very small living organisms called **micro-organisms**, or **microbes**, which are around us all the time but need to gain entry to the body before causing harm. Most microbes are so small that they can only be seen with a powerful microscope. There are three main types of microbe that can cause infection: **bacteria**, **viruses** and **fungi**. Microbes that cause disease are referred to as pathogens.

Louis Pasteur, a scientist in the 19th century who has become very famous, carried out a well known experiment to show the role of air-borne microbes in the contamination of drink or food. Before Pasteur's work it was assumed that when wine, juice or milk became contaminated, the microbes causing the contamination had spontaneously appeared (they appeared from nowhere!) – this was the theory of **spontaneous generation**. Pasteur carried out some research using strange 'swan neck' flasks (see Figure 6.1) to see whether in fact the microbes came from the air. He proved that microbes were not spontaneously created. Only the juice in flask B became contaminated, where microbes could gain entry through the open neck.

Pasteur's work has helped us understand a feature of many well known diseases in humans – that microbes have to gain entry to the body before they cause harm.

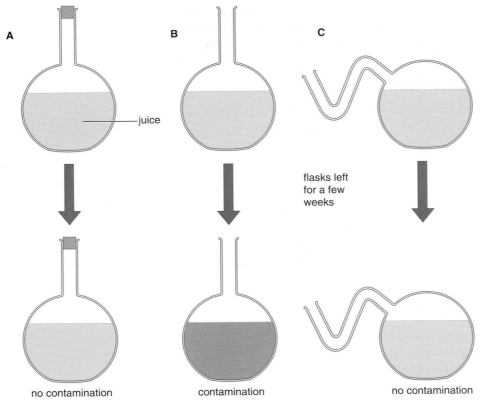

Figure 6.1 Pasteur's 'swan neck' experiment

> **1 a** In Pasteur's experiment, why would the flasks and their contents need to be sterilised by heating before being left?
>
> **b** Explain why the juice in flasks A and C did not get contaminated.

Examples of diseases caused by microbes

- **Bacterial diseases** include the sexually transmitted disease **gonorrhoea**, **tuberculosis (TB)**, which mainly affects the lungs, and **salmonella**, which is a major cause of food poisoning.
- **Viral diseases** include the **colds** and **flu** that almost all of us will have experienced; also **chickenpox**, **rubella**, **polio** and the potentially fatal condition **AIDS**.
- Common **fungal diseases** include **athlete's foot** and **thrush**.

Most of these diseases are infectious diseases, that is, they are passed from one person to another.

How can we defend against infectious disease?

The human body is well adapted to protect us against infection. The body is very successful at preventing most microbes from gaining entry, plus it has very effective defences against those microbes that do get in.

The **skin** itself is an excellent barrier to microbes, and the openings to the body such as the nose and the respiratory system are protected by **mucous membranes** that trap the microbes and prevent them getting any further. **Clotting** of blood at a wound is also important as a defence mechanism. The process of clotting stops more blood escaping but it also acts as a barrier against infection.

If a microbe does get into the body, it is the blood system that usually combats the invader. The blood is very effective in this role, but we are often ill for a period of time before the defence system gains the upper hand.

Antigens and antibodies

Invading microbes have chemicals on their surface that the body can recognise as being foreign. These chemicals are called **antigens**. They cause special white blood cells called **lymphocytes** to produce **antibodies**. As Figure 6.2 shows, these antibodies have a shape that matches the shape of the antigens on the microbes. The antibodies combine with the microbes (like a jigsaw puzzle) and cause them to clump together. Once clumped or immobilised, they are easily destroyed by other white blood cells called **phagocytes** in a process called **phagocytosis**.

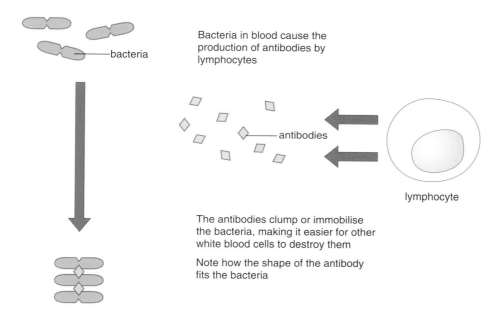

bacteria

Bacteria in blood cause the production of antibodies by lymphocytes

antibodies

lymphocyte

The antibodies clump or immobilise the bacteria, making it easier for other white blood cells to destroy them

Note how the shape of the antibody fits the bacteria

Figure 6.2 The action of antibodies

Phagocytosis

Phagocytes move around in the blood and can destroy microbes trapped by antibodies, or they can destroy microbes directly without antibody action. The phagocyte surrounds the microbe and engulfs (eats) it, as seen in Figure 6.3 on the next page. Eventually chemicals inside the phagocyte digest the microbe and destroy it.

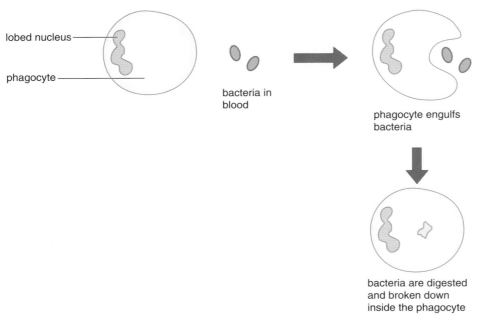

lobed nucleus

phagocyte

bacteria in blood

phagocyte engulfs bacteria

bacteria are digested and broken down inside the phagocyte

Figure 6.3 Phagocytosis in action

Immunity

Individuals who are protected against a particular infection or disease are described as being **immune** to that disease. Most people will be immune to a number of diseases. If someone is immune this means that his or her antibody levels have become high enough (or high enough antibody levels can be produced quickly enough) to combat the microbe should it gain entry to the body again. Figure 6.4 shows what happens in the period following first infection. The level of antibody rises as the white blood cells that produce the correct antibodies are stimulated by the presence of the microbe's antigens. After a period of time the antibodies reach a level that will:

- be high enough to combat the infection and allow the patient to recover
- be high enough to prevent the individual becoming ill from that particular disease in the months or years ahead (in reality it is not that the antibodies remain at a high level in the blood but that the first infection causes the production of special 'memory cells' that can very rapidly produce the antibodies that match the antigens of this microbe when required).

This type of immunity is called **active immunity**, as it is **the body that produces the antibodies** to combat the invading microbe. The graph in Figure 6.4 shows that, at least on first infection, there is a time factor in reaching the required antibody level, and so in some situations, for example when it is thought that an individual has been infected by a serious disease-causing microbe for the first time, a very rapid defence is needed to prevent illness.

Passive immunity can be used in this situation. This is the use of ready-made antibodies that are injected into the body. They can act very rapidly but can only last for a short time, because there are no memory cells to produce more antibodies. Figure 6.5 shows how the level of antibody peaks and drops. Note that the time scale is in days.

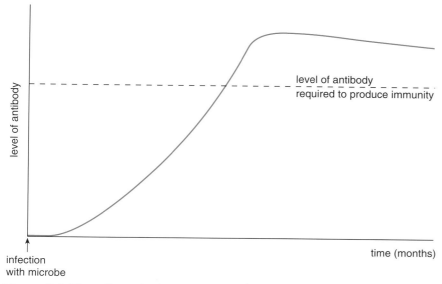

Figure 6.4 The effect of infection on antibody level

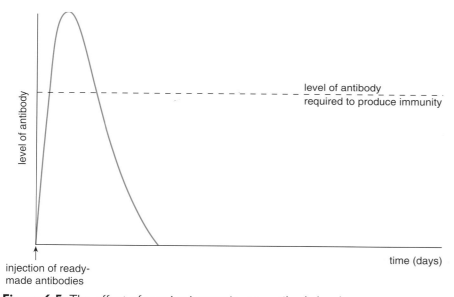

Figure 6.5 The effect of passive immunity on antibody level

Active immunity can also be developed through the use of vaccinations.

Vaccinations

Vaccination involves the injection of dead or modified pathogens (disease-causing microbes) into the body. The dead or modified microbes still have the antigens present that cause the body to produce the antibodies (and memory cells) at a high enough level to prevent the individual from becoming ill at a later time. The process is exactly the same as having caught the disease – except the big difference is you don't get ill! Sometimes we need more than one vaccination to make sure that we will remain immune for a reasonable period of time. Then a follow-up 'booster' is given. Figure 6.6 shows what happens following a vaccination that involves a booster.

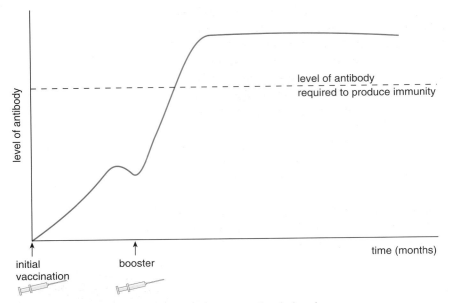

Figure 6.6 The effect of vaccination on antibody level

The medical profession recommends that children are vaccinated against a number of infectious diseases. The **MMR immunisation programme** is an example; this programme is designed to give protection against measles, mumps and rubella, all viral illnesses that used to be very common. Normally the first dose of the MMR vaccine is given between the ages of 1 and 2 years, with the second (booster) dose given three years later.

> **2** Why do you think most immunisation programmes are targeted at young children and not adults?
>
> **3** Why is it important that the microbes used in vaccination are dead or modified in some way?
>
> **4** Summarise the main differences between passive and active immunity. What are the advantages and disadvantages of each?

Vaccines: benefits and problems

The MMR immunisation programme is only one of a number of vaccination programmes that are in place in the UK. Children are vaccinated against polio, TB and other illnesses as well. However, there is often debate over whether to vaccinate or not, and some parents decide not to have their children vaccinated against MMR and other illnesses.

But why does this happen? The immediate benefits of vaccination are obvious, as children who are vaccinated are very much less likely to catch the illnesses they are vaccinated against. The more children who are vaccinated, the less likely it will be that an epidemic (a widely spread infection) will occur. The cost of treating patients with these illnesses will drop, because fewer people will be infected.

The problems associated with vaccinations are much less clear. Some children can feel unwell for a short period of time after a vaccination, and there are costs associated with vaccination programmes as well with treatment. However, it is the possibility of there being unknown (or as yet unproven) side effects to vaccinations that causes most concern for some people.

There have been suggestions that a possible link exists between the MMR vaccination and the development of autism (a permanent condition which causes the patient to have great difficulty in communicating with and understanding people). In 1998 this claim was made in the publication of some controversial research. This, when portrayed in the media, obviously had an effect on parents' attitudes to having their children immunised. Most scientists disagree with this viewpoint, however, and claim that there is no link at all between the MMR vaccination and autism.

The medical profession and the Government generally accept that there is no link – otherwise there would not be an immunisation programme. But it is easy to understand why some parents remain unsure whether to vaccinate or not.

This debate has resulted in many surveys and much further research to try to identify whether or not a link exists between the MMR vaccination and autism. Research is still ongoing. Recent evidence suggests that there is not a link.

In 2005 it was recorded that over 90% of eligible children in Northern Ireland were immunised with the MMR vaccination and that this was the highest uptake for a number of years. Statistics for England are not as positive; these show immunisation rates of just over 80% in 2004 compared with over 90% before the controversial research linking the MMR vaccination to autism was published.

A commonsense approach is probably the best. There is no doubt that for society a full immunisation programme will ensure that the outbreak of a particular disease is much less likely. Nonetheless, it is right that there is ongoing research into the safety of vaccinations and that everyone should be informed about medical issues that affect them.

Figure 6.7

ACTIVITY

Organise a classroom debate about the advantages and disadvantages of having the MMR vaccination. You will probably want to carry out some internet research about this first. What will happen (and is happening) if the number of children being immunised decreases? You may wish to debate whether children should be forced to become immunised by legislation, or whether this should be left to parental choice. What is the role of your school in immunisation programmes?

Travel and vaccination

People who travel to some foreign countries, particularly in Africa and the Far East, are expected, or sometimes required, to be vaccinated against certain diseases. This is because in some countries there are pathogens that can cause serious illnesses that do not exist (or are not common) in the UK. We therefore will not have built up antibody defences against them. It is not difficult to imagine the harm that could be caused by arriving back home from a holiday with an infectious disease that is usually not found in the UK.

> **5** Vaccinations that are necessary for foreign holidays have to be paid for, because they are not provided free by the NHS. Can you suggest why most vaccination programmes are free but those required for foreign travel are not?

Epidemics and pandemics

These two terms describe widespread infections. We use the term **epidemic** when the disease, such as flu, rapidly spreads through a town or a small region like Northern Ireland. A **pandemic** is much more widespread and may affect several countries, for example there is a lot of talk these days about the possibility of a bird flu pandemic.

Epidemics and pandemics are obviously more likely to happen if the microbe can be spread easily, as with flu, but also if it is more difficult to control such as when the disease-causing microbes **mutate** (change). This has happened with many types of flu in the past. Although there is a vaccination for flu, there is always the risk that this vaccination will not work if a slightly different variety of microbe (and flu) develops because of a mutation. The reason why AIDS is difficult to treat is because of the mutation of the virus that causes it.

> **6** Use the information in the paragraph above to explain why you can catch a cold or the flu more than once.

Antibiotics

Antibiotics are medicines that can be taken to help combat bacterial infections. Most people have had antibiotics at some time in their lives to defend against bacterial conditions such as septic throats or infected wounds in the skin. Antibiotics kill bacteria, as can be seen in the agar plate in Figure 6.8. Agar is a jelly-like substance that contains nutrients to help microbes to grow.

Antibiotics are not as specific as antibodies, in that they are not designed to combat only one type of bacterium. They usually act against a range of bacteria. However, different types of antibiotics have different effects on different bacteria. For this reason a GP may prescribe different antibiotics at different times for the same patient if the bacterial infections are different.

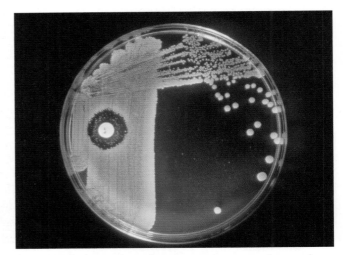

Figure 6.8 Agar plate showing a clear area (around the white circle on the left) where the antibiotic (penicillin) has killed bacteria growing on the jelly

Bacterial resistance to antibiotics

Bacterial resistance to antibiotics was used as an example of natural selection in Chapter 5. This is making many antibiotics ineffective against many bacteria and is becoming a major problem. The overuse of antibiotics in recent times is largely responsible. This has allowed many types of bacteria to come in contact with the main antibiotics and develop mutated resistant forms. It is these resistant forms that are now common. It is therefore very important that antibiotics are only used when they are really necessary.

'Superbugs' and MRSA

Some bacteria have developed resistance to the extent that they are now referred to as '**superbugs**' and these are responsible for a number of serious medical conditions. One example is **MRSA**, which is resistant to most types of bacteria and is a very serious problem in hospitals. It is life-threatening to the elderly in particular. The headline in Figure 6.9 is typical of many that have appeared in the press lately. There has been media speculation that superbugs are at their most dangerous in hospitals because of poor standards of hygiene in some hospitals. Is this really fair?

There is no doubt that high levels of hygiene are very important in preventing the spread of microbes, but other factors also allow superbugs to infect patients in hospital. Patients often have weak immune systems due to illness, or they may be recovering from surgery and have wounds allowing the microbes entry to the body. Nonetheless, new measures in hospitals include increased levels of hygiene such as the immediate cleaning of spillages of body fluids and the wearing of disposable gloves and so on.

Figure 6.9

Antibiotics and livestock rearing

It is thought that in recent years more than half the antibiotics produced throughout the world have been used on animals. They are used to treat infections in the animals concerned, and in intensive farming they are also commonly given to healthy animals to prevent infection. These antibiotics can also act as growth promoters, possibly because the animals use fewer resources in fighting infection and therefore faster growth rates result.

However, many types of bacteria have become resistant to these antibiotics because of the widespread use. As the same types of antibiotics are used to combat human infections, it is not surprising that many human disease-causing bacteria have become antibiotic resistant.

Following much research and debate, the use of antibiotics as growth promoters has been banned in Europe from 2006.

---

7 a Suggest why infectious diseases are likely to be more common in animals that are intensively farmed.

  b Suggest one economic reason for not banning the use of antibiotics as growth promoters.

Working with microbes in the laboratory

It is possible to grow microbes in the laboratory and to see the effect of antibiotics on them. When working with microbes in a school environment there are important health and safety precautions that need to be taken. These include:

- not eating or drinking in the laboratory
- culturing microbes in sealed containers
- not culturing microbes at body temperature
- sterilising or disposing of all equipment after use
- washing hands thoroughly after use.

It is very important that the microbes you are working with do not contaminate anything else. The safety measures listed above will help prevent this. It is also important that the microbes themselves are not contaminated by other microbes in the air or on surrounding surfaces. The use of **aseptic techniques** in the laboratory helps to prevent contamination. Figure 6.10 shows the aseptic techniques used prior to transferring microbes from a culture flask to an agar plate and then spreading them.

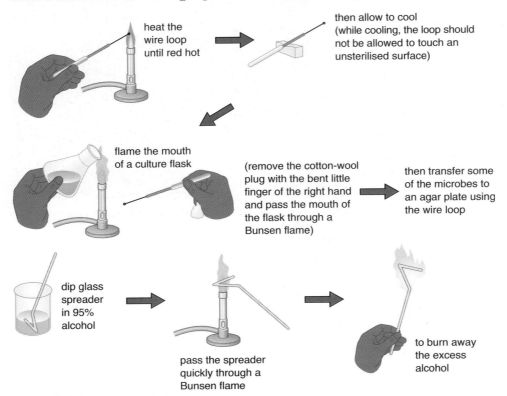

Figure 6.10 Aseptic techniques

Figure 6.11 shows how the microbes can be spread over an agar plate to allow them to grow and form a 'lawn' over much of the plate. After a series of 'spreads' the individual colonies formed are pure – they have each developed from one microbe, as the spreading has separated or diluted the microbes sufficiently. This **spread plate** method can be used to produce pure colonies of bacteria or fungi. The spread plate method of growing microbes was used in culturing the bacteria in Figure 6.8 (page 68).

(page 68)

ACTIVITY

Use aseptic techniques to spread a layer of bacteria on an agar plate. You do not need to follow the 'spread plate' technique exactly as described above, but instead spread the bacteria evenly over the agar. Place a 'multidisk', containing either different antibiotics or different strengths of the same antibiotic, on the agar. After a few days the effectiveness of the antibiotics can be determined by the size of the 'bacteria-free' area around each antibiotic.

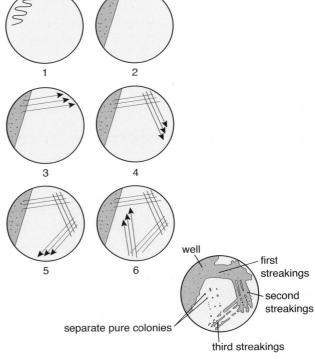

Figure 6.11 Producing pure colonies of a microbe

Discovering medicines

Medicines have been around for a very long time. Medicines are substances that help us recover from illnesses, or that reduce discomfort or pain. Some traditional medicines may seem very different from the types we get from the pharmacist today. Rubbing dock on nettle stings to reduce pain is a very old remedy, as is the use of iodine to help heal cuts.

Figure 6.12 Alexander Fleming at work in his laboratory

The discovery of medicines in earlier times often occurred by accident or chance. An example of this can be seen in one of the most famous medical discoveries of the last century – the discovery of **penicillin**, the first antibiotic. In 1928 **Alexander Fleming** was growing bacteria on agar plates and noticed that one of his plates had become contaminated with mould (fungi) – this is very likely to happen when culturing bacteria unless very effective aseptic techniques are used. The growth of mould did not surprise Fleming but he was surprised when he observed that the bacteria he was culturing did not grow around the edges of the mould. He concluded that the fungi produced a substance that prevented the growth of the bacteria. As the fungus causing the contamination was *Penicillium*, the anti-bacterial substance was named penicillin and the first antibiotic was born.

Fleming carried out some work with his anti-bacterial substance on animals but progress was hindered because he was unable to produce a pure form of the substance.

In the early 1940s two other British scientists, Florey and Chain, were able to isolate a pure form of penicillin and trial it on mice initially and then on humans, in a similar way to which drugs are tested today – see below. The large-scale production of penicillin then began. It has been in widespread use since then, but is now only one of a large number of antibiotics in use.

New medicines are continually being developed. The research and development of new medicines and drugs has made the pharmaceutical industry a major contributor to developed economies today.

Developing new medicines: the stages and the issues

There are a number of stages that new medicines and drugs go through before they become commercially available. Usually the process takes many years from start to finish.

The medicines or drugs need to be developed in the laboratory. This is described as **in vitro testing** and is used to see how effective the drugs are against cells grown in laboratory conditions. Unless the scientists find that in vitro testing has shown that the drug being tested works for the purpose intended and that living cells are not harmed by it, further testing of the drug is unlikely to take place.

Figure 6.13 In vitro testing in the laboratory

Animal testing is usually the next stage. This is a very contentious issue. Many people are very opposed to animal testing but it has been a very important part of the process of developing new drugs in the past. Scientists say that animal testing is needed, as testing on small groups of cells in the laboratory is very different from testing on entire animals with complete immune and other systems.

While no one likes the idea of animal testing, most feel that it is a necessary evil in ensuring that drugs are not harmful. Rabbits, guinea pigs, rats and mice are specially bred purely for medical research and there are very strict regulations to ensure that the animals are treated in as humane a way as possible.

Scientists cannot always be certain, however, that the effect a drug has on one of these small animals will be the same on a human. This is because we are different species and our bodies are not likely to act in exactly the same way. For this reason some very important animal testing is carried out on animals that are very similar to humans, such as chimpanzees and monkeys. This obviously presents a very difficult ethical issue. A lot of people would like to see effective alternatives to animal testing introduced as soon as possible.

Figure 6.14 Some people hold very strong views against animal testing ('vivisection')

Not surprisingly then, there is considerable investment in the development of alternatives to animal testing. More advanced in vitro testing methods enable scientists to have a better idea of how effective drugs will be, and of possible side effects. Computer modelling also allows the prediction of the effects of drugs.

ACTIVITY

Organise a debate or discussion about the rights and wrongs of animal testing. How do you think someone's views would be affected by having a close relative very seriously ill with a condition that could only be cured by the development of a new drug?

Clinical trials are necessary following the earlier stages in drug development described above. Before this stage everyone needs to be as sure as possible that the drug targets the illness and that there are no serious side effects. Clinical trials usually start with small-scale 'pilot' programmes, on volunteers who may be healthy or may have the illness at which the drug is targeted. Over time, trials with larger numbers of patients take place. The aims of these are:

- to see how effective the drug is
- to find out what the required dose is
- to see if there are any harmful side effects.

Only when the drug has been shown to be effective and safe with no or very limited side effects will it be **licensed** for use.

Figure 6.15 shows an advert asking for volunteers to take part in a clinical trial. Would you be willing to be a volunteer?

Volunteers wanted for medical research

Volunteers should be between 20 and 30 years old and currently taking no medication.

Volunteers will be asked to spend one night in a clinic and take part in a number of follow-up visits.

For further details contact …

Figure 6.15

Other drugs: their use and misuse

Medicines and most drugs are developed and used purely to help people recover from or cope with illnesses or to relieve pain, but some drugs are also used for 'recreational' purposes. Drugs alter the physical or mental state of individuals and it is for these reasons that some 'recreational' drugs are very popular in our society.

Alcohol: getting the balance right

Perhaps the most obvious recreational drug is **alcohol**. Alcohol has been a part of the culture of many human societies since history began, because it can give a sense of well-being and lead to a more relaxed state of mind. Many people think that taking alcohol in moderation has little harmful effect on the body and there is some evidence that small quantities of some alcoholic drinks, for example red wine, can help protect against heart disease.

However, excessive consumption of alcohol can have many harmful effects – some of the adverse effects on the body were discussed in Chapter 1 in relation to heart disease (see page 11).

Even in small quantities, alcohol can cause impaired judgement and a lack of inhibition, so it is not surprising that most developed countries have strict laws to prevent people driving after consuming alcohol (see Chapter 14). The same effects of alcohol mean that it is a major contributory factor to violence in society.

If excessive drinking takes place over a prolonged period, addiction (alcoholism) can result, and liver and brain damage can also occur.

As well as directly affecting the lives of individuals concerned, society as a whole is affected. Family breakdown can result, and alcohol abuse is a major cause of absenteeism in employment. Medical costs arising from accidents and violence after taking alcohol leave fewer resources for other areas.

Why do people drink?

People drink to be sociable, and usually because they enjoy what they are drinking. The sense of well-being and lack of inhibition discussed above also encourages some people to drink.

Drinking alcohol can obviously become a problem if people drink too much, but also if they drink for the wrong reason. It is not advisable to take alcohol to reduce stress, or to escape from a problem. When the effect of the alcohol wears off the problem or stress will still be there. Alcohol is actually a depressant, so the happier mood can be very short term.

Teenagers often start drinking or drink too much because of peer pressure from their friends. They are at particular risk from the harmful effects because they are inexperienced at coping with alcohol.

A particular concern is the development of **binge drinking** among young people. This involves drinking considerable quantities of alcohol over a short period of time and can have a very harmful effect on the body. Binge drinking in pubs and clubs is often associated with violence. Individuals may get involved in activities that they would avoid when not under the influence of alcohol. It is little wonder that many people are not in favour of the idea of 24-hour opening for pubs and clubs. The Government is hoping that longer opening hours will actually decrease the likelihood of binge drinking taking place, as there will not be a rush coming up to 'closing time'.

Figure 6.16 The sense of well-being is evident here – no one has had too much to drink

Figure 6.17 A consequence of binge drinking

Strategies to reduce alcohol intake

These include greater education about the effect of alcohol on the individual and on society, and making people aware of safe drinking limits. A glass of wine and a half pint or bottle of beer are each roughly equivalent to a 'unit' of alcohol. Health-promoting agencies publish and advertise details concerning safe drinking limits for men and women. The current recommended limits for alcohol consumption are:

- a maximum of 21 units per week for men, with no more than 4 units in any one day
- a maximum of 14 units per week for women, with no more than 3 units in any one day.

Smoking

The evidence of the harmful effects of smoking has been available for a long time.

Tar in the smoke can cause lung cancer and other conditions such as bronchitis and emphysema. **Nicotine** is the addictive substance in tobacco smoke; its presence makes it very difficult for smokers to give up the habit. Nicotine also can have a harmful affect on the heart and circulatory system.

The effect of another product, **carbon monoxide**, is equally harmful. The carbon monoxide combines more effectively with the oxygen-carrying red blood cells than oxygen itself does. The effect of this is that the blood of a smoker carries less oxygen than that of a non-smoker. This can have serious consequences for pregnant mothers who smoke. The developing fetus may not get as much oxygen as it needs and therefore may not grow as fast as it otherwise could. Evidence suggests that babies born to mothers who smoke during pregnancy have a lower birth weight on average than babies born to non-smoking mothers.

Even people who do not smoke can be harmed by cigarette smoke. **Passive smoking** has been shown to cause harm and has been one of the reasons why smoking bans in public places have been introduced over much of the British Isles including Northern Ireland.

> **ACTIVITY**
>
> Total or partial smoking bans in public places, including in pubs and clubs, have been introduced in parts of the British Isles. These bans have followed debates by the governments of the countries concerned. What types of arguments will the supporters and opponents of the ban have used to try to influence the final decision? Have a debate putting forward both sides.

Illegal drugs

Alcohol and tobacco are not illegal in the UK but a number of other substances, including cannabis, ecstasy, cocaine and heroin, are illegal. Nonetheless these drugs are used by considerable numbers of people for recreational purposes.

Cannabis is the most widely used illegal drug in the UK, partly due to its widespread availability and relatively low cost. It is thought of as a 'soft' drug and its illegality is seen as having limited enforcement (see page 76). When taken it can create a relaxed mood. There is an on-going debate as to whether taking cannabis makes the user more likely to go on to taking other, 'harder' drugs. There is some evidence that cannabis can lead to mental health problems in some people, particularly those who are most at risk of mental health problems for other reasons.

Figure 6.18 Some of the illegal drugs in use in the UK today

Ecstasy causes hallucinations or other mind-altered states and can make emotions feel more intense. Ecstasy is used by many clubbers as it gives a very obvious energy lift. It can cause damage to the brain and nervous system, and there are examples of ecstasy causing death: over 200 in the UK in the last 10 years.

Cocaine is a stimulant that often gives users a 'high'. It is expensive. Side effects of the drug can harm the body in many ways. It is very addictive, and as its effects are short lived, users can be very easily tempted to increase their dose. Death by overdose can result.

Heroin is made from morphine (a very strong painkiller). It can create a 'buzz' and a feeling of well-being in users. It is very addictive, can lead to death from an overdose and has many side effects. As heroin is often injected, many heroin addicts have contracted serious infections such as AIDS through sharing needles with other users. Additionally, heroin is very expensive to buy and many users have resorted to crime to fund their drug habit.

The changing legislation regarding drug use

A change in the legal status of cannabis has taken place recently. It was reclassified from a Class B to a Class C drug in 2004. Although still illegal, this reclassification suggests that the Government accepts that cannabis is not as harmful as the Class B and Class A drugs. Ecstasy, cocaine and heroin are all Class A drugs – seen as the most harmful – and possession of them incurs much greater penalties. Importing or selling any class of illegal drug is an extremely serious offence and incurs very heavy penalties.

While the changes in legislation in this area, as with increased pub opening hours and bans on smoking in public places, are the direct result of Government action, they are based on updated evidence coming from scientists about the medical effects of the substance in question. In addition, other interested groups, including health-promoting groups and legal 'think-tanks', contribute to the debate and provide the Government with an assessment of how a change in the law will affect society.

The Government will also take into account the 'mood of the community', in that they are likely to promote change only when it will be supported by a significant part of the population.

websites

www.mmrthefacts.nhs.uk
information on the MMR vaccine

www.patient.co.uk/
from the home page search for 'safe alcohol limits': useful information on alcohol consumption

www.talktofrank.com
very useful and easy-to-read information on drugs

Questions

1 When a foreign bacterium enters the body, the immune system responds as shown in the diagram.

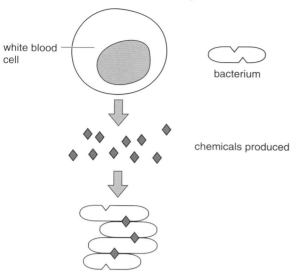

white blood cell

bacterium

chemicals produced

a Name the chemicals produced by the white blood cells to combat the bacteria. *(1 mark)*

b Explain the role played by these chemicals in combating bacteria. *(2 marks)*

c What type of immunity is described in the diagram above? *(1 mark)*

CCEA GCSE Science: Double Award (Modular) Foundation Tier March 2005

2 This mouse is infected with one type of bacterium.

Explain fully how the mouse's immune system combats the bacterial infection. *(4 marks)*

CCEA GCSE Science: Double Award (Modular) Higher Tier May 2005

3 The effect of increasing amounts of alcohol on the body is described in this diagram.

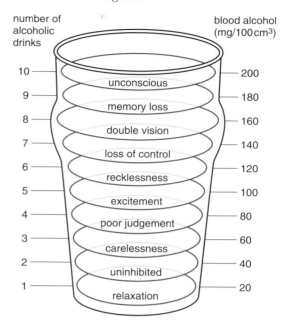

number of alcoholic drinks

blood alcohol (mg/100 cm³)

10	unconscious	200
9	memory loss	180
8	double vision	160
7	loss of control	140
6	recklessness	120
5	excitement	100
4	poor judgement	80
3	carelessness	60
2	uninhibited	40
1	relaxation	20

a What is the evidence in the diagram that even **one** drink can affect driving ability? *(1 mark)*

b How can a person's health be damaged by drinking a lot of alcohol over a long time period? *(1 mark)*

c Apart from damage to health, state **one** harmful effect of alcohol on society. *(1 mark)*

CCEA GCSE Science: Double Award (Modular) Foundation Tier November 2004

4 The development of new drugs and medicines are often the end result of a chance observation.

a Outline how a chance observation eventually led to the development of penicillin. *(2 marks)*

b The development of modern drugs and medicines often requires considerable financial investment and it may take many years before the drug is licensed for use by the general public. Describe and explain the main steps that are involved in drug development. *(4 marks)*

5 In a survey of the drinking habits of a group of 18–20-year-old males, 30% reported that they binge drink at least one night every week. Nearly three-quarters of the group who admitted to binge drinking stated that their behaviour after binge drinking often embarrassed them later.

a i What is binge drinking? *(1 mark)*

ii Suggest why the 18–20 age group was chosen for the survey. *(1 mark)*

iii Apart from causing embarrassment, state one other harmful effect binge drinking can cause an individual. *(1 mark)*

b Suggest **two** reasons why some people binge drink. *(2 marks)*

c Outline one strategy to reduce binge drinking. *(1 mark)*

Chapter 7

The effect of human activity on the world

By the end of this chapter you should know and understand:

➤ The balance and conflict between population growth and economic development and conservation
➤ Examples of air, land and water pollution and strategies to reduce their effects
➤ Global warming – its probable causes, its effects and possible remedial action
➤ Competition between living organisms and the effect of humans
➤ Methods of monitoring the environment
➤ Strategies to conserve resources and to preserve biodiversity

All living organisms have some effect on the world around them. However, only humans alter the environment in a way that affects, or has the potential to affect, almost all of the other plants and animals that share the planet with us.

Human population growth

The number of people living on the planet, and the very rapid rate of increase of the population, have brought about conflict with the conservation of our natural resources.

There are many reasons why the number of humans has risen so much, and in particular over the last century. These include improved diets, improved hygiene, and very important improvements to medical care such as the development of antibiotics and vaccinations. The increase in the number of people together with the desire, in developed countries, to have high standards of living, are contributing to changes in the environment in a number of ways.

Many of these changes are harmful. They include the using up of resources that will not be available to future generations, the polluting or destruction of natural habitats, and emissions into the atmosphere that contribute to climate change.

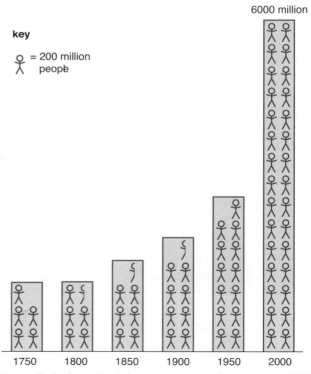

key

⚲ = 200 million
people

Figure 7.1 Growth of the human population since 1750

Using up resources

Humans are using up the world's **physical resources** at an alarming rate. It is possible that within your lifetime the world's natural reserves of oil will be used up. We probably have the technology to replace oil with other energy sources, but the same possibilities do not exist with the **living resources** – the plants and animals that are driven to the point of extinction.

A good example of the effect of humans on living resources is that of **fish stocks**. For centuries fishing has had little influence on the number of fish in the sea, but over the last few decades commercial fishing has become increasingly mechanised and the populations of the main commercial fish such as cod and herring have become very low.

There is now a greater understanding in many countries about the concept of **sustainability** of fish stocks (and other resources) and the need to conserve and build up the stocks that we have left. This has resulted in a number of strategies (some regulated at European level through the European Union's Common Fisheries Policy) to help rebuild our populations of threatened fish and to prevent other types of fish becoming threatened. These include:

Figure 7.2 The effect of decommissioning

- using **larger mesh sizes** in fishing nets. This avoids young fish being caught and so allows them to breed and sustain the fish population.
- **quotas**. These are restrictions on when fishing can take place for particular fish and limits on the numbers that can be caught.
- the **decommissioning of boats**. This reduces the number of working fishing vessels and involves paying compensation to the fishermen involved.

In our use of the world's resources we need to aim for **sustainable development**. This means developing our economy (maintaining or improving our lifestyle) but at the same time minimising our ecological 'footprint' (impact). Examples include the conservation of fish stocks and other resources for future use, the reduction of carbon dioxide emissions and other pollutants, and recycling waste materials.

ACTIVITY

Organise a debate about conserving fish stocks. This will probably include the issues surrounding the introduction of quotas and the decommissioning of boats. Will your knowledge of the precarious nature of some fish stocks such as cod affect which fish you buy? Would your attitude to the conservation of fish stocks change if you lived in an area largely dependent on the fishing industry, such as Kilkeel in County Down?

Polluting the environment

We pollute the world around us by adding harmful substances to the environment in sufficient quantities to cause harm. Although we have been producing harmful substances for centuries, it is only in recent decades that the quantities have been high enough to cause real harm. We are currently causing much damage to the **air**, **land** and **water** around us.

Air pollution

The burning of fossil fuels in homes, in industrial processes and power stations, and in vehicle and aeroplane engines produces large quantities of **carbon dioxide** that pollutes the air. The effect of rising levels of atmospheric carbon dioxide will be discussed in more detail later in this chapter (pages 82–86).

Acid rain

Fossils fuels also produce sulphur dioxide (and other gases including nitrogen oxides). When sulphur dioxide dissolves in water, acids such as sulphuric acid are produced. When the sulphur dioxide produced combines with rainwater, **acid rain** is the result. Much of the sulphur dioxide emitted in the UK is produced by the burning of fossil fuels in power stations and other large-scale industrial plants.

Figure 7.3 Fossil fuel power stations such as this one produce considerable quantities of sulphur dioxide

One of the main problems with acid rain is that it often falls in other countries, well away from the ones causing most of the pollution. This is because the prevailing winds often carry the clouds that will produce the acid rain for hundreds of miles before the rain actually falls.

But what is the effect of the acid rain on the area on which it falls? Over much of Europe many trees have been destroyed by the effects of acid rain. The acid rain causes the soil to become more acidic and this means that trees are no longer living in good growth conditions. The leaves or needles fall off and the trees eventually die.

Rivers and lakes are also badly affected. The acid rain causes the water to become too acidic for some species. It also causes the release of aluminium from compounds in the soil; this aluminium then makes its way into the rivers and lakes where it poisons fish.

Acid rain has become an important international issue, because its effects cross international borders. One way of reducing the release of the sulphur

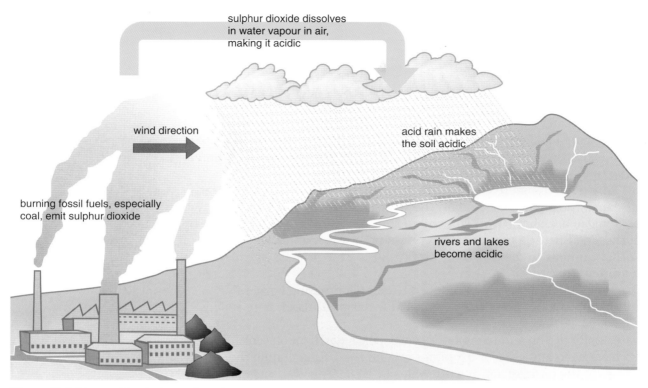

sulphur dioxide dissolves
in water vapour in air,
making it acidic

wind direction

acid rain makes
the soil acidic

burning fossil fuels, especially
coal, emit sulphur dioxide

rivers and lakes
become acidic

Figure 7.4 How acid rain is produced

dioxide and the other harmful chemicals produced by power stations and
other industrial complexes is to use filters that reduce the level of these
harmful gases emitted. There is now a greater awareness that other sources
of generating electricity, such as wind, water, solar and even nuclear power,
may be better long-term solutions than fossil fuels.

It has been estimated that the UK has reduced its sulphur dioxide
emissions by 80% over the last 25 years. This has resulted in the
re-colonisation by native species of many lakes that were seriously damaged
by acid rain.

Pollution on land

Much of our household and industrial waste
ends up in landfill sites. This is becoming a
major problem as we are starting to run out of
suitable sites.

An obvious solution is to increase the
proportion of waste that we recycle. It is also
possible to reduce the proportion of non-
biodegradable materials we use, for example
plastic yoghurt cartons, and replace these with
biodegradable packaging. But biodegradable
waste also presents environmental problems –
see page 174.

Recycling is discussed in more detail later in
this chapter (see page 90).

Figure 7.5 It is estimated that between 70 and 80% of
our rubbish ends up in landfill sites

Water pollution

Water pollution can have a particularly harmful effect, because our rivers, lakes and seas are relatively fragile environments and are easily damaged. We have already mentioned the effects of acid rain.

Every so often we read or hear about substantial fish kills in local rivers or lakes. This may be due to harmful chemicals being accidentally released from a factory, but many fish kills are a result of **slurry** (manure) or **silage** (compacted animal feed) effluent draining from farmland that borders the rivers or lakes. Silage effluent, slurry, untreated sewage and fertiliser run-off all serve to increase the **nitrate levels** of waterways.

But why does the increased nitrate level kill the fish? The high nitrate levels cause the algae that grow in the water to grow much faster. Many types of algae are short lived, and when they die they are broken down by bacteria. The bacteria use up the oxygen in the water and this causes fish and other animals to die due to lack of oxygen. This process is called **eutrophication**.

This type of pollution can be reduced through increasing farmers' environmental awareness, better control of fertiliser use and more secure storage of silage and slurry.

Water pollution on a much greater scale occurs when an oil tanker sinks. There have been a few major examples around the UK, including the *Sea Empress* off the coast of south-west Wales in 1996. This was one of the most serious oil pollution incidents in European history: 72 000 tonnes of oil was spilled. The oil spillages in such cases have caused environmental disasters, killing vast numbers of birds and marine species. Improved navigation systems and safety standards have reduced the number of major oil spillages in recent decades: in the 1990s worldwide there were less than a third of the number in the 1970s.

Figure 7.6 A fish kill caused by pollution

Global warming: a worry for us all

Most people will remember seeing a headline like that in Figure 7.7 in the newspapers or on television. Global warming and its effects are becoming much more widely known and recognised as a threat to the world as we know it.

We need to have some understanding of the carbon cycle before we can understand why global warming is occurring. Figure 7.8 shows a simplified diagram of the carbon cycle.

GLOBAL WARMING THREAT
to the planet – Government admits 'environmental crisis'

Figure 7.7

Carbon is a very important component of all living organisms; it is found in all proteins, carbohydrates and fats. The carbon cycle shows what happens to the carbon (often in the form of carbon dioxide) when key life processes such as respiration and photosynthesis take place, and also when organisms die and are recycled.

The carbon cycle has remained reasonably stable for centuries but there is now evidence that the cycle is becoming 'unbalanced', and this is generally believed to be largely due to human activity over the last century and particularly in the last few decades.

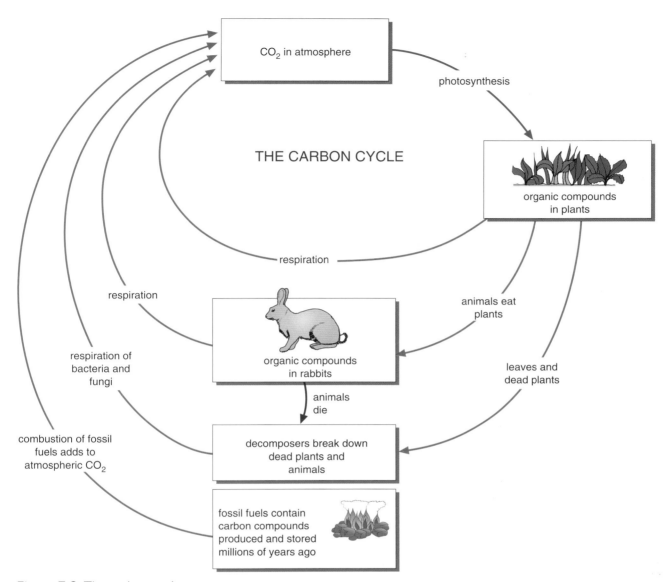

Figure 7.8 The carbon cycle

> 1   Suggest what human activities in the last century and in particular in the last few decades have caused an imbalance in the carbon cycle.

The role of humans in global warming

Figure 7.8 shows that there are many processes that return carbon to the atmosphere. The increased combustion of fossil fuels (and wood) increases the carbon dioxide levels in the atmosphere. The diagram also shows that atmospheric levels of carbon dioxide are reduced by photosynthesis. With the degree of deforestation that has taken place over much of the world, particularly in the great rainforests such as in the Amazon Basin, global photosynthesis has reduced. These two factors – increased combustion and reduced photosynthesis – have resulted in higher atmospheric carbon dioxide levels, which in turn are believed to cause global warming.

The link between higher carbon dioxide levels and global warming

The carbon dioxide and other 'greenhouse' gases, such as methane, form a 'blanket' around the Earth that helps to trap heat. Radiation from the Sun passes through the atmosphere (including the carbon dioxide blanket) and heats the Earth's surface. Some of this radiation is reflected back from the Earth, but much is prevented from leaving the Earth's atmosphere by the greenhouse gases in the atmosphere. The resultant effect is that this energy heats up the atmosphere. This is similar to how greenhouses heat up on a warm day – hence the term 'greenhouse effect'. This effect is important for life on Earth because without it the Earth would be too cold. However, the problem is that too much heat is now being trapped because of the increasing strength of the 'blanket', and global average temperature is increasing.

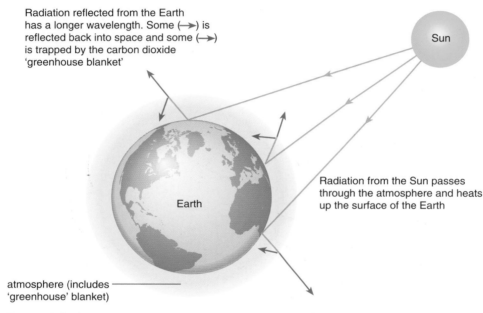

Figure 7.9 The greenhouse effect

The evidence for global warming

It is only very recently that most scientists and governments have accepted that global warming is a result of the activity of humans and not just part of the natural cycles of climate change that have occurred throughout the history of the world. Figure 7.10 shows how the carbon dioxide levels have been rising in the last century.

> **2** In the enlarged section of the graph in Figure 7.10 the annual variation in the carbon dioxide level is shown. Suggest what causes such a cycle each year.

It has been difficult to convince many people that the increase in carbon dioxide level has *caused* the increase in global temperatures and the resultant erratic climate effects.

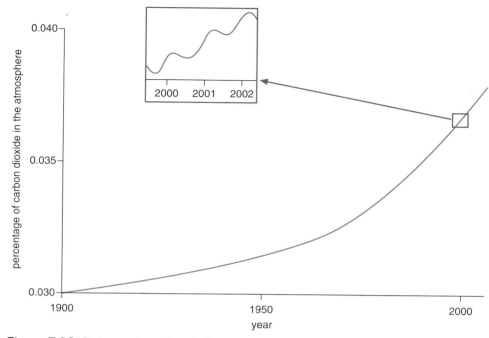

Figure 7.10 Rising carbon dioxide levels in the atmosphere

We have very strong evidence that global warming is occurring through an analysis of meteorological data. Our own average temperatures are gradually increasing and it is a rare year in the UK that we are not informed that we have broken a new record for having the warmest day or month or year, or the longest period without rain since records began.

The effects of global warming

Apart from the increase in temperatures, global warming has many other effects. The polar ice caps are melting at an increasing rate and there will be a resultant rise in sea levels. Other climate changes are also almost certainly caused by global warming. Of course there is evidence to show that hurricanes, great storms and floods have always happened, for example over a few days in 1953 storms and floods killed hundreds of people on the east coast of England and sank the Princess Victoria carrying passengers from Scotland to Northern Ireland. But there is no doubt that the frequency and intensity of extreme weather conditions on a world scale have become much greater in recent years.

Evidence for the increasingly turbulent nature of our climate is not difficult to find. The tornado that caused considerable damage in Birmingham in the summer of 2005 and Hurricane Katrina that caused widespread damage and loss of life in and around New Orleans in America in the same summer (see Figure 7.11 on the next page) may have been extreme examples but are now not unusual.

Changing weather patterns will also have other effects on the local regions affected. The vegetation that is characteristic of a particular country will change. As the UK gets warmer it is anticipated that crops not normally grown in large numbers, such as vines, will be able to be grown. However, globally the portent is not so good. Failing rains are already having a devastating effect on subsistence farming communities in parts of Africa and Asia.

Figure 7.11 The effects of extreme weather conditions in 2005: in Birmingham, UK (left) and New Orleans, USA (right)

What can be done to reduce the effects of global warming?

It is possible that if the increase in atmospheric carbon dioxide levels can be slowed down, stopped or even reversed, then global warming itself may be slowed down. Measures that will help include:

- reducing the burning of fossil fuels through the use of alternative energy sources, particularly for electricity generation
- greater energy efficiency, for example of car engines, or penalties through taxes for non-efficient vehicles
- energy conservation, for example by building well insulated homes and turning down central heating thermostats
- a slowdown in the rate of deforestation
- the planting of more woodland.

ACTIVITY

Organise a debate on global warming. You may wish to consider issues such as the evidence for global warming, the reasons why governments have been slow to accept that it is a crisis, and what you can do, as a school or an individual, to help.

Competition between organisms for resources and the effect of humans

Most living organisms live in close proximity to other living organisms. When this happens they usually compete for the resources they need to live. Competition for resources affects both plants and animals.

Imagine a group of oak seedlings growing closely together in a wood. It is probable that they are competing for a number of resources. These resources could include light, moisture, nutrients in the soil and even space. It is also possible that the competition between the seedlings might limit the growth of many (or all) of the seedlings and that some may not even survive due to this competition.

In the above example the competition is between members of the same species (oak seedlings). Competition can also be between different types of plants or animals. It is likely that seedlings (or trees) of different types will also compete with each other if they grow closely together as in a wood.

ACTIVITY **Investigate the effect of sowing density (number of seeds planted per pot) on the growth of seedlings. You could use pea or bean seeds. Plant different numbers in small plant pots or old yoghurt pots. You could compare the mass of the plants when only one is grown in the pot with the mass when a larger number is grown in the pot. Can you work out all the things (variables) you would have to keep constant to make your investigation a fair test? Work out other ways in which you could make your investigation more reliable.**

A good example of competition between animals is that of red and grey squirrels. Grey squirrels are native to North America and were only introduced to Ireland by people in the early part of the 20th century. Now they are very common, and the red squirrels have been pushed out of many wooded areas by the greys. These days red squirrels are only found in isolated pockets of woodland. It has been discovered that when both types of squirrels occur in the same broadleaved woodland they compete for the same food – nuts and fruits. The red squirrels lose out and are usually eliminated within 20 years.

Figure 7.12 The red and the grey squirrel

Why is the grey squirrel more effective at competing? The reason is that the smaller red squirrel can only digest ripe nuts, whereas the larger grey squirrel can feed on either unripe or ripe food. This means that the grey squirrels can obtain food for longer in the year and at times when the red squirrels struggle to find food. The outlook looks bleak for the red squirrel but in parts of the country attempts are being made to conserve the reds. Measures include:

- using special feeders that only the smaller red squirrels can use
- keeping some woodland areas free from greys by controlling their spread.

The competition between squirrels is a particular type of competition that has been brought about largely through the actions of humans, and it is a good example of how we have affected the countryside we live in.

There are many other examples that can be studied. You may be able to see the effect of another introduced organism, the rhododendron, in a wood near you. Rhododendrons are not native to the UK but can rapidly spread through woodland areas.

Figure 7.13
Rhododendron plants

3 Can you use Figure 7.13 on the previous page to suggest one reason why the rhododendron is such an effective competitor?

Another very effective coloniser, the zebra mussel, was accidentally introduced into the country in the 1990s and has rapidly spread. It is a voracious filter feeder that is able to affect the normal food chains in lakes when it occurs in large numbers. The mussel has recently spread to the Erne waterway system in Northern Ireland and, although there were attempts to prevent it reaching Lough Neagh, it was found there in 2005.

4 The zebra mussel can attach itself to the bottom of boats. Some boat owners transfer their boats by trailer between different waterways. Suggest what measures can be taken to prevent the spread of the zebra mussel.
5 The grey squirrel, the rhododendron and the zebra mussel are examples of a competitive invasive species. Describe the features that most competitive invasive species will have in common.

Monitoring change in the environment

It is very important that changes to the environment are monitored very closely, whether they are physical changes such as global warming or changes to the numbers or types of animals and plants that occur, such as described above.

The measuring of physical or **abiotic** factors includes the measurement of atmospheric carbon dioxide levels. Other abiotic factors that can be measured to determine the rate at which global warming is occurring include the size of the polar ice fields and sea levels. The monitoring of climate data can also provide further evidence.

Abiotic data can be used to provide information about other types of pollution and change. The measurement of chemicals such as nitrates in water can be used to give an indication of water quality and can show how effective anti-pollution and conservation measures are working.

The number and distribution of plants and animals also provide information about environmental change. This type of information is called **biotic** data. **Lichens** are very simple plants that often grow on the roof tiles of houses and also occur on the bark of trees. Lichens are often yellow or light grey in appearance.

Most lichens will not grow where there are high levels of air pollution. Not surprisingly, they are relatively rare in industrial towns and cities but quite abundant in many rural areas. By monitoring the extent of lichen growth over time it is possible to monitor pollution levels.

Another very good example of an animal whose numbers tell us something about the environment is the **corncrake**. This bird used to

Figure 7.14 Lichens

be very common over much of Ireland and Britain but its numbers have dramatically fallen. The increase in silage cutting and the reduction in the growing of hay contributed to eliminating the corncrake from Northern Ireland but it can still be found in parts of Donegal and the west of Scotland. The corncrake lays its eggs in hay fields or meadows, which provide shelter and food. The young chicks are well established and able to survive by mid/late summer when hay is traditionally cut. When silage is cut much earlier in the summer, and more frequently, the timescale for the rearing of chicks becomes too short and they do not survive.

In 2005 it was reported that corncrakes had returned to County Tyrone and Belfast. This could be evidence of more effective conservation measures creating the conditions for a return of this much-loved bird.

Figure 7.15 The corncrake

The distribution of the corncrake is one of the best examples of analysing the effect of humans on other organisms, but it is important to understand that very many species of plants and animals have had their numbers and distribution changed due to the influence of people, either directly or indirectly.

---

6 a   Suggest why parts of Donegal and the Western Isles of Scotland provide suitable habitats for the corncrake.
   b   Suggest how farmers could encourage the return of the corncrake to their land.

ACTIVITY

Find out about either an abiotic or a biotic factor that gives us some information about the environment. You could research one of the examples given above or another. When you collect this data, try to evaluate how valid it is and how reliable it is in giving information about the environment.

Conservation: the way forward?

There is at last an understanding in many influential circles that human activity has had a significant influence on the environment and that it is the responsibility of, in particular, the leaders of developed countries to retrieve the situation before it becomes irreversible. **Conservation** is both the preservation of resources (both physical and living) and their effective management to ensure the sustainability of the resources where possible.

In addition, there is an understanding that conservation is an issue that has to be managed at a global or regional (for example European) level, because of any conflict of interests that may exist in and between many countries. However, because of the difficulty of balancing the desire for economic and industrial development and the need to conserve resources, progress is often at a slower pace than conservationists would wish.

Strategies to reduce pollution, conserve natural resources and promote biodiversity

There are many examples of wide-ranging strategies that are being developed to reduce pollution, conserve resources and promote biodiversity (the range of species and numbers of each type of plant and animal that live in a particular area). Some of these various strategies will be considered below.

International cooperation and legislation

The role of international cooperation was evident in the development of the **Kyoto Protocol** in 1997. This was an international agreement, produced at a summit (a meeting of world leaders) on approaches to reduce the problems associated with climate change. A key agreement reached at the summit was that countries would reduce their pollution levels so that levels in 2010 would be no higher than the levels in 1990. Much of the focus was on carbon dioxide emissions, and a 'credit system' was proposed, whereby rich industrialised countries could purchase 'carbon credits' from poorer, less industrialised countries that produce less carbon emissions. The idea is that high levels of carbon dioxide pollution in some countries will be compensated for by low levels in others. It is also hoped that the need for high carbon emitters to buy carbon credits will encourage the reduction in their carbon emissions by improving the efficiency of their industrial processes or by switching to alternative fuels.

The difficulties in maintaining wide-scale international agreements were highlighted by the USA withdrawing its commitment to the agreed Kyoto targets in 2003. There have been (and will be) other attempts to agree an international consensus on approaches to climate change, but the perceived conflict between economic development and 'greener' practices in individual countries will ensure that progress will be slow.

An example of pollution reduction legislation at a European level is the **European Nitrates Directive**. The legislation is aimed at reducing nitrate levels in waterways, in an attempt to reduce eutrophication (see page 82) and other harmful effects caused by water that is too nutrient-rich. High nitrate levels in drinking water can be harmful to very young babies, as well as polluting the environment. The legislation is designed to ensure that farmers do not spread manure or fertiliser on fields during the winter months. In addition, they are required to have adequate storage facilities for slurry in place by January 2007 to prevent leakage.

> **7** Why do you think it is important not to spread fertiliser during the winter months?

Effective recycling

Recycling of waste materials not only helps to preserve natural resources. It also plays a part in reducing carbon emissions, through saving energy in the harvesting/mining, processing and transporting of raw materials and, in some cases, in the manufacture of the end product. Recycling also reduces other pollutants, such as the greenhouse gas methane from landfill sites (see page 174). Although the UK has been well behind many other countries in terms of the percentage of waste recycled, progress is being made, partly as a result of European legislative requirements and partly due to local initiatives.

Recycling in Northern Ireland has been greatly influenced by European Directives as well as local (N.I.) legislation and policy. Many councils have developed a 20-year strategic plan for waste management. Typical targets include the recovery of 40% of household waste by 2010, of which 25% is to be achieved through recycling and composting. Northern Ireland has some distance to go in its recycling targets: in the period 2004–5 only 18.9% of household waste was sent for recycling.

By 2005 at least three types of refuse bin had been distributed to households in most areas of Northern Ireland. Two of these are intended for recyclable material (see Figure 7.16) to help meet the targets for waste management. This makes it much easier for people to sort their waste for recycling so should significantly increase the total amount recycled.

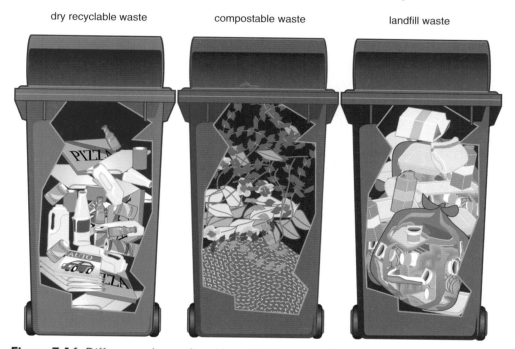

dry recyclable waste   compostable waste   landfill waste

Figure 7.16 Different colour refuse bins will help meet the recycling targets

8 The brown bins (see Figure 7.16) are usually not collected from December to February. Explain why this is so.
9 How efficient do you think your school or college is at recycling and at conserving energy? What type of information would you need to allow you to answer this question?

Strategies to maintain biodiversity

There is legislation aimed at maintaining biodiversity, as well as cooperation between countries and interested groups within each country. Also essential is an increased general awareness of the need to promote biodiversity. The identification of priority habitats and of species that are at greatest risk has been important. The Northern Ireland Biodiversity Strategy, developed by the Department of Environment, identifies conservation priorities and outlines the strategies necessary.

By prioritising which habitats and species are most at risk, it is possible to concentrate resources in conserving these. The development of **Nature Reserves** helps safeguard habitats and the species that live there and also helps raise public awareness of important conservation issues. **Areas of Special Scientific Interest** (**ASSI**s) are important at a national level and

Special Protection Areas (**SPA**s) at a European level. In Northern Ireland, ASSIs include particularly good examples of bogs, grasslands, lakes, woods and sand dune systems. Rathlin Island and the Foyle Estuary are examples of SPAs that have valuable populations of rare birds.

Individual land owners such as farmers can **set-aside land** that can be used to promote conservation and biodiversity.

Figure 7.17 Murlough Nature Reserve, County Down

Charities supporting wildlife and other conservation groups have important roles to play. **The National Trust**, the **Royal Society for the Protection of Birds** (**RSPB**) and the **Ulster Wildlife Trust** are examples of organisations that purchase and/or manage land to conserve threatened habitats or species that live within these habitats. They manage some designated conservation areas such as nature reserves and Areas of Special Scientific Interest. They also raise public awareness of conservation issues and can lobby the Government concerning key environmental issues.

ACTIVITY

Research some of the groups mentioned above on the internet. Try to identify the main aims and objectives of the organisation.

websites

www.carbontrust.co.uk
information on carbon emissions and climate change
www.habitas.org.uk
website of Ulster Museum Sciences
www.ulsterwildlifetrust.org
details on this large conservation organisation and its role in Northern Ireland
www.nationaltrust.org.uk
link to Conservation, Heritage and Learning and then to Climate Change
www.ntni.org.uk
website of the National Trust in Northern Ireland
www.nhm.ac.uk
use the Nature Online link to access pages on environmental change and biodiversity
www.rspb.org.uk
website of the Royal Society for the Protection of Birds
www.ehsni.gov.uk
links to information in a Northern Ireland context on climate change, biodiversity and specially designated areas such as nature reserves and ASSIs

Questions

1 The graph shows the number of fish and average nitrate levels in a number of rivers.

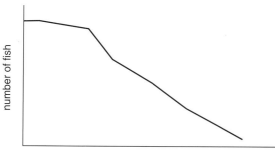

a i Use the graph to describe the relationship between river nitrate levels and the number of fish. *(1 mark)*
ii Suggest what may have caused the high nitrate levels in some rivers. *(1 mark)*
iii Draw a flow diagram to show how high nitrate levels can result in fish death. *(3 marks)*
b Explain how legislation can be used to reduce nitrate levels in rivers. *(2 marks)*

2 The development of a satellite to monitor the size of the polar ice caps is one method of estimating the rate and effects of global warming. Other data being collected includes atmospheric carbon dioxide levels.
a Describe and explain the link between atmospheric carbon dioxide levels and global warming. *(3 marks)*
b Suggest **two** reasons why global warming has been ignored by many world leaders for so long. *(2 marks)*

3 The diagrams show the predicted change in temperatures over the British Isles during this century.

winter   **summer**

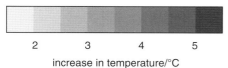

increase in temperature/°C

a Give **two** differences between the summer and winter predictions. *(2 marks)*

Carbon dioxide gas is thought to play an important role in these predicted changes.
b Give **one** source of the carbon dioxide in the atmosphere. *(1 mark)*
c Explain how carbon dioxide is thought to cause temperature changes. *(3 marks)*

CCEA GCSE Science: Biology (Higher Tier) June 2004

d Although most people and governments are beginning to accept that it is the levels of carbon dioxide in the atmosphere that cause global warming, the link between carbon dioxide and global warming is not accepted by everyone.
i Suggest how the graph below could be used to provide evidence that high carbon dioxide levels cause global warming. *(1 mark)*

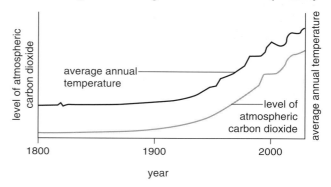

ii Suggest how someone could argue that the graph does **not** prove the link between higher atmospheric levels of carbon dioxide and global warming. *(1 mark)*

4 Copy and complete the table.

Environment	Polluting substance	Effect
air	acid rain	
water		eutrophication (rapid growth of plants and death of fish)
	household rubbish	litter

(3 marks)
CCEA GCSE Science: Single Award (Modular) Specimen Paper (Foundation Tier) 2006 (part question)

5 a The table shows some gases produced by a petrol and a diesel engined car of the same type and size.

Gas	Mass of gas produced/g per km	
	Petrol	Diesel
carbon dioxide	188	138
carbon monoxide	1.068	0.1
nitrous oxides	0.127	0.339

i Explain why encouraging people to drive diesel cars would help reduce global warming. (*1 mark*)

ii State **one** way carbon monoxide can harm human health. (*1 mark*)

iii Describe **one** way this diesel engine could be harmful to the environment. (*2 marks*)

b The flow diagram shows some causes of algal blooms.

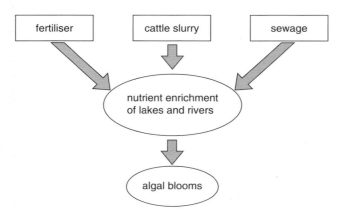

i Name the nutrient which causes the enrichment of lakes and rivers. (*1 mark*)

ii Name this type of water pollution (*1 mark*)

iii Suggest how the nutrients from fertilisers and cattle slurry spread on a field, could reach a river. (*2 marks*)

iv Explain how nutrients draining into the water can harm organisms living in lakes and rivers. (*5 marks*)

CCEA GCSE Science: Biology (Higher Tier) 2004 (part question)

6 The maps show the distribution of red and grey squirrels in Ireland in 1998.

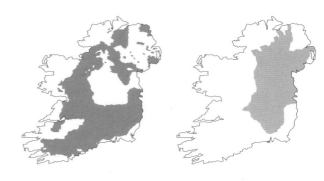

red squirrel distribution   grey squirrel distribution

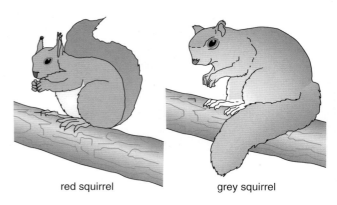

red squirrel   grey squirrel

Grey squirrels are non-native species.

i What is meant by a non-native species? (*1 mark*)

ii Give **one** difference, visible in the drawing, between a red and a grey squirrel. (*1 mark*)

iii Use the maps to describe **one** difference in squirrel distribution. (*1 mark*)

Grey squirrels now outnumber the red squirrels by 66 : 1.

iv Give **one** reason why grey squirrels now outnumber the red. (*1 mark*)

Grey squirrels build up in large numbers in broad-leaved woodland but only reach similar numbers to the red in conifer woods.

v Suggest **one** thing that could be done to help conserve the red squirrel in this country. (*1 mark*)

CCEA GCSE Science: Single Award (Modular) Specimen Paper (Foundation Tier) 2006 (part question)

Chapter 8

Acids and bases

Learning objectives

By the end of this chapter you should know and understand:

➤ That acids and bases have a wide range of uses in the home and everyday life
➤ The names of common acids and bases found in the home
➤ How acids react with kettle fur, metallic oxides and rust, and explain these using word equations
➤ That indigestion is caused by hydrochloric acid, and how it is cured by neutralisation using indigestion tablets containing oxides, hydroxides or carbonates
➤ The word equations for curing indigestion
➤ The test for carbon dioxide
➤ How baking powder in cake mixture produces bubbles of carbon dioxide
➤ The word equations to show the effect of heat and acids on sodium hydrogencarbonate
➤ Why sherbet fizzes when moist
➤ The word equations to show how sodium hydrogencarbonate reacts with citric acid and tartaric acid
➤ That hazard symbols alert users to the dangers of some chemicals
➤ The use of universal indicator to determine the pH of solutions and their classification as acidic, neutral or alkaline
➤ The use of pH sensors to follow a neutralisation reaction
➤ That pH indicators can be made from natural dyes
➤ What a compound is, and use formulae of simple and complex compounds
➤ How to construct symbol equations to describe the reactions covered in this chapter

We are familiar with many **acids** and **bases** in everyday life (see Figure 8.1). Gastric juice contains hydrochloric acid, which aids digestion in the stomach. Citric acid is responsible for the sour taste in lemons. Methanoic acid (formic acid) causes the sting in nettles and in ants.

Bases are the opposite of acids, and many bases are used as 'antacids' to **neutralise** acids. Examples in everyday life are the use of a base to cure acid indigestion in the stomach, caused by excess hydrochloric acid, and farmers spreading lime on fields to neutralise acid in the soil.

Figure 8.1a Acids used in everyday life

Figure 8.1b Bases used in everyday life

Acids

Table 8.1 highlights a number of acids encountered in the home.

Table 8.1 Acids met in the home

Name	Natural occurrence	Weak or strong acid
hydrochloric acid	stomach	strong
phosphoric acid	cola drinks	fairly strong
ethanoic (acetic) acid	vinegar	weak
tartaric acid	grapes	weak
methanoic (formic) acid	nettle or ant sting	weak
citric acid	citrus fruits	weak
oxalic acid	rhubarb	weak
butanoic acid	rancid butter	weak

From Table 8.1 it is seen that both hydrochloric acid and phosphoric acid are strong acids. Quite often these acids are used to remove the tarnish of metal oxides from metal surfaces. This happens because these oxides are basic oxides. They react with an acid to produce a **salt** and **water**. For example:

hydrochloric acid + copper(II) oxide → copper(II) chloride + water
(acid)   (base)   (salt)   (water)

To help you to remember how to write the word equation for an acid reacting with a base, it is best to learn the following rule:

acid + base → salt + water

A **salt** is the general product of neutralising an acid with a base. Examples are copper chloride, copper sulphate and sodium chloride (common salt).

Rust, which is hydrated iron(III) oxide, can be removed using a combination of the strong acids, sulphuric acid and phosphoric acid. A big advantage of using this combination of acids is that one of the products, iron(III) phosphate, acts as a protective layer. It stops the iron from reacting and rusting further:

phosphoric acid + hydrated iron(III) oxide → iron(III) phosphate + water

There are examples where a strong acid cannot be used to remove rust, for example, on clothes. A strong acid would attack the cloth, so a weak acid must be used. Oxalic acid is particularly effective, as its combines very readily with iron. The clothes must be well washed after cleaning, because oxalic acid is poisonous. Another weak acid, citric acid, from lemons or other citrus fruit, can be used to clean oxidised copper or brass surfaces:

citric acid + copper(II) oxide → copper(II) citrate + water

Ethanoic acid (acetic acid, vinegar) should not be used to clean copper surfaces, because it produces the compound copper(II) ethanoate, which is more toxic than copper citrate. This weak acid can be used to remove deposits of insoluble calcium carbonate and magnesium carbonate formed in kettles in areas that have temporary hard water. These insoluble metal carbonates are generally referred to as **kettle fur**. They react with vinegar to produce the soluble compounds, magnesium ethanoate and calcium ethanoate. After the removal of these insoluble carbonates, the heating element in the kettle becomes much more efficient in heating the water. The word equation for the reaction of calcium carbonate with ethanoic acid is:

ethanoic + calcium → calcium + water + carbon
acid   carbonate   ethanoate   dioxide

---

1 Give the names of the acids that cause
  a indigestion
  b the sting in nettles and in ants
  c the bitter taste in vinegar.
2 Name the acid that
  a is present in rancid butter   **d** makes rhubarb taste bitter
  b causes the sharp smell in vinegar   **e** removes the scale in kettles.
  c makes lemons taste bitter

Bases

Bases are chemicals that are commonly used in the home as medicinal antacids and as cleaning agents. Indigestion is caused when there is a build-up of excess hydrochloric acid in the stomach. It can be cured by taking indigestion tablets, which contain a weak base. The base reacts to **neutralise** the acid. Note that a soluble base is called an **alkali**, giving rise to an **alkaline** solution.

A typical reaction for the neutralisation of hydrochloric acid is:

hydrochloric + sodium → sodium + carbon + water
acid   hydrogencarbonate   chloride   dioxide
(acid)   (hydrogencarbonate)   (salt)   (carbon dioxide + water)

$$HCl + NaHCO_3 \rightarrow NaCl + CO_2 + H_2O$$

See page 106 for how to write symbol equations.

A general equation can be written to show how carbonates and hydrogencarbonates react with acids:

acid + **carbonate** *or* → **salt** + **carbon dioxide** + **water**
hydrogencarbonate

Table 8.2 gives a list of the common bases used as commercial antacids. From Table 8.2 it is seen that the **antacids** used can be classified as **carbonates**, **hydrogencarbonates**, **hydroxides** and **oxides**.

Table 8.2 Commercial antacids

Carbonates	Hydrogencarbonates	Hydroxides	Oxides
magnesium carbonate	sodium hydrogencarbonate	aluminium hydroxide	aluminium oxide
calcium carbonate		magnesium hydroxide	magnesium oxide

Nowadays many of the antacid tablets are **effervescent**. They are made from a weak acid and a hydrogencarbonate, for example, citric acid and sodium hydrogencarbonate. In these effervescent tablets, the hydrogencarbonate is always in excess. This ensures that the final solution is alkaline.

This type of antacid has an advantage. It avoids the user having to cope with large volumes of carbon dioxide, which are produced very quickly when more traditional antacid tablets (such as sodium hydrogencarbonate) are used to neutralise excess acid in the stomach.

As well as being an important antacid, sodium hydrogencarbonate plays a key role in baking. When it is heated, it produces carbon dioxide. This causes food mixtures, for example, bread, cake or buns, to rise and produce a lighter honeycomb texture with many bubbles throughout (Figure 8.2). During this **thermal decomposition** reaction, sodium hydrogencarbonate breaks down to produce carbon dioxide. The word equation is:

sodium → sodium + water + carbon
hydrogencarbonate   carbonate   dioxide

$$2NaHCO_3 \rightarrow Na_2CO_3 + H_2O + CO_2$$

To show that the gas given off is carbon dioxide, it is bubbled through limewater, and the limewater turns milky (see opposite).

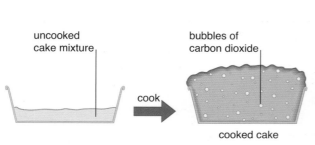

Figure 8.2a Carbon dioxide released during cooking causes the cake mixture to rise

uncooked cake mixture

bubbles of carbon dioxide

cook

cooked cake

Figure 8.2b The finished cake has a light texture full of holes

One of the products of the thermal decomposition of sodium hydrogencarbonate is sodium carbonate, and this gives the cooked food an unpleasant alkaline taste. Often, baking soda is used instead to make food mixtures rise in baking. Baking soda is a mixture of sodium hydrogencarbonate and tartaric acid (or its salt, potassium hydrogentartrate). When these substances react, they produce carbon dioxide. This causes food mixtures to rise. The sodium tartrate produced does not have the unpleasant alkaline taste of sodium carbonate.

The equation for the production of carbon dioxide is:

tartaric   +   sodium   →   sodium   +   carbon   +   water
  acid   hydrogencarbonate   tartrate   dioxide

In baking soda, it is important to use a weak acid like tartaric acid. Strong acids like hydrochloric acid would produce carbon dioxide too quickly. If a strong acid is used, the food mixture releases all the carbon dioxide long before the mixture has baked. As a result, the food mixture would not have risen properly to provide the desired honeycomb structure.

Testing for carbon dioxide gas

When carbon dioxide is bubbled through limewater, the limewater turns milky (Figure 8.3).

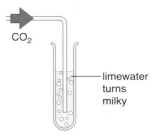

Figure 8.3 The limewater test for carbon dioxide

ACTIVITY

Honeycomb or hokey-pokey is the sweet substance inside Crunchie bars. As in baking, the honeycomb structure is achieved by the thermal decomposition of sodium hydrogencarbonate. The following procedure can be used to make honeycomb.

- Place 5 tablespoons of sugar and 2 tablespoons of golden syrup into a beaker.
- Measure out 1 teaspoon of baking powder.
- Heat the sugar and syrup gently over a low heat until all the sugar dissolves.
- Heat for a further 4 minutes with continuous stirring.
- When the mixture boils, remove the heat and keep stirring.
- Add in the baking powder and stir. Pour the mixture onto a piece of greaseproof paper or aluminium foil.
- Leave to cool. The product is honeycomb.
- Describe the appearance of the honeycomb you have made.

3 When potassium hydrogencarbonate is heated strongly, it produces carbon dioxide.
   a   Name the two other products in the above reaction.
   b   How would you show that the gas given off is carbon dioxide?
   c   Name another substance that will break down when it is heated strongly.
   d   What name is given to a reaction where a substance is broken down by heat?
4 Write a word equation to show how hydrochloric acid is neutralised by sodium hydrogencarbonate in curing indigestion.

> **5** Complete the following word equations to show how bases react with acids:
> **a** calcium carbonate + hydrochloric acid → .... + ... + ...
> **b** magnesium oxide + sulphuric acid → .... + ...
> **c** aluminium hydroxide + ... → aluminium ethanoate + water
> **d** .... + ... → magnesium tartrate + water
> **e** potassium hydrogencarbonate + ...
>   → potassium chloride + ... + carbon dioxide

Double-action baking powder

Chemists have modified tartaric acid in baking soda to control the rate at which carbon dioxide is produced in baking. It is now referred to as **double-acting**. Tartaric acid has been replaced with a mixture of potassium hydrogentartrate and calcium dihydrogendiphosphate. The potassium hydrogentartrate produces carbon dioxide when making the 'wet' baking mixture, causing the mixture to rise. Calcium dihydrogendiphosphate is slower to dissolve in the wet baking mixture. It only produces carbon dioxide when the mixture is heated in the oven. Here the bubbles of gas are trapped, causing the mixture to rise during heating.

A similar type of reaction to this occurs when people eat sweets that contain sherbet (Figure 8.4). When placed in the mouth, sherbet has a fizzing sensation. This is due to the production of carbon dioxide by the reaction of citric acid with sodium hydrogencarbonate.

The reaction is:

sodium hydrogencarbonate + citric acid → sodium citrate + carbon dioxide + water

Figure 8.4 When sherbet dissolves in your mouth, it produces carbon dioxide – it fizzes

> **ACTIVITY**
>
> Commercial sherbet is a mixture of citric acid, sodium hydrogencarbonate and sugar. To make some sherbet, all you have to do is thoroughly mix 2 teaspoonsful of citric acid, 1 teaspoonful of sodium hydrogencarbonate and 9 teaspoonsful of icing sugar. When mixing is complete, store the sherbet in a dry sealed container, because water vapour in the air will cause the citric acid to react with the sodium hydrogencarbonate. Citric acid and sodium hydrogencarbonate can both be purchased in a chemist's shop. Describe what you observe when water is added to sherbet (Figure 8.5).

Figure 8.5 Fizzing sherbet

Hazardous chemicals

Many materials or commercial products in the home have harmful properties. Their containers must be labelled with **hazard symbols** to identify the dangers (Figure 8.6). Hazard symbols have been internationally agreed and are easily recognised. Words beside or below the symbols indicate the type of hazard. Figure 8.7 shows the hazard symbols on some things you will find in the home or school laboratories.

Explosive

A substance likely to explode.
e.g. ammonium dichromate

Toxic

Substances which can cause death.
They may cause problems if swallowed,
inhaled or absorbed through the skin.
e.g. chlorine, sulphur dioxide

Harmful

Substances similar to toxic
substances but not as harmful
e.g. aspirin, iodine, ethanol

Radioactive

Substances which give out
radiation that can cause
harmful effects such as cancer
e.g. cobalt-60, plutonium-239,
radium-226

Corrosive

Substances which attack and destroy
living tissues, including eyes and skin.
e.g. concentrated sulphuric acid,
concentrated sodium hydroxide

Irritant

Substances which are not corrosive
but can cause reddening or
blistering of the skin
e.g. dilute sulphuric acid, iodine solution

Highly flammable

Substances which can catch fire easily
e.g. petrol, ethanol

Figure 8.6 Some hazard symbols

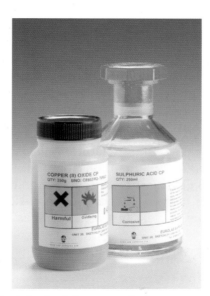

Figure 8.7 Products in the home and harmful chemicals in the laboratory display hazard symbols on their labels

6 **a** Why are hazard symbols used to warn people of the dangers of chemicals?
  b What is the difference between a 'harmful' substance and a 'toxic' substance?
7 Look in your home for chemicals with hazard symbols. Draw the symbols and give their meanings.

Acids, alkalis and the pH scale

The **pH scale** is a measure of how **acidic** or **alkaline** a solution is. **pH** is measured using a pH meter or using universal indicator paper, which turns different colours for different pH values. Figure 8.8 on the next page shows the colour of litmus and the colour of universal indicator in solutions with various pH values.

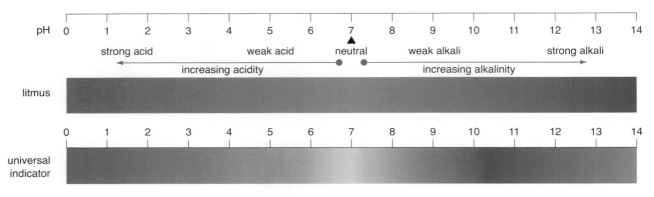

Figure 8.8 The colours of litmus and universal indicator in solutions of different pH

The pH scale runs from 0 to 14. Chemists use universal indicator to tell if dissolved substances are acidic, neutral or alkaline. A neutral solution has a pH of 7. Below pH 7 a solution is acidic, and above pH 7 a solution is alkaline.

- The **lower the pH** value below 7, the **stronger the acid**.
- The **higher the pH** value above 7, the **stronger the alkali**.

Many **indicators** are natural plant extracts, which change colour if they are mixed with acids or alkalis. Red cabbage, beetroot and blackcurrant are three examples of plants that contain natural indicators. **Universal indicator** is a special indicator. It contains a mixture of dyes that have been specially chosen to give a range of colour changes similar to those in the visible spectrum or a rainbow. The colour that a substance turns universal indicator is used to classify it as an acid, as an alkali or as a neutral solution.

Table 8.3 gives the pH values for a number of foods and chemicals found in the home or at school.

Table 8.3 The pH values for some foods and chemicals

Food	pH	Chemical	pH
lemon juice	2.5	dilute hydrochloric acid	1.0
apples	3.0	water	7.0
orange juice	3.5	ethanol	7.0
tomatoes	4.5	soap	8.0
banana	4.5	sodium hydrogencarbonate	8.0
carrots	5.0	ammonia solution	10.0
potatoes	5.5	dilute sodium hydroxide	13.0
tuna	6.0		
sardines	6.0		
salmon	6.5		
butter	6.5		

Hydrochloric acid with a low pH of 1 is classified as a strong acid. Orange juice, which contains citric acid, with a higher pH of 3.5 is classified as a weak acid. Sodium hydroxide with a high pH of 13 is classified as a strong alkali. Sodium hydrogencarbonate with a lower pH of 8 is classified as a weak alkali.

ACTIVITY

Use *Publisher* to design a poster on acids and bases in everyday life. Your poster should include a table or spreadsheet to display information about acids, bases and their pH values.

8 The table shows the preferred pH values of soils for growing different plants.

pH of soil	Plant	Acidic or alkaline
3.5–5.0	potato	
5.0–7.0	rhubarb	
5.5–7.0	radish	
7.0–8.5	pink hydrangea	

a   Copy and complete the table, by filling in whether the plants' soil type is acidic, alkaline or neutral.

b   Which plants would you grow if your garden soil had a pH of 6.5?

c   Hydrangea petals can be blue or pink depending on the pH of the soil. What type of substance can be extracted from hydrangeas?

ACTIVITY

The following method can be used to extract the colouring from red cabbage. Use it as an indicator to show whether substances are acidic or alkaline.

● Take 5 large red cabbage leaves and place them in a blender that is half full of water.

● Blend the mixture for a few minutes. Then filter the mixture to obtain the purple/blue indicator liquid.

● Add the indicator to a weak acid, such as vinegar. There will be a colour change from blue to red. Add the indicator to an alkaline solution of washing soda. There will be a colour change from blue to green.

● The indicator can now be used to test for a range of acids and alkalis.

Neutralisation reactions

When the right amount of an alkali is added to an acid, they cancel each other out. This reaction is known as **neutralisation**. As the final solution is neutral, it is possible to use universal indicator to tell when neutralisation takes place. The neutralisation reaction between hydrochloric acid and the alkali, sodium hydroxide, can be followed using universal indicator as shown in Figure 8.9.

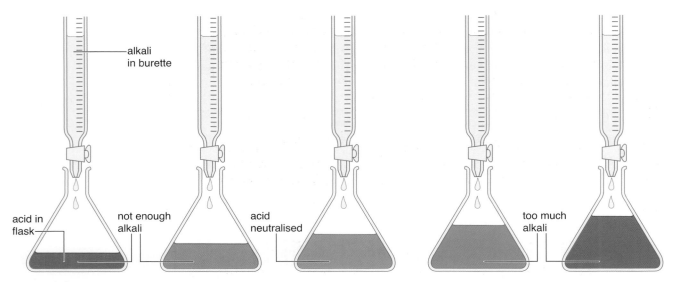

Figure 8.9 Adding alkali to an acid

During this neutralisation reaction, in which sodium hydroxide is added to hydrochloric acid, the solution becomes less acidic and the pH starts to rise. At the neutralisation point, the solution has a pH of 7. The universal indicator is then green. When further sodium hydroxide is added, the solution rapidly increases its pH. The solution becomes alkaline, as shown by the blue/purple colour of the universal indicator.

During neutralisation of an acid and an alkali, a salt and water are formed. The reaction can be represented by the following equation:

hydrochloric acid + sodium hydroxide → sodium chloride + water

$$HCl + NaOH \rightarrow NaCl + H_2O$$

The general word equation for an acid reacting with an alkali is:

acid + alkali → salt + water

In this reaction, hydrochloric acid reacts to give salts called chlorides. Table 8.4 shows the names of the salts produced by different acids.

Table 8.4 How salts are named

Acid	Salt
hydrochloric, HCl	chloride
sulphuric, H_2SO_4	sulphate
phosphoric, H_3PO_4	phosphate
nitric, HNO_3	nitrate
ethanoic, CH_3COOH (or CH_3CO_2H)	ethanoate
methanoic, HCOOH (or HCO_2H)	methanoate
tartaric	tartrate
oxalic	oxalate
citric	citrate

ACTIVITY

Plan and carry out an investigation using a pH sensor to find out how the pH changes during the neutralisation of hydrochloric acid and sodium hydroxide. The sodium hydroxide is added to the hydrochloric acid as in Figure 8.9. Include a graph of pH value against volume of sodium hydroxide added in your results section.

ACTIVITY

Plan an experiment to compare the effectiveness of different brands of indigestion tablets. You should consider which tablets are best at neutralising acids. Also consider the cost of different brands of tablets.

Writing formulae of metal compounds

Before studying the formulae of compounds, it is important to be clear about the meaning of some important terms:

- An **atom** is the smallest part of an element that can exist. For example, copper is composed of copper atoms.
- An **element** is a substance composed of one type of atom only. For example, oxygen, bromine and iron are all elements.
- A **compound** is a substance that contains atoms of two or more elements chemically joined together. For example, water H_2O (two hydrogen atoms and one oxygen atom), sodium chloride NaCl and methane CH_4 are compounds.
- A **molecule** consists of atoms chemically joined together. It may be an element, for example H_2, or a compound, for example CO_2.
- An **ion** is an atom or molecule that has lost or gained electrons, and so has a positive or negative charge.

When elements react, their atoms join with other atoms to form compounds. This involves transferring, gaining or sharing electrons. The atoms are held together by **chemical bonds**. Often the atoms form charged ions that bind strongly with ions of the opposite charge.

Table 8.5 shows the different charges on ions, which are used to work out the formulae of compounds for GCSE Science.

Table 8.5 Charges on various ions

Positive ion 1+	Symbol
sodium	Na^+
potassium	K^+
hydrogen	H^+
ammonium	NH_4^+

Positive ion 2+	Symbol
calcium	Ca^{2+}
magnesium	Mg^{2+}
copper(II)	Cu^{2+}
iron(II)	Fe^{2+}
zinc	Zn^{2+}

Positive ion 3+	Symbol
aluminium	Al^{3+}
iron(III)	Fe^{3+}

Negative ion 1−	Symbol
hydrogencarbonate	HCO_3^-
chloride	Cl^-
hydroxide	OH^-
ethanoate	CH_3COO^-

Negative ion 2−	Symbol
oxide	O^{2-}
carbonate	CO_3^{2-}
sulphate	SO_4^{2-}

Writing formulae

The following examples show how chemists work out the formulae of compounds.

- Sodium chloride: ions are Na^+ and Cl^-, charges are same size, so formula is **NaCl**.

- Sodium oxide: ions Na^+ and O^{2-}, two Na^+ needed to balance O^{2-}, so formula is **Na_2O**.

- Sodium carbonate: ions Na^+ and $CO_3{}^{2-}$, so formula is **Na_2CO_3**.

- Calcium hydroxide: ions Ca^{2+} and OH^-, two OH^- needed, so formula is **$Ca(OH)_2$**; brackets around OH because there is more than one atom in the hydroxide ion.

- Potassium sulphate: ions K^+ and $SO_4{}^{2-}$, so formula is **K_2SO_4**.

- Magnesium ethanoate: ions Mg^{2+} and CH_3COO^-, so formula is **$(CH_3COO)_2Mg$**; note that this is written with the metal on the right (see also questions 9e and 10b).

- Aluminium oxide: ions Al^{3+} and O^{2-}, so formula is **Al_2O_3**.

---

9 Write formulae for the following compounds:
   a calcium carbonate
   b potassium hydroxide
   c sodium sulphate
   d magnesium hydrogencarbonate
   e calcium ethanoate
   f potassium chloride.
10 Name the following compounds:
   a $Mg(OH)_2$
   b CH_3COONa
   c $Ca(HCO_3)_2$.

Writing symbol equations

i Consider the following word equation:

$$\text{potassium hydroxide} + \text{hydrochloric acid} \rightarrow \text{potassium chloride} + \text{water}$$

In writing the symbol equation, first write the formulae of all the reactants and products. Then check to see that the equation is balanced. There must be the same numbers of atoms on each side of the equation. So first we write:

$$KOH + HCl \rightarrow KCl + H_2O$$

Looking at the equation, you can see that there are the same numbers of atoms on each side. So the equation is already balanced.

ii   Consider the following word equation:

   sodium hydroxide + sulphuric acid → sodium sulphate + water

Writing the symbol equation gives the following:

$$NaOH + H_2SO_4 \rightarrow Na_2SO_4 + H_2O$$

To balance the equation, we must have the same number of atoms on each side. We must take $2NaOH$ and $2H_2O$. So the balanced equation is:

$$2NaOH + H_2SO_4 \rightarrow Na_2SO_4 + 2H_2O$$

iii Next consider the word equation for the thermal decomposition of sodium hydrogencarbonate:

   sodium hydrogencarbonate → sodium carbonate + carbon dioxide + water

Putting the formulae into the symbol equation:

$$NaHCO_3 \rightarrow Na_2CO_3 + H_2O + CO_2$$

The equation is not balanced. You can see that to get the same number of atoms on each side, you need to take $2NaHCO_3$. This now gives:

$$2NaHCO_3 \rightarrow Na_2CO_3 + H_2O + CO_2$$

---

11 Complete the following word equations:
   a   potassium hydrogencarbonate → water + ... + ...
   b   hydrochloric acid + calcium carbonate → .... + ... + ...
   c   sulphuric acid + calcium hydroxide → .... + ...
   d   hydrochloric acid + zinc oxide → .... + ...

---

12 Write balanced symbol equations for the four reactions in question 11.

---

websites

www.sambal.co.uk/indicators.html
useful information on the meaning of acid, alkali, pH, indicator and neutralisation

http://kidshealth.org/kid/health_problems/stomach/indigestion.html
interesting material on indigestion

www.s-cool.co.uk
revision of acids, alkalis, pH and neutralisation: search for 'acids and alkalis'

www.gcsechemistry.com/ukop.htm
good for revision of this chapter

www.vickicobb.com/scienceyoueat.html
details on how to make a red cabbage indicator

www.creative-chemistry.org.uk/gcse/revision/equations/02.htm
provides several tests on balancing symbol equations

Questions

1 a What happens in a neutralisation reaction when an acid reacts with a base? *(1 mark)*

  b Write word equations for the following reactions:
   i iron oxide + phosphoric acid
   ii zinc oxide + hydrochloric acid
   iii copper oxide + ethanoic acid *(3 marks)*

2 a Why can lemons be used to clean a tarnished copper pot? Write a word equation for the reaction taking place. *(3 marks)*

  b Why shouldn't vinegar be used to clean tarnished copper surfaces? *(1 mark)*

  c Name **three** substances that could be used to cure indigestion. *(3 marks)*

3 Roberta and Mark experimented with making honeycomb. They decided to add various quantities of sodium hydrogencarbonate (baking soda) to a heated mixture of sugar and honey. The mixture was then quickly stirred and poured into a greased tin. They wanted to get honeycomb that would rise to the greatest height.

  a Roberta and Mark wanted to keep the investigations valid. Which **three** of the following statements do you feel are important for a valid test?
   i The same amount of sugar/honey mixture should be used.
   ii The same size of container should be used to heat the mixture.
   iii The same amount of sodium hydrogencarbonate should be used each time.
   iv The mixtures should be heated for the same length of time.
   v The mixtures should be heated to the same temperature.
   vi The same size of greased tin should be used. *(3 marks)*

  b Their results are shown below.

Amount of baking soda (g)	5	10	15	20	25	30
Height of honeycomb (cm)	2	3	2	5	6	6

   i Suggest a reason why the maximum height of 6 cm was reached even though more baking soda was used. *(1 mark)*

   ii Mark suggested one of the readings was incorrect. Which amount of baking soda appeared to give a false reading and suggest a reason for this? *(2 marks)*

   iii Roberta suggested better honeycomb would be made if a small amount of vinegar was added to the sugar mixture. Why do you think this would make honeycomb reach an even greater height? *(1 mark)*

CCEA GCSE Science: Single Award (Modular)
Specimen Paper (Foundation Tier) 2006

4 A group of students investigated the thermal decomposition of sodium hydrogencarbonate. Their teacher told them that it decomposed according to the equation given below. They were asked to heat 16.8 grams of the sodium hydrogencarbonate and this should produce 10.6 grams of sodium carbonate.

sodium hydrogencarbonate → sodium carbonate + carbon dioxide + water

The students obtained the following results:

Mass of crucible	= 120.0 g
Mass crucible + sodium hydrogencarbonate **(before heating)**	= 136.8 g
Mass crucible + sodium hydrogencarbonate **(after heating)**	= 126.4 g

  a Calculate the mass of sodium carbonate formed. *(1 mark)*

  b Give a reason why the mass of sodium carbonate formed was not equal to the predicted amount. *(1 mark)*

  c Suggest a way of improving the experiment to get a value the same as the predicted value. *(1 mark)*

  d Give **one** important safety precaution that the students must take. *(1 mark)*

  e Write a balanced symbol equation to show the thermal decomposition of sodium hydrogencarbonate. *(3 marks)*

CCEA GCSE Science: Single Award (Modular)
Specimen Paper (Higher Tier) 2006

5 a Which of the following 'best' describes a chemical indicator?
   1 always shows a change in colour
   2 does not change colour if a substance is neutral
   3 tells us whether a substance is an acid
   4 changes colour depending on pH *(1 mark)*

  b Farmers sometimes add lime to the soil to improve its quality. Select **two** statements from the following list that best explain the reason for adding lime.
   1 lime has a low pH
   2 lime adds alkali to the soil
   3 lime adds acid to the soil
   4 lime neutralises acid soil
   5 lime fertilises the soil *(2 marks)*

  c Write down the correct chemical symbol for the following elements.
   i sulphur
   ii lithium
   iii chlorine *(1 mark)*

CCEA GCSE Science: Single Award (Modular)
Specimen Paper (Foundation Tier) 2006

6 The diagram shows sulphuric acid being added to sodium hydroxide solution.

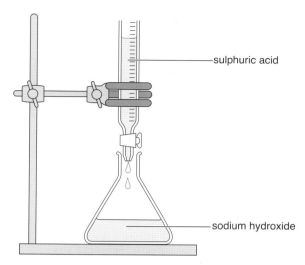

The pH value of the solution is taken and recorded. Which of the following graphs shows how the pH value changes during the experiment? *(1 mark)*

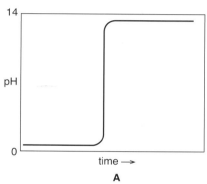

A

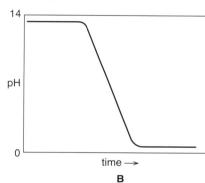

B

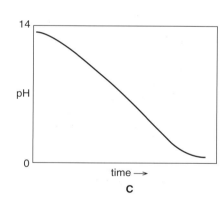

C

CCEA GCSE Science: Single Award (Modular)
Specimen Paper (Foundation Tier) 2006 (part question)

7 The following hazard symbols are found on a bottle of methylated spirits.

a Name **two** dangers when handling methylated spirits. *(2 marks)*

b Draw the symbol you would expect to find on a substance which is poisonous. *(1 mark)*

c Smoke alarms have the following symbol on their cover.

What sort of material is found in a smoke alarm? *(1 mark)*

d A substance has the following hazard symbol on its label.

What does this tell us about this substance? *(1 mark)*

CCEA GCSE Science: Single Award (Modular)
Specimen Paper (Foundation Tier) 2006 (part question)

Chapter 9

Food processing

By the end of this chapter you should know and understand:

➤ That food needs preserving, because microbes feed on food and make it go bad
➤ That microbes cause food poisoning
➤ How food processing involves methods of treating food to improve its taste, flavour and colour
➤ That food processing preserves food, controls its pH, stops its oxidation and makes it last longer
➤ The advantages and drawbacks of using food additives
➤ The seven main types of food additives, and the particular function of each
➤ That food colourings can be investigated using chromatography
➤ That food additives must be tested and approved before use
➤ That additives may be tested on animals to ensure that they are not dangerous to human health
➤ The ethical issues involved in food additive testing with animals
➤ Why people have worries about the dangers of some additives, as they can cause allergies, hyperactivity and other health problems

Why the need for food processing?

Since earliest times people have realised the need to **preserve** food to stop it from going bad. At that time, the main ways of preserving foods were by drying it, cooking it, salting it or keeping it cool. Similarly, at that time people also realised that certain additives such as herbs and spices could be added to preserve and enhance the flavour of food. Chinese people have for a long time used MSG (monosodium glutamate: the sodium salt of glutamic acid) as an ingredient of soy sauce. On its own, MSG has only a faint meaty taste; but when it is added to processed food, it has a very powerful flavour-enhancing effect. Food technologists use MSG to flavour many foods, especially processed meat products.

The early ideas of keeping food from going off have now been developed into the science of food processing. So **food processing** is the different ways of treating food to improve it and make it last longer. Virtually all of the food you eat has been processed in some way or another (Figure 9.1).

Microbes, that is, **bacteria** and **fungi**, feed on our food. If they are not stopped, they will grow in the food and cause it to go bad. In addition, some microbes produce harmful chemicals, which lead to food poisoning. It is not surprising that a major aim of food processing is to stop the growth of bacteria and fungi.

Figure 9.1 Food is processed in many different ways

ACTIVITY

Investigate how temperature and pH affect the rate at which apples or other fruits ripen and turn brown. Remember that you can only change one factor at a time!

Preserving food

There are several ways of preserving foods. These involve either killing the **microbes** or slowing down the rate at which they reproduce. The methods are as follows:

- salting
- drying
- freezing
- canning

- pickling in oil or vinegar
- adding chemical preservatives
- irradiation with gamma rays (see page 263).

1   Suggest a method of preserving the following foods. Give a different method for each.
   a   fish
   b   peas
   c   beetroot
   d   coffee

Food additives

In addition to food preservatives, food technologists also add other chemicals to improve and preserve foods. If you check the labels on tinned or packed foods, you will find a list of the various ingredients and food additives (see Figure 9.2).

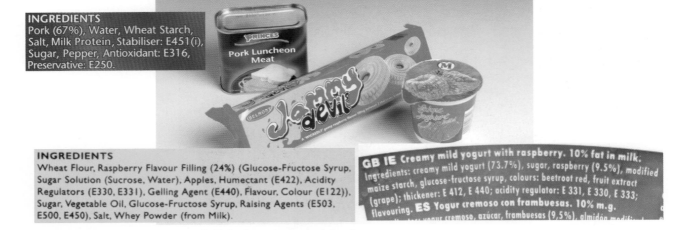

INGREDIENTS
Pork (67%), Water, Wheat Starch, Salt, Milk Protein, Stabiliser: E451(i), Sugar, Pepper, Antioxidant: E316, Preservative: E250.

INGREDIENTS
Wheat Flour, Raspberry Flavour Filling (24%) (Glucose-Fructose Syrup, Sugar Solution (Sucrose, Water), Apples, Humectant (E422), Acidity Regulators (E330, E331), Gelling Agent (E440), Flavour, Colour (E122)), Sugar, Vegetable Oil, Glucose-Fructose Syrup, Raising Agents (E503, E500, E450), Salt, Whey Powder (from Milk).

GB IE Creamy mild yogurt with raspberry. 10% fat in milk. Ingredients: creamy mild yogurt (73.7%), sugar, raspberry (9.5%), modified maize starch, glucose-fructose syrup, colours: beetroot red, fruit extract (grape); thickener: E 412, E 440; acidity regulator: E 331, E 330, E 333; flavouring. **ES Yogur cremoso con frambuesas. 10% m.g.**

Figure 9.2 Additives need to be labelled on packaged foods

There are many different food additives. They can be classified into seven major groups:

- colourings
- flavourings
- anti-oxidants
- sweeteners
- emulsifiers
- acids and bases
- stabilisers and preservatives.

These groups of food additives are regulated by governments. This means that companies must have government permission to use them. All food additives are also regulated by European Community legislation. They have been labelled with a different E number.

Colourings

The importance of the colour in food is well recognised. The attractiveness of fruit and vegetables is mainly due to their colour (Figure 9.3), which is caused by the presence of very small amounts of colouring matter. The attractive colouring in carrots and tomatoes is caused by substances called carotenoids. Where the natural colour of a processed food is unattractive, coloured substances may be added. Cochineal (from a type of insect) can be used to colour foods red. Saffron (from the saffron crocus plant) and annatto (from the fruit of a tropical tree) are used to produce a natural yellow colour for foods.

Figure 9.3 Strong colours can increase the attractiveness of foods

Most colourings now have an E number beginning with the number 1. For example, the green colouring added to peas has the E number E124.

ACTIVITY

Scientists use chromatography to identify the colouring agents added to foods. Figure 9.4 shows how to check the orange colouring in an orange drink:

1 A spot of the drink and spots of some permitted food colourings are put on chromatography paper.
2 The chromatography paper is rolled up and the bottom is dipped into a small amount of a suitable solvent.
3 The solvent is allowed to rise up the chromatography paper, and the colours separate.
4 The chromatography paper is removed from the solvent, dried and examined.

As the solvent moves up the chromatography paper, the dyes are carried along with the solvent. The dyes move up the paper at different rates. The rate depends on their solubility in the solvent and how strongly they are attracted to the paper. Those that are most soluble in the solvent and are not attracted strongly to the paper travel a long distance up the paper. Those that are less soluble in the solvent and are attracted strongly to the paper travel only a short distance up the paper. From the chromatogram in Figure 9.4, we can see that the orange drink contained the two permitted colours 2 and 3.

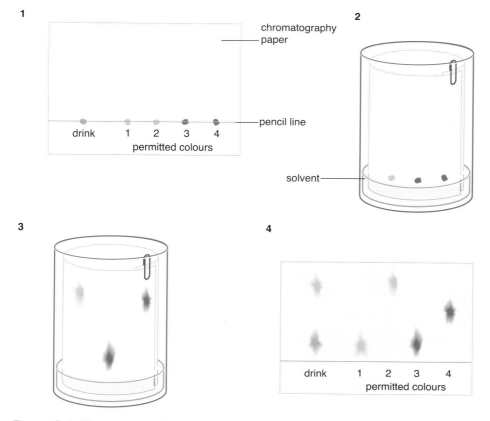

Figure 9.4 Chromatography can be used to check the food colours in a drink

Flavourings

Flavour is an important factor in the processing of foods, as this is detected by our senses of taste and smell. The senses of taste – salt, bitter, sour and sweet – are detected by the taste buds located on the tongue, palate and cheeks. Smell is detected by sensitive cells at the top of the nasal cavity.

Herbs, spices, coca, peppermint, vanilla, orange and lemon are examples of natural flavourings. Many of the synthetic flavourings belong to a family of organic compounds called **esters**. Esters are used as artificial fruit flavourings (see Table 9.1). Unlike other food additives, flavourings do not have an E number assigned to them.

Table 9.1 Esters that are used as flavourings

Name of ester	Use
ethyl methanoate	rum, raspberry and peach essences
ethyl ethanoate	apple, pear, strawberry and peach essences
pentyl ethanoate	pear, pineapple and raspberry essences

ACTIVITY

For safety reasons, this synthesis of the flavouring, pentyl ethanoate, should be done as a teacher demonstration.

- Put 4 cm^3 of pentanol (amyl alcohol) into a Pyrex boiling tube and carefully add 1 cm^3 of concentrated sulphuric acid.
- Add 4 cm^3 of glacial ethanoic acid.
- Warm the test tube gently with shaking.
- Allow the boiling tube to cool.
- Pour the contents of the tube into 50 cm^3 of sodium carbonate solution.
- Carefully smell the artificial flavouring made.

Anti-oxidants

Fatty foods and others such as cakes and biscuits contain fat and are prone to atmospheric oxidation. When the fats get oxidised, the food deteriorates and becomes **rancid**. Air oxidation is also responsible for fruit and vegetables developing a brown colour. Anti-oxidants are added to foods to stop fats getting oxidised and tasting bad. Fats contain vitamin E as a naturally occurring anti-oxidant, but there is not enough of it to prevent air oxidation of stored foods. One of the common anti-oxidants added to foods is BHT, with an E number of E321. BHT is the shortened name for the organic compound called butylated hydroxyl toluene. It is used to stop fats getting oxidised in food products like potato crisps and butter.

Sweeteners

Sugar is a natural product, quite cheap, readily available and very soluble in water. But it has two major disadvantages in foods:

- It is not sweet enough for a number of manufactured food products.
- Its high energy value makes it unattractive for slimming products.

Sugar also contributes to obesity and tooth decay.

Sweeteners are an alternative to sugar. An example of a sweetener is sorbitol, with an E number of E420. It is used in diabetic chocolates. Generally sweeteners have an E number that starts with a 4 or 6.

Emulsifiers

When water and oil are added together, the oil forms a layer on top of the water. The liquids do not dissolve in each other. The liquids are said to be **immiscible**. When the oil and water are shaken, the two liquids are dispersed in each other. It is now described as an **emulsion**. On standing, the two liquids separate. The emulsion is described as being unstable. There are two types of emulsion, either **oil-in-water** or **water-in-oil**. In an oil-in-water emulsion, the oil droplets are dispersed through the water. In a water-in-oil emulsion, the water droplets are dispersed in oil.

For water and oil to form a stable emulsion, an emulsifier must be added. One common emulsifier is GMS (or glyceryl monostearate), which has an E number of E471. This emulsifier is used in ice cream and salad cream (both oil-in-water emulsions). Lecithin (E322) is used in margarine (water-in-oil emulsion) and mayonnaise (oil-in-water emulsion). Emulsifiers have E numbers beginning with a 3 or 4.

Milk is an example of a natural emulsion. It is stabilised by natural emulsifiers in the milk. Many food products that contain fats have emulsifiers added, for example margarine, cooking fats, salad dressings and ice cream.

Acids and bases

These are added to foods to control pH and so act as preservatives. By controlling pH, it is possible to stop the growth of bacteria and fungi. Sulphur dioxide (E219) is a widely used preservative for fruit juices, wines, beer and cider. Other acids such as ethanoic acid, citric acid and tartaric acid can be added to foods to preserve them. The base sodium hydrogencarbonate (E500) is added to preserve tinned custard.

> **ACTIVITY**
>
> Collect the labels or empty packets of around 20 different foods from your home. From the information on the labels, decide which of the ingredients are additives and which are foods. Create a spreadsheet or table showing the name of each different food additive, its E number, and the type of additive it is, e.g. anti-oxidant, colouring, preservative, etc. Also record if there are any foods that do not contain additives. Compare your findings with the other students in your class.

> **2** You are eating some green sweets that contain a mixture of two dyes – blue and yellow. Describe an experiment you could carry out to show that the sweets contained these two dyes. Include suitable diagrams and a list of equipment.
>
> **3 a** What is meant by a food additive?
> **b** Butter contains the food additive BHT, with an E number of E321. Why is BHT added to butter?
> **c** Why are potato crisps packed in bags containing nitrogen instead of air?

> **ACTIVITY**
>
> In groups, discuss whether there is a need for food processing, and whether it would be possible to do without processed foods and to live on natural, organic foods only. Your group should then present your ideas to the class and highlight the advantages and disadvantages of processing foods.

Should additives be used?

There is still much debate about adding chemicals to food. Some people argue that all additives are tested to make sure they are not harmful to people's health. They cannot be used unless they fulfil all the Government's health and safety legislation. Nevertheless, from the results of animal testing, a number of additives have been withdrawn and banned from being used in food manufacture. One example was in the USA, where a permitted food colouring dye known as Butter Yellow was banned after it was shown that it caused animals to develop liver tumours.

Because of rigorous testing and legislation, the number of food additives has been reduced. Many people, however, still have serious concerns about the use of food additives (Figure 9.5). Their arguments are based on the fact that some people are allergic to a number of additives. It is claimed that these can cause dizziness, headache, nausea, tiredness and stomach pain. There is also evidence that sulphur dioxide, the food preservative in alcoholic drink, can bring on asthmatic attacks. Additionally there have been reports that food additives are responsible for the hyperactivity of children. Some people claim that food additives cause behavioural difficulties with school-children, and this affects their learning and emotional response. There needs to be further research into the effects of food additives on young people.

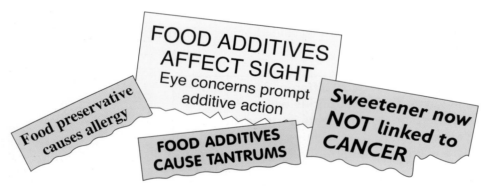

Figure 9.5 Food additive 'scares' can make the headlines in newspapers

ACTIVITY

Find out further information from libraries and the internet on the possible effects of some food additives on the behaviour of children. Make a poster to display your findings. Compare your work with other students' research.

ACTIVITY

Food additives are tested on animals to see if they are safe before they are used for human consumption. Make out a list of reasons for or against testing food additives on animals.

websites

http://archive.food.gov.uk/hea/teachers/english/info.html
useful information on food labelling and the preserving of food

www.eufic.org
www.food.gov.uk/safereating/chemsafe/additivesbranch/enumberlist
these two sites give extensive information on food additives and legislation covering them

http://news.bbc.co.uk/1/hi/health/2352709.stm
a report on the possible dangers of using the food additive monosodium glutamate (MSG)

www.yesmag.bc.ca/projects/paper_chroma.html
a project to separate coloured dyes using chromatography

Questions

1 a Why are food preservatives added to food products? Give **three** advantages and **three** disadvantages of adding preservatives to food.   *(6 marks)*

b A certain brand of margarine contains three food additives: E320, E202 and E160. Explain why each additive had been added to the margarine.   *(6 marks)*

c Suggest suitable food additives that could be added to the following foods: cheese and onion crisps, jam, tinned beans, chocolate, powdered milk.   *(5 marks)*

2 Many foods contain natural colourings that can be made up from a number of dyes. Explain how you could show that a food colouring contained more than one dye (a labelled diagram would help to support your method).   *(5 marks)*

3 Janice is 5 years old, sleeps only 4 hours at night and is very overactive throughout the day. After visiting the doctor, it is felt that the green colouring E142 is causing this hyperactivity. What advice should be given to Janice's parents to help overcome this problem?   *(2 marks)*

4 For centuries many people have added different substances to foods to preserve and improve them. The Chinese have been using sodium glutamate in soya sauce to increase its flavour. On its own, sodium glutamate has only a faint meaty taste. However, when added to processed food and other additives, it has a powerful flavour enhancing effect.

Sodium glutamate is known to cause flushing, dizziness and palpitations and although scientists do not think that it is harmful, sodium glutamate is no longer added to food prepared specifically for babies and infants.

Most food additives are controlled by government legislation and permission must be given before a food processing company can use a food additive. All regulated additives have a number and if it is regulated by the European Community then the number will start with an E.

E numbers starting with 1 are colourings
E numbers starting with 2 are preservatives
E numbers between 300 and 321 are anti-oxidants
E numbers starting with 5 are acids or bases
E numbers starting with 4 or 9 are sweeteners

a What causes food to go bad?   *(1 mark)*

b Why are people worried that food additives are a danger to health?   *(1 mark)*

c Why is sodium glutamate not used in processed food for babies?   *(1 mark)*

d Who has responsibility to allow new food additives to be used in the food processing industry?   *(1 mark)*

e Sodium glutamate is a food additive with an E number E621. What type of food additives are:

i sulphur dioxide E219?

ii sodium hydrogencarbonate E500?

iii sorbitol E420?   *(3 marks)*

CCEA GCSE Science: Single Award (Modular)
Specimen Paper (Higher Tier) 2006 (part question)

5 During 2005 a red colouring Sudan 1 was found to be present in imported chilli powder. This powder was used to make Worcester sauce. This sauce was sold to food processors who used small quantities of it in making different types of foodstuff.

Sudan 1 is a red dye normally used in boot polish. It is not permitted to be used in foodstuffs in the EU. Tests on animals show that a form of cancer can develop when it is eaten. No cancer, however, has been found to develop in humans.

As a result of the discovery over 400 processed foods were removed from shelves. The Food Standards Agency stated that there is no real risk to health.

a Why do you think the makers of chilli powder used Sudan 1 rather than an approved colouring?   *(1 mark)*

b Give **two** reasons why the Food Standards Agency stated that there was little risk if contaminated foods were eaten.   *(2 marks)*

CCEA GCSE Science: Single Award (Modular)
Specimen Paper (Higher Tier) 2006 (part question)

Chapter 10

The Earth's rocks

Learning objectives

By the end of this chapter you should know and understand:

➤ That there are three different types of rock – igneous, sedimentary and metamorphic

➤ What fossils are and how they provide evidence for changes in the Earth

➤ The concept of deep time and how the dating of rocks provides evidence for the age of the Earth (4500 million years)

➤ Archbishop Ussher's theory on the age of the Earth and how it compares with the modern method of dating rocks

➤ The development of the modern theory on the shape of the surface of the Earth, including Wegener's theory of continental drift and plate tectonics

➤ The size and structure of the Earth

➤ The process of sea-floor spreading

➤ How sea-floor spreading produces a pattern in the magnetism recorded on sea floors

➤ That volcanoes and mountain building are likely to occur at the edge of tectonic plates and describe the process of volcanic eruption

➤ How earthquakes occur and use the Richter scale to interpret their intensity

➤ That no theory will accurately predict when a volcano will erupt or an earthquake will happen

➤ How tsunamis occur during volcanoes, earthquakes and landslides

➤ That the surface of the Earth is constantly changing, with new land masses being created and existing ones being partially covered by sea

➤ That changing climate and tectonic plate movement can accelerate these changes

Types of rock

The study of rocks is very important. About 4500 million (4.5 billion) years ago the Earth was a massive ball of fire. As it cooled down, it formed layers, with a solid crust of rocks around the surface of the Earth. These rocks are classified into three major groups, according to the way in which they were formed:

● igneous
● sedimentary
● metamorphic.

Figure 10.1 shows how the three rock types are related.

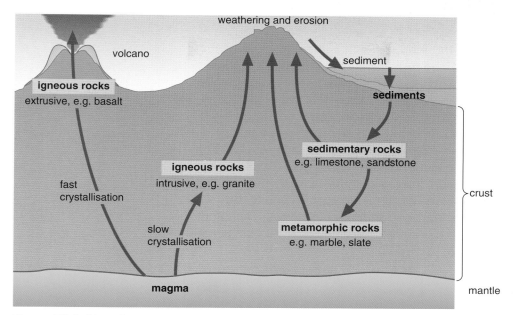

Figure 10.1 How the three rock types were formed

Igneous rocks

This type of rock was formed by solidification of the hot, molten magma found in the Earth's mantle (Figure 10.1). **Magma** is a mobile mixture of liquids, solid rock and gases. When the magma cools down and solidifies, the resultant igneous rock is composed of interlocking crystals.

Igneous rock formed from volcanic lava will have a small crystal size due to fast cooling at the Earth's surface. This type of igneous rock is dark in colour and is termed **extrusive**. An example of this rock type is **basalt**, which makes up the Giant's Causeway (Figure 10.2, left) and the Antrim Plateau.

Magma deep below the Earth's crust cools down very much more slowly. This causes the rocks to have a much larger crystal size. Crystals vary from a few millimetres to a few centimetres in size. This type of igneous rock is known as **intrusive**. An example of this rock type is **granite**, which is found in the Mournes (Figure 10.2, right) and the high ground of Dartmoor.

Figure 10.2 Igneous rocks: basalt rocks on the Giant's Causeway, County Antrim (left) and granite rocks in the Mourne Mountains, County Down (right)

Sedimentary rocks

Sedimentary rocks are formed by the accumulation and compacting of weathered (broken) rock material, the remains of living organisms (shells and plants) and chemical deposits. As the layers of sediment build up, over thousands of years, they get pressed together. As a result, water gets squeezed out and the layers glue together to form sedimentary rock. There are many sedimentary rocks, each one being distinguished by its main components. Organic sedimentary rocks are formed from living things. For example, shells form **limestone**, while peat layers form coal. Rock salt is formed from the evaporation of water from seas or lakes. Clay minerals form shale, sand forms **sandstone**, and larger fragments such as gravel form conglomerate. There are lots of examples of sedimentary rocks throughout Ireland. Two famous examples are the limestone deposits in Fermanagh and the Burren in County Clare (Figure 10.3, left).

Figure 10.3 Sedimentary rocks: limestone hills of the Burren, County Clare (left) and sandstone rocks at Scrabo Hill, County Down (right)

Metamorphic rocks

Rocks buried deep below the Earth's surface are subjected to high temperatures and high pressures. The minerals and the physical structures in these solid rocks are transformed or **metamorphosed**. The new type of rock is called metamorphic rock. Under these conditions sedimentary rocks are changed into harder rocks. Examples are the conversion of limestone into **marble** (Figure 10.4, left) and mudstone into **slate** (Figure 10.4, right).

Figure 10.4 Metamorphic rocks: marble quarry in Connemara (left) and slate on Valencia Island, County Kerry (right)

1 a   Why are basalt and granite referred to as igneous rocks?
  b   Explain why the crystals in granite are larger than those in basalt.
  c   Name two sedimentary rocks.
2 Marble is a metamorphic rock.
  a   How are sedimentary rocks converted into metamorphic rocks?
  b   Which sedimentary rock is transformed into marble?
  c   Give one use of marble.

Fossils and rocks

Fossils are often found in sedimentary rocks.
Fossils are the remains of ancient life, for
example, the animals and plants that died and
became part of the layers of sediment in the rocks.
They display patterns that help scientists to
determine the ages of rocks. The relative ages of
rock sequences can be established mainly on the
basis that newer layers lie on top of older layers.
Figure 10.5 shows us how fossils provide evidence
for the ages of rocks.

Rock layers of similar age contain similar fossil
remains of ancient life. Rock layers of different
ages contain different fossil remains. This type of
rock dating is known as the **rock record**.
Scientists have used the fossil record to define a
number of geological periods. These geological
periods are the basis of the **geological timescale**, which provides a standard system to study
geological age. Fossils in rocks have also provided
evidence for the theory of continental drift (see
page 124). It has been shown that the kinds of
rocks continue from one continent across into
another continent. Thus old rocks in South
America lie next to old rocks in Africa. Likewise,
young rocks lie next to young rocks in these
continents. The fossil remains in the rocks in both
continents also match up. The location of these
fossils provides evidence that there have been
changes in the Earth over periods of time (see
Figure 10.8, page 124).

The geological time-line (or **deep time** as it often referred to) is a way of
helping to understand the immensity of time. It also helps us to develop a
better understanding of evolutionary changes. The time-line and the events it
portrays provide a framework for understanding geological time. As deep
time extends to thousands of millions of years, it takes a lot of getting used
to. In terms of the planet we live on, our lifetime is only a blink of the eye
compared to the age of the Earth. The time-line in Figure 10.6 on the next
page, based on a single year, gives an idea of the relationships between
geological events in the story of the Earth.

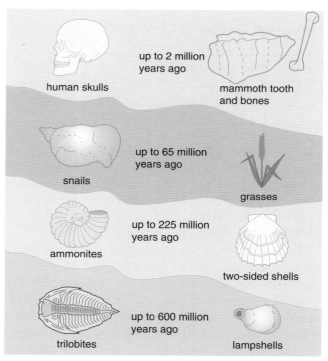

Figure 10.5 The age of a layer of rock can be
estimated from the fossils in it

up to 2 million
years ago

human skulls

mammoth tooth
and bones

up to 65 million
years ago

snails

grasses

up to 225 million
years ago

ammonites

two-sided shells

up to 600 million
years ago

trilobites

lampshells

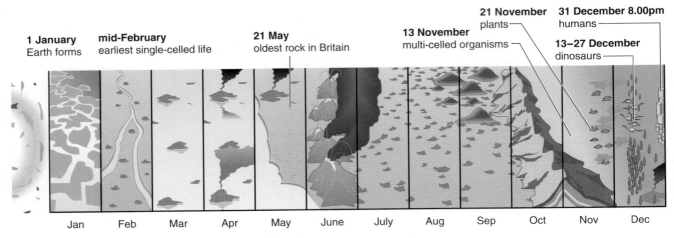

1 January
Earth forms

mid-February
earliest single-celled life

21 May
oldest rock in Britain

13 November
multi-celled organisms

21 November
plants

31 December 8.00pm
humans

13–27 December
dinosaurs

Jan   Feb   Mar   Apr   May   June   July   Aug   Sep   Oct   Nov   Dec

Figure 10.6 Time-line of Earth's history: 4500 million years contracted to one year

3 a What are fossils?
b In what type of rock are fossils often formed?
c How do scientists use fossils to find out the relative ages of rocks?

The very oldest rocks contain few fossils, and some rocks do not contain fossils at all. So other methods are necessary to find the age of such rocks. Additionally, rocks that contain fossils only provide a relative date and not an absolute date. The main method of determining the age of a rock is by **radiometric dating**. This method is based on the rate of decay of a radioactive element (see Chapter 19).

To date a rock, a scientist works out the amount of an undecayed radioactive element and the amount of decayed or 'daughter' elements, and then finds their ratio. The basis of the method is as follows. Younger rocks contain more of the original undecayed element. Older rocks contain a higher proportion of the daughter elements. The rates of decay are constant. So the ratio of the concentration of the original element to the daughter element shows how long the rock has been decaying. This is used to calculate the age of the rock.

There are a number of radioactive elements that are used to work out the age of a rock. These include uranium-238, potassium-40 and carbon-14. Each of these elements has its own **half-life**. This is the time it takes for half of the original radioactive element to decay to its daughter element. For example, carbon-14 has a half-life ($t_{1/2}$) of 5730 years. This means that the amount of carbon-14 halves every 5730 years. When carbon-14 decays, it forms nitrogen-14. This is used to work out the age of old objects.

- Uranium-238 has a half-life of 4500 million years and is used to date the oldest rocks. Here the amount of uranium-238 is compared to the amount of lead-206.
- Potassium-40 has a half-life of 1300 million years. Rocks are dated using this radioactive element by comparing the proportion of potassium-40 to argon-40.
- Carbon-14, with a half-life of 5700 years, is used to date substances less than 30 000 years old.

Using radiometric dating, it has been calculated that the Earth's crust is approximately **4500 million years old**.

As a result of radiometric dating of rocks, scientists believe that some of the earlier theories on the date of creation are inaccurate. One such theory was developed in 1658 by the Dublin-born James Ussher. While Archbishop of Armagh, Ussher became determined to approximate when the universe was created. Using the *Book of Genesis* to count the generations of ancestors, he concluded that the universe was created on the 23 October 4004 BC. If this date is used to calculate how old the Earth is, it would be just over 6000 years old. This value is very different from the 4500 million years put forward by scientists.

> **4 a** What is the meaning of half-life?
> **b** Name two radioactive elements that are found in rocks.
> **c** Give the approximate age of the Earth from radioactive dating.

Earth's layers

Scientists have put forward a structure of the Earth from studies on the density of the Earth and from an analysis of **seismic waves** (shock waves from earthquakes). In Figure 10.7 we see that the Earth is composed of a layered structure, with a **core**, a **mantle** and a thin solid **crust**.

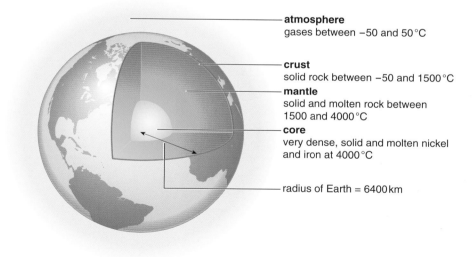

atmosphere
gases between −50 and 50 °C

crust
solid rock between −50 and 1500 °C
mantle
solid and molten rock between
1500 and 4000 °C
core
very dense, solid and molten nickel
and iron at 4000 °C

radius of Earth = 6400 km

Figure 10.7 The structure of the inside of the Earth

- The **crust** is a thin layer of low density solid rock. It has an average thickness of about 33 km but it may be as much as 75 km.
- The **mantle** is mostly a moderately dense solid with some molten rock, and is almost 2900 km thick. Both temperature and pressure rise towards the interior.
- The **core** is more than 2900 km below the surface and is composed of the densest materials, nickel and iron. The outer part of the core is liquid, while the inner part is solid. Temperatures are in the region of 4000°C.

During the formation of the Earth, the temperature inside it was very high. The insulating properties of the layers have helped to maintain this high temperature. In addition, rocks like granite that contain radioactive elements such as potassium and thorium provide heat energy during their decay.

---

5 Draw a diagram to show the main layers that make up the Earth. Label the diagram to show what the Earth's radius is. Also show what the distance around the Earth is, from the South Pole to the North Pole.

6 Explain where the heat inside the Earth comes from.

Continental drift theory and plate tectonics

Continental drift

The formation of the continents has been an issue of great debate for centuries. Early scientists and philosophers firmly believed that the continents formed when the Earth's molten crust cooled down and shrank. Central to their thinking was the idea that, because of their size and mass, the continents always remained in fixed positions.

Alternative ideas were highlighted as far back as 1620. In that year the English philosopher Francis Bacon noticed the similarity in shape of the South American and African coastlines on either side of the South Atlantic Ocean. This jigsaw-like fit (Figure 10.8) has been a source of inspiration and speculation for **continental drift** theory. It was first put forward in 1558 by the American, Antonio Snider, who tied his ideas in with the Biblical tale of the Great Flood. Snider imagined a single great land mass before the Flood, slowly being hardened and split open by internal heat, producing great cracks edged by volcanoes. Eventually the land mass drifted apart while the waters of the Flood rushed into the cracks between the old world and the new world.

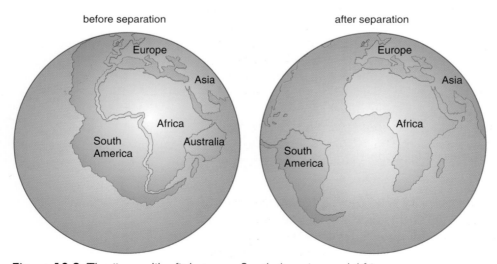

Figure 10.8 The jigsaw-like fit between South America and Africa

There were weaknesses in Snider's theory. But the idea of the Earth splitting along lines of volcanic activity fits well into the theory of continental drift, or under its modified new name of **plate tectonics** (see page 127).

In spite of Snider's theory, the idea of continental drift never got off the ground in the 19th century. It was only in 1915 that attention was given to this theory. It was then that the German scientist Alfred Wegener put forward a logical and coherent account of how continental drift may have occurred. He put forward the following ideas (see Figure 10.9):

1 Originally there was only one continent called 'Pangaea'.
2 Around 200 million years ago, it started to break up and form continents.
3 These continents were able to move, and they ploughed through the weaker crust of the ocean floor like icebergs through the sea.

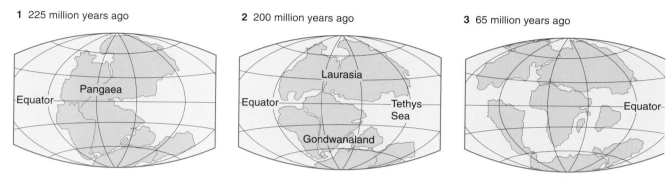

Figure 10.9 The break-up of Pangaea as suggested by Wegener

Wegener showed that the continents fitted together like a jigsaw, especially in the case of South America and Africa. He also highlighted the following evidence for continental drift:

● The rock pattern continued from one continent across the joint and into another continent. There was a good fit of old rocks in South America lying next to old rocks in Africa, and similarly for young rocks in both these continents.
● A past period of glaciation can be found in rocks not only in South America and Africa but also in Australia, Antarctica and India. The rock layers laid down during the Ice Age (about 200 and 350 million years ago) can be clearly distinguished in all these continents. The area they covered can be accounted for very nicely by a region of glaciation around the South Pole – but only if these continents were stuck together, and roughly centred over the pole, at a critical period 200–350 million years ago.
● The remains of living organisms (coal beds and fossil remains) found on different continents match up across the 'joint'. These include the remains of identical creatures that lived only in fresh water, now separated by the salty expanse of the Atlantic Ocean.

With so much evidence in its favour, it was difficult to see how the theory of continental drift could fail to be taken seriously. But it took another 40 years before the theory of continental drift became acceptable. Wegener's theory was rejected because geologists at the time did not accept that continents could drift. They believed the continents were in fixed positions. Additionally, they thought that mountain ranges connecting continents had sunk over a period of time, and that there had been many climatic changes throughout time.

Two further developments supported the theory and allowed it to be modified into the modern theory of plate tectonics. First, the computerised research work of Edward Bullard at the University of Cambridge confirmed the jigsaw fit of the continents. Second, some crucial research in the 1950s provided important information on the magnetism of the sea floor, and allowed the continental drift theory to be improved.

ACTIVITY

Investigate more fully the reasons why it took 40 years for Wegener's theory of continental drift to be accepted.

The studies of the ocean floor showed that, in the middle, there was a huge mountain range called a **mid-ocean ridge**. This ridge is greater than 50 000 km long, 450 m high and in places 800 km across. Magma from volcanoes on the mid-ocean ridge cools and crystallises on the ocean floor. This is now known as **sea-floor spreading**. Scientists discovered that there were unusual magnetic variations in these rocks on the ocean floor. When they analysed the results, they surprisingly found that there were stripes of differently magnetised rocks on either side of the mid-ocean ridge. As well, the pattern of the stripes was the same on both sides of the ridge (see Figure 10.10).

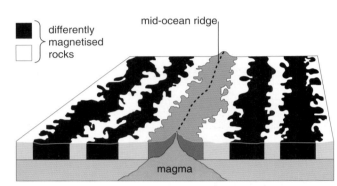

Figure 10.10 The pattern of differently magnetised stripes on each side of a mid-ocean ridge

In the early 1960s scientists explained the reason for magnetic striping of rocks on the ocean floor. Their explanation was based on the fact that the mid-ocean ridge was considered an area of weakness on the ocean floor. Along this ridge, magma could erupt and form a new ocean floor to either side of the ridge (sea-floor spreading). The magnetic stripes were in this new rock. Magnetic properties are due to iron minerals such as magnetite or other magnetic material in volcanic rock. These magnetic materials are incorporated into the new rocks' crystal structure. The rocks take on a weak magnetism which is aligned by the Earth's magnetic field. The youngest rocks are close to the crest of the ridge. Because of this, they have similar polarity to the Earth's current magnetic field. Moving out from the ridge the stripes of parallel rocks get older and show alternating stripes of normal and opposite (reversed) polarity (Figure 10.11).

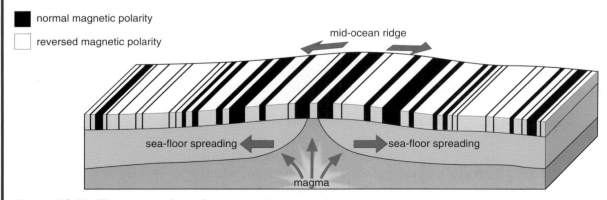

Figure 10.11 The theory of sea-floor spreading to explain the magnetic striping

The research into the formation of the mid-ocean ridge and the magnetic striping patterns of rocks on the ocean floor provided evidence for Wegener's continental drift theory. It convinced scientists that most of his ideas were correct. Geologists now accepted Wegener's belief that, over time, the ocean floor could move. Small forces (on a geological scale) could move the continents through the ocean floor. The idea that the continents were fixed was now thrown out, and the continental drift theory became accepted. Wegener's theory of continental drift has now been replaced by the theory of **plate tectonics**.

7 a   What is meant by continental drift?
   b   Explain how evidence for continental drift was provided by
      i   the shapes of different continents
      ii   fossils
      iii rocks.
8 a   Explain the meaning of sea-floor spreading.
   b   Use the idea of sea-floor spreading to explain how the continents move.

9   What evidence exists to support sea-floor spreading?

Plate tectonics

In this theory, the Earth's crust is not considered to be a continuous shell of rock. Instead, it is envisaged as cracked and broken into a number of large **tectonic plates**, as shown in Figure 10.12. There are two types of tectonic plate: **continental plates** and **oceanic plates**.

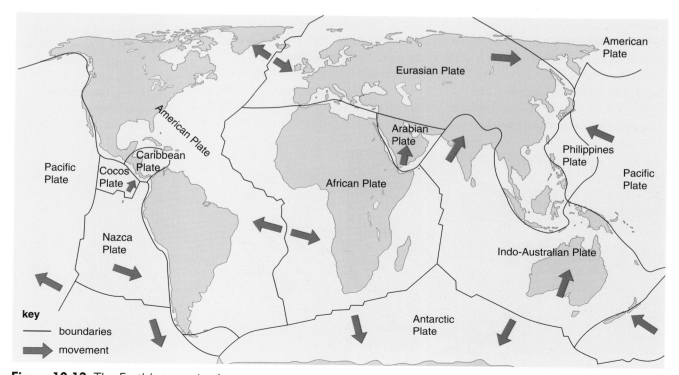

Figure 10.12 The Earth's tectonic plates

Plate tectonics is a study of how the plates move and how they interact with each other. As these large plates, which make up the crust, are less dense than the mantle, they float on it. With the Earth's core at a temperature of around 4000°C, this causes slow-moving convection currents in the mantle. These convection currents cause movement of the plates, which float on the mantle. Space satellite measurements show that such movement is causing North America and Europe to move apart at a rate of about 4 cm per year.

The theory of plate tectonics can be used to describe many geological features such as earthquakes, volcanoes, tsunamis, the formation of mountains and the burial of rocks.

Earthquakes, volcanoes and tsunamis

Earthquakes, volcanoes and tsunamis generally occur around plate boundaries where there are weaknesses in the crust. We shall look at each in turn.

Earthquakes

An **earthquake** is caused by the stresses and strains that are set up when two continental plates move past each other. This means that they generally occur at plate boundaries, where the plates slide past each other (Figure 10.13) or where one plate slides under another (see page 130). The forces involved in these processes are very large. They can cause the plates to bend. If these forces are released suddenly, then an **earthquake** occurs. The ground shakes violently, and this causes breaks and cracks to develop in the ground. This often produces major damage to buildings, bridges and other structures (Figure 10.14), and may result in serious injuries and loss of life.

These breaks caused by horizontal movement of plates are known as tear faults. Two well-known examples are the San Andreas Fault in California and the Great Glen Fault in Scotland (Figure 10.15).

Earthquakes vary greatly in scale or magnitude. The magnitude of an earthquake is determined by the intensity of the seismic waves it produces. **Seismic waves** are the vibrations from earthquakes that travel through the Earth. They are recorded on instruments called **seismographs**. The time, location and magnitude of an earthquake can be determined from the data recorded by seismograph stations.

In 1935 Charles F. Richter established a special scale for use with seismograph records. On the **Richter scale**, each value is 10 times larger in magnitude than

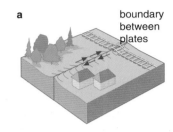

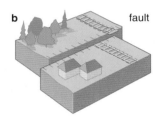

Figure 10.13 How an earthquake happens
a The two plates bend as they slide past each other. The ground is displaced
b The stresses are suddenly released as the ground shakes and breaks. A fault has been formed

Figure 10.14 Devastation after the major earthquake in northern Pakistan, October 2005

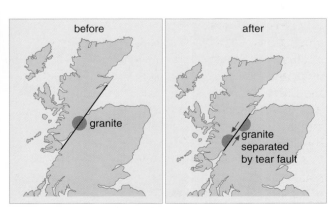

Figure 10.15 Scotland before and after the Great Glen Fault

Table 10.1 The Richter scale

Richter scale	Damage
1 to 3	Recorded on local seismographs, but not felt by people
3 to 4	Often felt by people, but no damage to structures
5	Felt widely, and slight damage near the centre of the earthquake
6	Damage to poorly constructed buildings and other structures within tens of kilometres from the earthquake's centre
7	'Major' earthquake, causes serious damage up to about 100 km. Recent examples in Taiwan, Turkey, Kobe (Japan) and California earthquakes
8	'Great' earthquake, causes great destruction and loss of life over several hundred kilometres. An example was in San Francisco in 1906
9	Rare great earthquake, causes major damage over a large region of more than 1000 km. Examples include Chile in 1960 and Alaska in 1964

the value one unit lower. For example, a value of 2 is 10 times that of 1, a value of 3 is 10 times that of 2, a value of 4 is 10 times that of 3, and so on. So a value of 4 is 1000 times greater than a value of 1. Table 10.1 shows how the numbers on the Richter scale are related to the damage caused by the earthquake.

Earthquakes present particular hazards because their effects can be so violent and widespread. Also they are very difficult to forecast. Linking earthquakes to plate boundaries has identified the areas most likely to be affected. But identifying exactly where and when an earthquake will take place has so far proved impossible. Some earthquakes that have caused a lot of damage have taken place outside plate boundaries. Such earthquakes are less frequent. Almost every earthquake is a surprise. Even though the 1989 earthquake of San Francisco was expected, the precise timing was not forecast.

Much research is being carried out to improve the detection and analysis of seismic waves. All earthquakes that take place are monitored. But earthquakes are due to stresses and strains set up in rocks below the Earth's surface. Apart from monitoring past and present patterns, there is little that can be done to predict when the next earthquake will take place. On 8 October 2005 the devastating Pakistan/Kashmir earthquake struck South Asia (Figure 10.14). It caused the death of 80 000 people and injured many more. As many as 3 million people were left homeless. Most of them spent the winter in tents, vulnerable to severe winter cold and disease.

Volcanoes

Whereas earthquakes are caused by plates moving past each other, setting up stresses and strains in the Earth's crust, a **volcano** is caused by plates moving apart. When this takes place, the Earth's crust is stretched. In areas of weakness, the crust may crack. Molten magma and gases can escape through the cracks, resulting in a volcano (Figure 10.16).

Approximately 80% of volcanoes occur along plate boundaries in the ocean floor. This is because of sea-floor spreading, which was discussed earlier (page 126). If plates move far enough apart, then some of the surface rocks may sink.

Figure 10.16 Mount Merapi spewing hot lava near a village in Yogyakarta, Indonesia

As far as local people are concerned, an important difference between volcanoes and earthquakes is that volcanoes are predictable. Prior to eruption, there are rumblings from the volcano indicating that an eruption is about to take place. Although there are signs, it is not easy to say how violent the eruption might be.

What happens when plates collide?

Continental crust is that crust that lies under the continents. The crust that lies under the oceans is called oceanic crust. The two crusts are different. The continental crust is made of less dense rocks like granite. It is thicker than the oceanic crust, which is made of more dense rocks like basalt. When two plates move towards each other, the more dense oceanic plate sinks below the less dense continental plate (Figure 10.17). Areas where this takes place are called **subduction zones**.

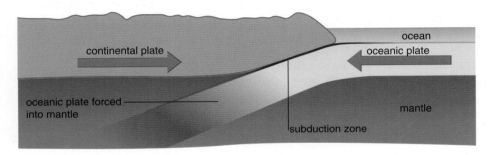

Figure 10.17 Collision of a continental plate with an oceanic plate

During this process the oceanic crust can be forced into the mantle. At the temperatures in the mantle, this oceanic crust will melt to form magma. While this is happening to the oceanic crust, the continental crust is also undergoing change, as it is squashed and lifted into folds (Figure 10.18). This latter process continues for millions of years, leading to the formation of mountain ranges. An example of this is the Andes in South America. These mountains were caused by the American Plate colliding with the Nazca Plate. These new mountain ranges replace the older ones, which are worn away by erosion and weathering.

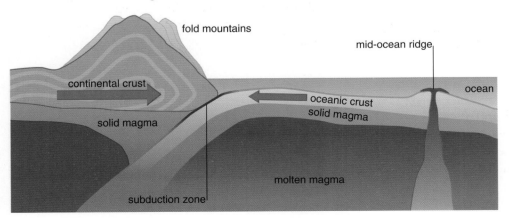

Figure 10.18 The collision can result in the formation of mountain ranges

> **10 a** What is the name of the Earth's plate that we are standing on?
> **b** Name a plate that has only ocean on it.
> **c** If a plate moves 5 cm in a year, calculate its speed in mm/day.
> **d** What is a plate boundary?

Tsunamis

A **tsunami** is a natural phenomenon consisting of a series of waves generated when one or more vertical displacements occur within the ocean. Earthquakes, volcanoes and submarine landslides can generate tsunamis. They can rapidly and violently flood coastlines, causing devastation, property damage, injuries and loss of life due to injuries or drowning. The most common cause of a tsunami is an undersea earthquake (Figure 10.19). Even if the earthquake on its own is too small to cause a tsunami, it may cause an undersea landslide capable of generating a tsunami.

Typically, undersea earthquakes give rise to between three and five distinct waves (crests), the second or third of which is the largest. In the deep water of the open sea, a person would probably not notice a tsunami. The height of the wave in the open water would be less than one metre. But the height of the wave can build up to 30 m or more as the wave approaches a coastline, perhaps thousands of miles from the origin of the tsunami. A notable exception was the landslide-generated tsunami in Lituya Bay, Alaska, in 1958. This produced a wave 525 m in height!

On 26 December 2004 an earthquake in the Indian Ocean triggered a series of lethal tsunamis that killed over 160 000 people (Figure 10.20). This makes it the most deadly tsunami recorded in history. The tsunami killed people over a huge area. This ranged from the immediate vicinity of the earthquake in Indonesia, Thailand and the north-eastern coast of Malaysia, to thousands of kilometres away in Bangladesh, India, Sri Lanka, the Maldives and even as far as Somalia in East Africa. Unlike the Pacific Ocean, there is no organised alert service covering the Indian Ocean. This has been partly due to the absence of tsunamis since 1883.

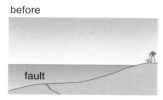
before
fault

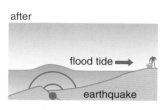
after
flood tide →
earthquake

Figure 10.19 Vertical displacement within the ocean can lead to a tsunami

Figure 10.20 Tidal wave hitting Penang, Malaysia, following the December 2004 tsunami

> **11** Use the theory of plate tectonics to explain what happens during
> **a** a volcano
> **b** an earthquake
> **c** a tsunami.
> Include diagrams where possible.

The changing surface of the Earth

The shape of the Earth's surface is continually changing. Many of these changes can be explained in terms of the theory of plate tectonics. For example, plate tectonics explains continents moving apart, sea-floor spreading and volcanic activity. Another major factor affecting the shape of the Earth is global warming, which has led to climatic changes. With continued melting of ice in the Artic and Antarctic, and the expansion of sea water on heating, sea levels will rise. Places just above sea level will disappear, for example Tuvalu and the Maldives.

websites

www.arm.ac.uk/history/ussher.html
detail on the work of James Ussher

www.moorlandschool.co.uk/earth/tectonic.htm
lots of information on continental drift and plate tectonics

www.infoplease.com/ce6/sci/A0813370.html
outlines the theory of continental drift

www.pbs.org/wgbh/aso/tryit/tectonics/intro.html
information on plate tectonics and the theory of continental drift

www.infoplease.com/ce6/sci/A0839323
excellent geology site, including information on plate tectonics, earthquakes and volcanoes

www.volcanoes.com/
describes the science behind volcanoes

http://news.bbc.co.uk/1/hi/in_depth/4136289.stm
excellent reference for the 2004 Indian Ocean tsunami

Questions

1 a Complete the following sentences using the following words:

igneous   sedimentary   metamorphic

i Fossils are usually found in _____ rocks.
ii Marble is an example of a _____ rock.
iii The Giant's Causeway is made up of
_____ rock.   (*3 marks*)

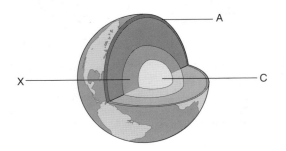

b The diagram shows a section of the Earth.
Complete the following sentences about the Earth.
i The outermost part of the Earth (labelled A) is
called the _____ .   (*1 mark*)
ii The Earth has an overall diameter of
12 800 _____ .   (*1 mark*)
iii As we move closer to the centre of the Earth
(labelled C) the temperature _____ .   (*1 mark*)
iv Around the innermost centre of the Earth is a layer of
material (labelled X) called the _____ .   (*1 mark*)

c When scientists looked at the shape of continents, many thought that the continents of Africa and South America seemed to fit together like pieces of a jigsaw.

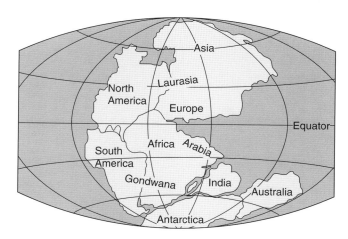

In the early 20th century, A. Wegener proposed that the continents had moved apart by continental drift.

Give **three** pieces of evidence to suggest that continents were once closely joined.   (*3 marks*)

CCEA GCSE Science: Single Award (Modular) Specimen Paper (Foundation Tier) 2006

2 Give **two** reasons why the theory of continental drift put forward by Wegener was not initially accepted.   (*2 marks*)

3 a The diagram below shows the names of some rock types and some rock descriptions.

name of rock	description
basalt	crystals smaller than 0.5 mm, dark in colour
granite	hard, brittle, grey rock, splits into sheets
slate	crystals bigger than 0.5 mm, light in colour

Copy the diagram and draw a line from each name to its correct description. Each name must be joined to a different description.   (*3 marks*)

b Give **one** example of each of the following rock types. Choose your answers from the following list:

basalt   limestone   granite   slate

i a sedimentary rock   (*1 mark*)
ii a metamorphic rock   (*1 mark*)
iii an extrusive igneous rock   (*1 mark*)
iv an intrusive igneous rock   (*1 mark*)

4 A, B and C are three plates of the Earth's crust. They are moving in the directions of the arrows.

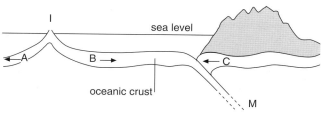

a i Name **one** natural occurrence that can happen at plate boundaries.   (*1 mark*)
  ii Give **two** conditions that exist at I that cause igneous rock to form.   (*2 marks*)
  iii Give **two** conditions that exist at M that cause metamorphic rock to form.   (*2 marks*)
b How can igneous rocks form sedimentary rocks in a different place?   (*4 marks*)

5 a The diagram shows a volcano.

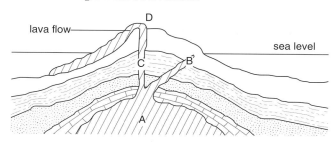

  i Will the cooling be fastest at A, B, C, or D?   (*1 mark*)
  ii Where will the largest crystals be formed when the molten rock cools?   (*1 mark*)
  iii Give **two** conditions needed for sedimentary rocks to be changed to metamorphic rocks.   (*2 marks*)
b Earthquakes and volcanoes can occur around plate boundaries.
  i What causes an earthquake?   (*1 mark*)
  ii What instrument detects earthquakes?   (*1 mark*)
c Heat is generated inside the Earth by the decay of radioactive elements. Some energy is released in volcanoes. Name **two** other effects of this thermal energy on the inside of the Earth.   (*2 marks*)

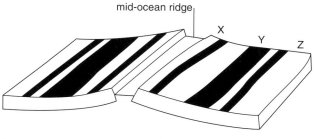

d The rocks on part of the ocean floor show a pattern of 'magnetic stripes' on both sides of a mid-ocean ridge.
  i Where would you find the youngest rock, at X, Y or Z?   (*1 mark*)
  ii Where would you find the oldest rock?   (*1 mark*)

Chapter 11

Atomic structure and the Periodic Table

By the end of this chapter you should know and understand:

➤ That atoms can be described as particles having a nucleus surrounded by moving electrons, and know the relative mass and charge of a proton, electron and neutron

➤ The different ideas put forward to explain the structure of atoms by Dalton, Thomson, Rutherford and Bohr

➤ The atomic structure of the first 20 elements in the Periodic Table in terms of protons, neutrons and electrons, and use the terms atomic number and mass number

➤ The work of Newlands and Mendeleev in the development of the Periodic Table, and examine how ideas changed from early Greek thinking

➤ That the position of an element in the Periodic Table relates to its electronic structure

➤ That elements with similar properties are grouped together in the Periodic Table, e.g. alkali metals, alkaline earth metals, halogens and noble gases

➤ That metallic character decreases on moving across the Periodic Table from left to right

➤ That helium, neon and argon are known as the noble gases

➤ That the alkali metals react with water, and relate the rate at which they react to their position in the Periodic Table

➤ That the metals magnesium, zinc, iron and copper can be placed into a reactivity series based on their reactions with dilute acid

➤ How a more reactive metal can displace a less reactive metal from a solution of its salt, and predict where an unfamiliar element should be placed in a reactivity series based on comparative information

Atomic structure

Table 11.1 summarises our present-day understanding of atomic structure. The atom is composed of a very dense, positively charged nucleus made up of protons and neutrons, with negatively charged electrons orbiting around the nucleus. The radius of an atom is very small and only measures about 10^{-8} cm.

Table 11.1 Mass, charge and position of protons, electrons and neutrons

Particle	Relative mass (atomic mass units)	Relative charge	Position
neutron	1	0	nucleus
proton	1	+1	nucleus
electron	1/1840	−1	in orbit around nucleus

> **1** Draw a diagram to represent the present-day model of the atom. Show clearly the positions of the particles that make up the atom, and label them with their relative charge and relative mass.

Historical ideas about atomic structure

Theories of atomic structure date back to almost 2000 years ago. It was then that the Greek philosophers **Democritus** and **Leucippus** first put forward the idea that matter was made up of small, invisible particles, called atoms. Unfortunately, their theory was not taken seriously. Instead, the simpler ideas of another famous Greek philosopher **Aristotle** were considered more acceptable. He believed that matter was composed of the four basic 'elements': air, earth, fire and water. He said that these four 'elements' could be used to explain matter and its behaviour. These ideas were not to change until much later.

John Dalton's theory

It was not until 1808, when **John Dalton** (Figure 11.1) published his *Atomic Theory*, that the significance of the particulate nature of matter was taken seriously by scientists. In his theory Dalton stated that:

- All elements are made up of small invisible particles called atoms.
- Atoms cannot be created or destroyed.
- Atoms of different elements have different properties.
- When atoms combine, they form molecules or compounds, which Dalton called 'compound atoms'.

Dalton's research provided important explanations for the structure of compounds and molecules. It was used to determine the atomic masses of the known elements.

Figure 11.1 John Dalton

The 'plum pudding model' of J. J. Thomson

It was not until 1897, when **J. J. Thomson** (Figure 11.2) discovered the electron, that Dalton's atomic theory was modified to provide a new model of atomic structure. Thomson put forward the 'plum pudding' model of the atom. His idea was that, in atoms, there are negative **electrons** embedded in a sphere of positive charge. This was just like currants (or plums) embedded in a Christmas (plum) pudding. Thomson also explained that the atom was neutral because it contained equal numbers of positive and negative charges.

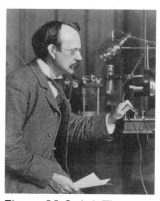

Figure 11.2 J. J. Thomson

The work of Ernest Rutherford and Niels Bohr

Thomson made important progress in understanding atomic structure. But he made the incorrect assumption that the mass of an atom was only due to the electrons. In 1911 his assumption was shown to be incorrect. Then, **Ernest Rutherford** (Figure 11.3) showed that the atom consisted of electrons revolving around a positively charged nucleus. He called the positive particles **protons**, and gave them a mass of one atomic mass unit. Rutherford compared his model of electrons revolving around a positive nucleus (Figure 11.4) to that of the planets revolving around the Sun. On a relative scale, this model of the atom could be compared to a small pea at the centre of a football pitch. The small pea is the nucleus, with the remainder of the pitch representing the space occupied by the revolving electrons.

Figure 11.3 Ernest Rutherford

In the same year as Rutherford put forward his model of the atom, **Niels Bohr** modified the model and suggested that the electrons travelled in stable circular orbits. These orbits had different amounts of energy. Electrons could jump from one orbit to another by loss or gain of given amounts of energy. The model of the atom suggested by Bohr is still used nowadays. However, it was modified in 1932, when **David Chadwick** showed that the nucleus consisted of two different types of particles, protons and new particles called **neutrons**. The neutron was found to have a similar mass to a proton but, unlike a proton, it had no charge. It has been shown that all atoms apart from hydrogen contain neutrons.

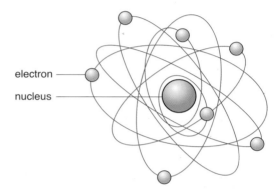

electron

nucleus

Figure 11.4 Rutherford's model of the atom

2 Name the scientist who discovered the
   a electron
   b proton
   c neutron.

ACTIVITY

Use the internet to investigate the different ideas put forward to explain the structure of matter and atoms, in particular the work of Dalton, Thomson, Rutherford, Bohr and Chadwick. Produce an article, a *PowerPoint* presentation, or a poster to show how the theory of atomic structure changed with time and with new information.

Figure 11.5 Niels Bohr

Atomic number and mass number

The terms **atomic number** and **mass number** are used to provide scientists with important information about the number of protons, neutrons and electrons contained in atoms.

> **The atomic number (Z) of an element is the number of protons in an atom of that element.**

Since atoms are neutral, there are always the same number of electrons and protons in each atom. The atomic number of an element can be obtained from the Periodic Table. It is represented by the subscript at the left-hand side of the symbol, for example, $_{11}Na$. This tells us that a sodium atom has 11 protons and 11 electrons.

The mass number (A) of an element is the number of protons and neutrons in the nucleus of an atom of that element.

Like the atomic number, the mass number can be obtained from the Periodic Table. For the element in question, it is the superscript at the left-hand side of the symbol, for example, ^{23}Na. This means that for sodium the number of protons and neutrons added together is 23. The number of neutrons can be obtained by subtracting the atomic number from the mass number, for example, for an atom of sodium $23 - 11 = 12$ neutrons.

---

3 Explain the meaning of the terms **atomic number** and **mass number**.

4 Calculate the numbers of electrons, protons and neutrons in the following:
   a $^{19}_{9}F$ **b** $^{31}_{15}P$ **c** $^{40}_{18}Ar$
   d $^{106}_{46}Pd$ **e** $^{56}_{26}Fe$ **f** $^{64}_{29}Cu$

5 Why do atoms have no charge?

6 Copy and complete the table below.

Element	Atomic number	Number of neutrons
	19	20
manganese	25	
bromine		45

How electrons are arranged in atoms

It is now understood that the atom is composed of:

- a very small, dense, positively charged **nucleus** made up of **protons** and **neutrons**
- negatively charged **electrons** orbiting the nucleus in **shells**.

For GCSE Science, the following guidelines will apply when filling electrons into shells:

1 Electrons are filled into shells starting from the first shell (sometimes called the first energy level). This is the one closest to the nucleus.

2 Moving out from the first shell, electrons are then filled into the second shell, third shell and so forth.

3 The first shell can hold up to two electrons. The other shells can hold up to eight electrons.

4 Before filling electrons into a new shell, it is important that the previous existing shell has been filled.

Filling electrons into shells for hydrogen and helium

Figure 11.6 shows how the electrons are arranged in the first shell for the two lightest elements, hydrogen and helium.

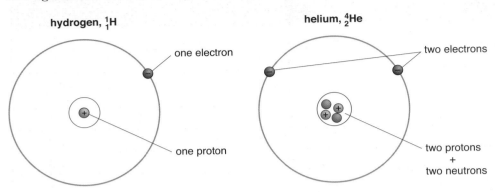

Figure 11.6 Electronic structures of hydrogen and helium

Filling electrons into shells for nitrogen and sodium

Nitrogen has seven electrons. The first two electrons are filled into the first shell. The remaining five electrons are placed in the second shell (Figure 11.7, left). Sodium has 11 electrons. Two are used to fill the first shell. The next eight electrons fill the second shell. The remaining one electron goes into the third shell (Figure 11.7, right). These electronic structures are often shortened to nitrogen 2,5 and sodium 2,8,1 as shown.

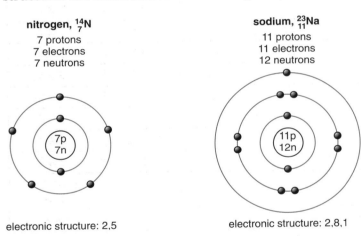

Figure 11.7 Electronic structures of nitrogen and sodium

> **ACTIVITY**
>
> **Make a poster to show the electronic structures of sodium and fluorine. Write a few lines to explain where the electrons, protons and neutrons are placed in the atom. Also say how the electrons are arranged in shells.**

Structure of the first 20 elements

In Table 11.2 the atomic number and mass number of the first 20 elements (atomic numbers 1 to 20) have been used to work out the number of protons, electrons and neutrons that each element contains. The last column provides a description of each element's electronic structure in terms of electrons in shells.

Table 11.2 Electronic structures of the first 20 elements

Element	Symbol	Atomic number	Mass number	Number of protons	Number of electrons	Number of neutrons	Electronic structure (electrons in shells)
hydrogen	^1_1H	1	1	1	1	0	1
helium	^4_2He	2	4	2	2	2	2
							first shell is full
lithium	^7_3Li	3	7	3	3	4	2,1
beryllium	^9_4Be	4	9	4	4	5	2,2
boron	$^{11}_5B$	5	11	5	5	6	2,3
carbon	$^{12}_6C$	6	12	6	6	6	2,4
nitrogen	$^{14}_7N$	7	14	7	7	7	2,5
oxygen	$^{16}_8O$	8	16	8	8	8	2,6
fluorine	$^{19}_9F$	9	19	9	9	10	2,7
neon	$^{20}_{10}Ne$	10	20	10	10	10	2,8
							second shell is full
sodium	$^{23}_{11}Na$	11	23	11	11	12	2,8,1
magnesium	$^{24}_{12}Mg$	12	24	12	12	12	2,8,2
aluminium	$^{27}_{13}Al$	13	27	13	13	14	2,8,3
silicon	$^{28}_{14}Si$	14	28	14	14	14	2,8,4
phosphorus	$^{31}_{15}P$	15	31	15	15	16	2,8,5
sulphur	$^{32}_{16}S$	16	32	16	16	16	2,8,6
chlorine	$^{35}_{17}Cl$	17	35 or 37	17	17	18 or 20	2,8,7
argon	$^{40}_{18}Ar$	18	40	18	18	22	2,8,8
							third shell is full
potassium	$^{39}_{19}K$	19	39	19	19	20	2,8,8,1
calcium	$^{40}_{20}Ca$	20	40	20	20	20	2,8,8,2

The development of the Periodic Table

Around the mid-19th century many chemists were researching and publishing information on the properties of elements. More and more they realised that it was necessary to bring some type of order to the huge amount of information that was available on the already discovered elements. Considerable attention was given to the idea that elements could be arranged in terms of their properties and atomic weights (now called **relative atomic masses**).

In 1866, an English chemist, **John Newlands**, published the **Law of Octaves**, where he ordered the known elements in terms of their increasing relative atomic mass. Newlands proposed that the eighth element was a repetition of the first, just like the eight notes of an octave of music. Thus starting from lithium, Li, and moving on eight places we arrive at sodium, Na, an element with very similar properties to lithium. In the same way we could show this eighth relationship for a number of other elements. Newlands' arrangement of some of the elements in octaves is shown below.

H	Li	Be	B	C	N	O
F	Na	Mg	Al	Si	P	S
Cl	K	Ca	Cr	Ti	Mn	Fe
Co and Ni	Cu	Zn	Y	In	As	Se
Br	Rb	Sr				

Newlands had made a significant contribution to the classification of the elements. But his work was rejected by other scientists for these reasons:

- His classification assumed that all elements had been discovered, even though a number of new elements had been recognised a few years prior to his publication. No gaps were left for undiscovered elements. The discovery of new elements would immediately destroy his arrangement of octaves.
- Newlands grouped some elements together which were not alike. For example, manganese was grouped with nitrogen, phosphorus and arsenic. Copper was grouped with lithium, sodium, potassium and rubidium.
- In forming the octaves, Newlands found it necessary to place two elements in one position, as can be seen for cobalt and nickel in the diagram above.

Newlands had identified important periodic properties between certain elements based on his Law of Octaves. It was the Russian chemist **Dmitri Mendeleev** (Figure 11.8) in 1869 who received the main credit for arranging the elements in the Periodic Table. Like Newlands, he arranged the elements in order of their increasing relative atomic mass. He also placed elements with similar properties in the same vertical column as shown in Figure 11.9. However, Mendeleev realised that there were elements that had not been discovered and he left gaps for them. The gaps also helped him to keep similar elements in the same vertical columns. The vertical columns of elements were called **Groups** and the horizontal rows of elements were called **Periods**.

Figure 11.8
Dmitri Mendeleev

	GROUP							
	I	II	III	IV	V	VI	VII	VIII
Period 1	H							
Period 2	Li	Be	B	C	N	O	F	
Period 3	Na	Mg	Al	Si	P	S	Cl	
Period 4	K	Ca	*	Ti	V	Cr	Mn	Fe Co Ni
	Cu	Zn	*	*	As	Se	Br	
Period 5	Rb	Sr	Y	Zr	Nb	Mo	*	Ru Rh Pd
	Ag	Cd	In	Sn	Sb	Te	I	

Figure 11.9 Part of Mendeleev's Periodic Table

Mendeleev predicted that, through time, elements would be discovered that would fill the gaps he had left in his Periodic Table. He also predicted the properties of many unknown elements with amazing accuracy. For example, in the gaps below aluminium and silicon he predicted the properties of two unknown elements, eka-aluminium and eka-silicon. Later when the two elements were discovered (1875 and 1886 respectively) they were called gallium and germanium. They had properties almost identical to those predicted by Mendeleev. Confidence in the Periodic Table soared.

The accuracy of Mendeleev's predictions influenced other scientists. Soon it became accepted that the Periodic Table was a suitable way of ordering the elements and their properties.

The modern Periodic Table

The modern Periodic Table (Figure 11.10) is based on that of Mendeleev. However, there are a number of changes:

- Mendeleev placed the elements in order of relative atomic mass. However, in the modern Periodic Table elements are placed in order of their atomic number. When Mendeleev placed elements in order of relative atomic mass, he found that in some instances he had to reverse the order of elements. For example, he had to put tellurium, Te = 128 and iodine, I = 127. According to ordering by relative atomic mass, Mendeleev should have placed iodine before tellurium. However, he realised that for iodine and tellurium to fit into their proper groups, he had to reverse the order. This problem is now overcome using atomic number, where tellurium = 52 and iodine = 53.

Figure 11.10 Modern Periodic Table

- A family of very unreactive elements, called the noble gases or Group 0 elements, has been discovered and inserted.
- The transition metals have been taken out and placed as a block of metals between Group II and Group III.
- Some of the groups have been given common names as well as group numbers (Table 11.3).

Table 11.3 Group names in the Periodic Table

Group number	Name	Elements
I	alkali metals	lithium, sodium, potassium, rubidium, caesium and francium
II	alkaline-earth metals	beryllium, magnesium, calcium, strontium, barium and radium
VII	halogens	fluorine, chlorine, bromine, iodine and astatine
0	noble gases	helium, neon, argon, krypton, xenon and radon

- Non-metals are found at the right-hand side of Figure 11.10, with the thick line acting as a division between metals and non-metals.

Along the steps of the thick line there are some elements that are classified as semi-metals. Semi-metals are elements with properties between those of metals and non-metals. They generally look like metals but are brittle like non-metals. One example of such intermediate behaviour is the fact that they are semi-conductors. Their electrical conduction properties are between those of metals and non-metals. Silicon and germanium are two examples of semi-conductors. Graphite, which is a form of carbon, is an unusual non-metal. It is a good conductor of electricity, a property typical of metals. This property is explained by the structure of graphite, which has a mobile cloud of free electrons in layers.

Trends in the Periodic Table

We have already seen that, as we move across a period, the properties of the elements gradually change from metals through to semi-metals to non-metals. This trend in Period 3 can be seen in Table 11.4.

Table 11.4 Properties of elements in Period 3

Property	Sodium Na	Magnesium Mg	Aluminium Al	Silicon Si	Phosphorus P	Sulphur S	Chlorine Cl	Argon Ar
Electronic structure	2,8,1	2,8,2	2,8,3	2,8,4	2,8,5	2,8, 6	2,8,7	2,8,8
Group	I	II	III	IV	V	VI	VII	VIII
Valency	1	2	3	4	3 or 5	2	1	0
Metal/non-metal	metal	metal	metal	semi-metal	non-metal	non-metal	non-metal	non-metal
State	solid	solid	solid	solid	solid	solid	gas	gas
Melting point (°C)	98	650	659	1410	44	119	−101	−189
Oxide	basic	basic	acidic or basic	acidic	acidic	acidic	acidic	−

7 From the Periodic Table, give the symbol for an element that is:
   a   a noble gas
   b   an alkaline-earth metal
   c   a halogen
   d   an alkali metal.
8 Use the Periodic Table to name:
   a   a metal in Period 3 with three electrons in its outer shell
   b   a non-metal in Period 2 that belongs to Group VII
   c   a noble gas with two electrons in its outer shell
   d   an element that forms a stable ion by gaining two electrons.
9 Give three features of the Periodic Table developed by Mendeleev.

The alkali metals: reaction with water

All the alkali metals react vigorously with water to produce hydrogen and an alkaline solution of the metal hydroxide (see Figure 11.11). For Li, Na and K all three metals float on the surface of the water, melt and as they rapidly move around often break into flame. Moving down the group, the reactions become more vigorous.

a

b

c

Figure 11.11 The reactions of **a** lithium, **b** sodium and **c** potassium with water

Lithium reacts with water, forming a steady stream of hydrogen gas and an alkaline solution of lithium hydroxide:

$$\text{lithium} + \text{water} \rightarrow \text{lithium hydroxide} + \text{hydrogen}$$
$$2\text{Li} + 2\text{H}_2\text{O} \rightarrow 2\text{LiOH} + \text{H}_2$$

Sodium reacts vigorously with water, producing hydrogen gas. Sometimes the hydrogen gas ignites and burns with a bright yellow flame because the reaction is highly exothermic:

$$\text{sodium} + \text{water} \rightarrow \text{sodium hydroxide} + \text{hydrogen}$$
$$2\text{Na} + 2\text{H}_2\text{O} \rightarrow 2\text{NaOH} + \text{H}_2$$

Potassium reacts violently, and the hydrogen ignites immediately because the reaction is very fast and highly exothermic:

$$\text{potassium} + \text{water} \rightarrow \text{potassium hydroxide} + \text{hydrogen}$$
$$2\text{K} + 2\text{H}_2\text{O} \rightarrow 2\text{KOH} + \text{H}_2$$

Chemical reactivity of metals

Although many metals take part in the same reactions, some metals are more reactive than others. We already saw this when we considered the reactions of Group I metals with water. Here the metals become more reactive as the group is descended. By observing the behaviour of different metals in the same reactions, it is possible to place them in order of reactivity.

Reaction with dilute acid

Copper, iron, magnesium and zinc can be placed in dilute acid, usually hydrochloric acid. All but copper will react, producing the metal salt and giving off hydrogen. As before, magnesium is the most reactive, then zinc, and iron is the least reactive. The general equation is

$$\text{metal} + \text{acid} \rightarrow \text{metal salt} + \text{hydrogen}$$

for example $\quad Zn + 2HCl \rightarrow \quad ZnCl_2 + \quad H_2$

Calcium, potassium and sodium would all, of course, react with dilute acid. But these reactions are never carried out in a school laboratory – they would be much too vigorous!

Displacement reactions

When magnesium metal is placed in a solution of copper sulphate, a reaction occurs. But if copper metal is placed in a solution of magnesium sulphate, there is no reaction. The magnesium can **displace** the copper from its salt:

$$Mg + CuSO_4 \rightarrow MgSO_4 + Cu$$

But the copper cannot displace the magnesium. This is an example of the general rule that a more reactive metal will displace a less reactive metal from a solution of its salt.

---

10 In which of the following would a displacement reaction occur?
  a calcium and potassium chloride solution
  b magnesium and iron nitrate solution
  c zinc and copper chloride solution
  d iron and sodium sulphate solution
  e magnesium and zinc chloride solution

Placing an unfamiliar element in the reactivity series: examples

You need to be able to use given data to place elements in a reactivity series.

1 Silver does not react with water (hot or cold), it does not react with dilute hydrochloric acid nor does it react with a copper sulphate solution. Where would it fit into the reactivity series given earlier?

Answer: below copper.

It would fit beside copper because of its lack of reaction with water and with dilute hydrochloric acid. But because it cannot displace copper from copper sulphate, the silver must be less reactive than copper.

2 A new metal has been discovered. It does not react with cold water but it reacts when heated in steam. It was placed in different salt solutions with the following results. Place this new metal in the reactivity series.

Metal salt solution	Observation
$MgSO_4$	no reaction
$Al_2(SO_4)_3$	no reaction
$ZnSO_4$	no reaction
$FeSO_4$	reaction
$CuSO_4$	reaction

Answer: below zinc and above iron.

The lack of reaction with cold water puts this metal below calcium. The reaction with steam puts the metal above copper. It cannot displace magnesium, aluminium or zinc, so it must be below zinc. It can displace iron, so it is above iron.

3 Four metals M, N, O and P were added to separate test tubes of dilute hydrochloric acid. N and O reacted, but M and P did not. When metal N was placed in a solution of a salt of metal O, there was no reaction. When metal M was placed in a solution of a salt of metal P, there was a reaction. Place these metals in descending order of reaction.

Answer: O, N, M, P.

N and O are more reactive than M and P because they do react with dilute acid and M and P do not. N is less reactive than O because it cannot displace O from its salt. M is more reactive than P because it can displace P from a solution of its salt.

websites

web.buddyproject.org/web017/web017/
gives a history of the Periodic Table, information on metals and non-metals, and trends in the Periodic Table

www.watertown.k12.wi.us/hs/teachers/buescher/atomtime.asp
an 'atomic structure timeline' which explores discoveries

www.visionlearning.com/library/module_viewer.php?mid=50
useful material on atomic theory and matter

www.chemsoc.org/viselements/
information on the Periodic Table and properties of the elements

www.webelements.com/index.html
a visual interpretation of the Periodic Table

www.periodictable.com
an interactive Periodic Table, including its history

Questions

1 a Copy the diagram and label it to show where the protons, neutrons and electrons are in this atom.

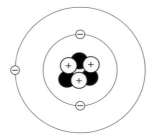

(3 marks)

b Name the element shown above. You may find the Periodic Table useful. *(1 mark)*

2 Use the Periodic Table to help you fill in the blanks in the table below.

Element	Relative atomic mass	Number of protons	Number of electrons	Number of neutrons
boron	11	5		6
	39		19	20
lithium	7	3	3	

(4 marks)

3 This question is about some elements in the Periodic Table.

a i How many electrons has a silicon atom in its outer shell? *(1 mark)*

ii Give the common name for
[A] Group 7 elements *(1 mark)*
[B] Group 1 elements *(1 mark)*

iii From **Period 3** name an element which is found in
[A] Group II *(1 mark)*
[B] Group V *(1 mark)*

b Argon is a noble gas used inside light bulbs.

i Why is argon used inside light bulbs instead of air? *(1 mark)*

ii Show how the electrons of argon are arranged. *(1 mark)*

iii Why does the arrangement of electrons in argon make it suitable for use inside light bulbs? *(1 mark)*

4 The table represents a number of the elements in the Periodic Table.

I	II			III	IV	V	VI	VII	O
									4 He 2 helium
			1 H 1 hydrogen						
7 Li 3 lithium	9 Be 4 beryllium			11 B 5 boron	12 C 6 carbon	14 N 7 nitrogen	16 O 8 oxygen	19 F 9 fluorine	20 Ne 10 neon
23 Na 11 sodium	24 Mg 12 magnesium			27 Al 13 aluminium	28 Si 14 silicon	31 P 15 phosphorus	32 S 16 sulphur	35.5 Cl 17 chlorine	40 Ar 18 argon
39 K 19 potassium	40 Ca 20 calcium								

a What name is given to the horizontal rows in the Periodic Table? *(1 mark)*

b Name an element, from the table, which has only one electron in its outer shell. *(1 mark)*

c From the table, name the alkaline-earth metal which reacts most vigorously with water. *(1 mark)*

5 This question is about the physical and chemical properties of the alkali metals.

a The table lists some physical properties of alkali metals.

Element	Melting point (°C)	Boiling point (°C)	Density (g/cm³)
lithium	180	1347	0.53
sodium	98	883	0.97
potassium	64	774	0.86
rubidium	39	688	1.53
caesium	28	678	1.88

i Which of the alkali metals is a liquid at 35°C? *(1 mark)*

ii How do the boiling points of the alkali metals vary down the group? *(1 mark)*

iii Name a metal in the table which would sink if placed in water. *(1 mark)*

b Potassium hydroxide, like sodium hydroxide, is a base. It reacts with sulphuric acid to form a solution containing potassium sulphate

i Describe how you could obtain crystals of potassium sulphate from potassium sulphate solution. *(2 marks)*

ii Give the chemical formula of potassium sulphate. *(1 mark)*

iii Why should a chemist **not** try to make potassium sulphate by reacting potassium with sulphuric acid? *(1 mark)*

c   The reaction of the Group I metal rubidium (Rb) with
water is given by the word equation

rubidium + water → rubidium + hydrogen
hydroxide

   i   Write a balanced symbol equation for this
reaction.   (*2 marks*)
   ii From your knowledge of the reaction of sodium
with water, predict **three** things you would expect
to see, **apart from bubbles of gas**, if a small piece
of rubidium was placed in water.   (*3 marks*)

6   Mendeleev was responsible for much of the early
development work on the Periodic Table.
   a   Give **two** ways in which Mendeleev's Periodic Table is
different from the one we use today.   (*2 marks*)
   b   Helium, neon and argon belong to the same group in
the Periodic Table. What is the namegiven to this
group and why are its members very unreactive?
                                             (*3 marks*)

The elements magnesium and calcium are reactive metals
with similar chemical properties.
   c   How can you tell from the Periodic Table that
magnesium and calcium are reactive metals with
similar chemical properties?   (*2 marks*)
   d   Chlorine, bromine and iodine belong to Group VII of
the Periodic Table. Which of these elements would you
expect to be least reactive and why?   (*2 marks*)

7   The table shows the results obtained when four metals
were reacted in turn with solutions of salts of the other
three metals.

Metal	Solution			
	Lead nitrate	Magnesium nitrate	Copper(II) sulphate	Iron(II) nitrate
Lead		no reaction	reacts quite slowly	no reaction
Magnesium	reacts quite quickly		reacts very quickly	reacts quite slowly
Copper	no reaction	no reaction		no reaction
Iron	reacts quickly	no reaction	reacts quickly	

   a   Magnesium powder reacts very quickly with the
copper(II) sulphate solution. What **two** other changes
would you expect to see in this reaction?   (*2 marks*)
   b   Complete the word equation for the reaction
between magnesium and copper(II) sulphate:

magnesium + copper(II) → .... + ...
sulphate
                                             (*1 mark*)

   c   Use the information in the table to list the **four** metals,
lead, magnesium, copper and iron, in order of their
reactivity, putting the **most** reactive first.   (*2 marks*)

CCEA GCSE Science: Single Award (Modular) Specimen Paper
(Higher Tier) 2006 (part question)

Chapter 12

Oils, polymers and other materials

Learning objectives

By the end of this chapter you should know and understand:

- That coal is mainly carbon, and that crude oil and natural gas are hydrocarbons
- How oil is separated by fractional distillation
- The uses of the different fractions in crude oil, and the implications for our economy as oil reserves run down
- That each fraction contains hydrocarbons with a similar number of carbon atoms
- The structural formulae of alkanes (C_1–C_4) and be able to draw them
- The importance of thermal and catalytic cracking, and write word and symbol equations for the cracking and combustion of alkanes
- The impact on the environment of the burning of hydrocarbon fuels
- Polymerisation reactions and how to make nylon
- The symbol equations for the polymerisation of ethene, propene and vinyl chloride
- The commercial importance of the polymerisation of various monomers
- That there are two types of synthetic plastics (thermoplastics and thermosetting polymers), and that there are a number of natural polymers (silk and wool)
- The properties and uses of metals, plastics, fibres and ceramics, and explain why modern materials have replaced traditional ones
- The implications for manufacturers of traditional materials as their uses decline
- What composite materials are, and their advantages and disadvantages
- How nanotechnology can produce new properties in materials, and that a smart material is one whose properties alter with the conditions.

Fossil fuels

Most of the energy we use in our homes, industry, schools, offices and transport comes from **fossil fuels**. When fossil fuels burn, the chemical energy of the fuel is converted into heat energy. In the home, the energy from fossil fuels is used mainly for lighting and cooking. In industry, much is used in the manufacture of materials such as fertilisers, plastics, paints, metals, glass and other useful substances. Coal, oil and natural gas are all examples of fossil fuels, and were formed over many millions of years from dead animals and plants.

Coal is mainly composed of carbon. The hardness of coal and the percentage of carbon in it depend on the temperature and pressure at which it was formed. Anthracite is a hard coal that contains around 95% carbon. It was formed at a higher pressure and temperature than bituminous coal, which contains around 70% carbon. The higher the percentage of carbon in a coal, then the greater the heat content of that coal.

Natural gas, which is mainly methane, is used to provide heat in many homes. Natural gas contains small amounts of ethane, propane and butane. It is almost always found with deposits of crude oil.

Crude oil is a sticky, dark brown liquid, and is a mixture containing hundreds of different organic substances. Most of these substances are **hydrocarbons**. These are molecules that are composed of carbon and hydrogen atoms only. Some of the hydrocarbons in oil have only a few carbon atoms in each molecule. But there are some with over 70 carbon atoms in the molecule. The hydrocarbons in crude oil can be gases, liquids or solids. For example, the **alkanes** methane (CH_4), ethane (C_2H_6), propane (C_3H_8) and butane (C_4H_{10}) are all gases (Table 12.1). The alkanes with 5 to 15 carbon atoms are colourless liquids, for example, petrol (octane, C_8H_{18}). The alkanes with more than 15 carbon atoms are white waxy solids, for example, decosane ($C_{22}H_{46}$) is a low-melting white solid.

ACTIVITY

Use the internet or other resources about the chemical industry to make out a poster on chemicals from oil. Alternatively, produce a spreadsheet to show the different fractions from crude oil, their boiling point range and the important uses of each.

---

1 What element is the main constituent of coal?
2 Crude oil and natural gas are hydrocarbons.
   a What is the meaning of the term hydrocarbon?
   b Natural gas is mainly methane. Name three other gases that are present in small amounts in natural gas.
   c Name a liquid hydrocarbon that is found in crude oil.

Table 12.1 The first four members of the alkanes

Name	Molecular formula	Structural formula	State at room temperature	Boiling point (°C)
methane	CH_4	H—C—H (with H above and H below)	gas	−162
ethane	C_2H_6	H—C—C—H (with H's)	gas	−89
propane	C_3H_8	H—C—C—C—H (with H's)	gas	−49
butane	C_4H_{10}	H—C—C—C—C—H (with H's)	gas	−1

Fractional distillation and cracking of crude oil

Fractional distillation

The hydrocarbons in crude oil have different boiling points. Because of this they can be separated by using **fractional distillation**.

During fractional distillation, crude oil is separated into groups of hydrocarbons that have a similar number of carbon atoms in each molecule.

Fractional distillation takes place in a steel tower as shown in Figure 12.1. The tower is very hot at the base and cooler at the top. Crude oil is fed in and heated in a furnace. The vapours are then fed into the fractionating tower. As the vapour mixture rises up the tower, different vapours condense at different levels and are separated. The smaller hydrocarbon molecules with the smallest number of carbon atoms in each molecule have the lowest boiling points. They will rise to the top of the tower. The larger hydrocarbons with the highest boiling points will condense lower down in the tower.

Figure 12.1 shows that most of the fractions obtained from crude oil can be used as fuels. These fractions are LPG (liquid petroleum gas), petrol, naphtha, paraffin, diesel and candle wax. They are classified as fossil fuels, as is crude oil.

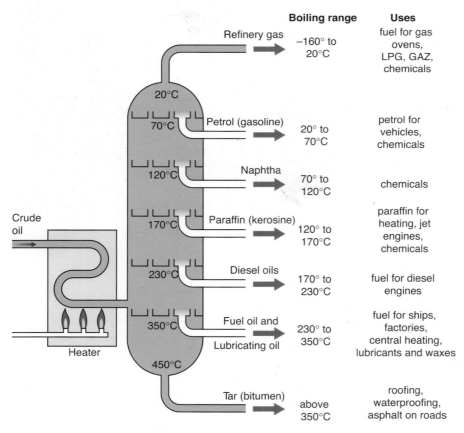

Figure 12.1 The products obtained by fractional distillation of crude oil and their major uses

Cracking of hydrocarbons

In oil refineries it is found that there is a greater demand for the **lighter fractions**, refinery gas and petrol, than for some of the **heavier fractions**. This is due to the high demand for petrol, bottled gas and monomers such as propene and ethene to make plastics. Table 12.2 compares the percentages of the different fractions in crude oil with the percentage demand for them in everyday life.

Table 12.2 Comparison of the composition of crude oil with everyday demand for the fractions

Fraction	Percentage in crude oil	Percentage in everyday demand
fuel gas	2	4
petrol	6	22
naphtha	10	5
kerosine	13	8
diesel oil	19	23
fuel oil and bitumen	50	38

Fortunately chemists can convert the heavier fraction molecules into smaller molecules by **cracking**. This provides more of the lighter fractions to meet the demands of the petrochemicals industry. Figure 12.2 shows a catalytic cracking plant at an oil refinery.

Cracking is used to convert the heavier fractions of oil into more useful products by breaking large hydrocarbon molecules into smaller molecules. Cracking by means of high temperature (up to 1000°C) is called **thermal cracking**. When a catalyst is used, it is called **catalytic cracking**. A zeolite catalyst is generally used. This reduces the temperature to around 500°C. Cracking requires high temperatures because, during the process, strong covalent bonds between carbon atoms must be broken. A lot of energy is required to break these strong bonds.

Figure 12.2 The catalytic cracking plant at an oil refinery

Consider the cracking of decane ($C_{10}H_{22}$) in the naphtha fraction to produce petrol or octane (C_8H_{18}) and ethene (C_2H_4), as below:

$$\text{decane} \rightarrow \text{octane} + \text{ethene}$$
$$C_{10}H_{22} \rightarrow C_8H_{18} + C_2H_4$$

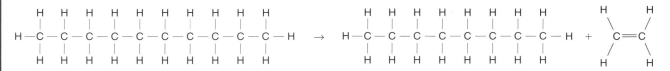

Figure 12.3 Catalytic cracking of decane

Decane in the naphtha fraction produces two important smaller hydrocarbon molecules: petrol, which is used as a fuel for car engines, and ethene, which is used to make polythene in the plastics industry. Petrol is a mixture of alkanes that contain about eight carbon atoms. The petrol obtained from cracking is a better quality fuel than that obtained from fractional distillation. In the oil refinery, petrol obtained from cracking is blended with that obtained from fractional distillation to improve the petrol's quality.

During the cracking of decane (as shown in Figure 12.3) only one of the hydrocarbons produced is an alkane (octane). The other is an **alkene** (ethene). When the molecular formula of octane (C_8H_{18}) is taken away from decane ($C_{10}H_{22}$), the molecule remaining has the molecular formula C_2H_4 and is called ethene. Because it contains a double bond between the two carbon atoms, it is known as ethene not ethane.

ACTIVITY

Carry out an information search on where oil deposits are and where there are likely to be future reserves of oil found. Why do you think the estimates of oil reserves constantly change? (Consider both scientific and political reasons.) Why is there concern about future supplies and the need to find alternative energy sources? Discuss and evaluate the implications for our economy as oil resources run down.

3 Explain how the different fractions in crude oil are separated by fractional distillation.

4 Complete the table below on the uses of the different fractions of crude oil.

Name of fraction	Boiling range (°C)	Example of use
refinery gas		fuel for gas cookers
petrol	20 to 70	
	70 to 120	chemicals
	120 to 170	heating oil
diesel		fuel for diesel engines
fuel oil	230 to 350	
	above 350	asphalt on roads

5 This question is about the cracking of the molecules in a heavy fraction of crude oil into lighter and smaller molecules.
  a What is the meaning of the term cracking?
  b Why is cracking carried out in the petrochemical industry?
  c Write a symbol equation to show the cracking of decane into octane and ethene.
  d Give two important uses for the products of the reaction above.

Combustion of alkanes

Combustion is the most important reaction of alkanes. In a plentiful supply of oxygen, alkanes burn to form carbon dioxide, water and heat energy. Because of the large amount of heat energy given out when they burn, alkanes are good fuels. Figure 12.4 gives the pictorial representation for the reactant and product molecules when methane burns in excess oxygen.

Figure 12.4 The combustion of methane, CH_4

The word equation can now be written for the reaction between methane and oxygen:

methane + oxygen → carbon dioxide + water + heat energy

The symbol equation for the reaction between methane and oxygen is:

$$CH_4 + 2O_2 \rightarrow CO_2 + 2H_2O + \text{heat energy}$$

We can also write symbol equations for ethane and propane burning in excess oxygen:

$$2C_2H_6 + 7O_2 \rightarrow 4CO_2 + 6H_2O + \text{heat energy}$$
ethane

$$C_3H_8 + 5O_2 \rightarrow 3CO_2 + 4H_2O + \text{heat energy}$$
propane

Environmental impact of burning hydrocarbons

Carbon dioxide (CO_2) levels in the atmosphere from the burning of hydrocarbon ('fossil') fuels are continually building up. This is contributing to global warming, through the greenhouse effect. You can read about this on pages 82–86.

In its 2006 UK Climate Change Programme, the Government set carbon dioxide emission levels to help to reduce the problem of global warming. Limits have also been set for other air pollutants, such as particles, carbon monoxide, lead, sulphur dioxide and the oxides of nitrogen, through Government legislation such as the Clean Air Act and the Air Quality Strategy. Additionally, the problem of the greenhouse effect is being addressed by the use of alternative fuels to replace hydrocarbons, for example renewables and hydrogen fuel cells.

Commercially important polymers

Polymers from alkenes

The word **polymer** comes from the Greek and means many parts. Chemists use the word polythene (or polyethene) to describe a molecule that has been made from many ethene molecules chemically joined or added together in long chain molecules. Reactive small molecules like ethene that react to make up the polymer are called **monomers**. The process of joining the molecules together is called **polymerisation**. For alkenes, the polymerisation reaction is also called **addition polymerisation**.

Figure 12.5 shows the general equation for the polymerisation of ethene. Polythene is made by heating ethene at high pressure in the presence of a catalyst (Figure 12.6).

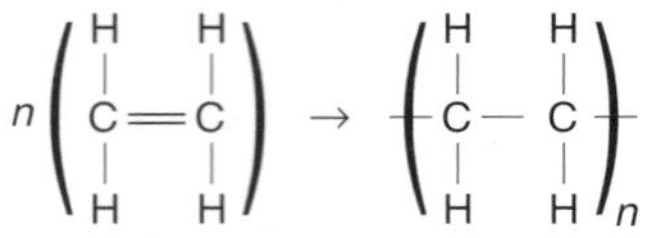

$$n\left(\begin{array}{c} H \ \ H \\ | \ \ \ | \\ C = C \\ | \ \ \ | \\ H \ \ H \end{array}\right) \rightarrow \left(\begin{array}{c} H \ \ H \\ | \ \ \ | \\ C - C \\ | \ \ \ | \\ H \ \ H \end{array}\right)_n$$

Figure 12.5 General equation for polymerisation of ethene; n has a value between 500 and 1500

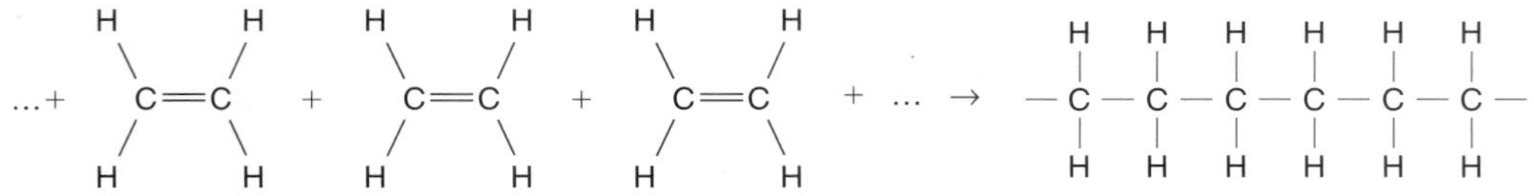

Figure 12.6 How ethene monomers join up to form the long chain of polythene

Nylon

Nylon is an important polymer. The reaction to make nylon is a different type of reaction from the addition polymerisation of alkenes. Nylon can be made by allowing its two different monomers to react at the interface between two suitable solvents. The following is a good demonstration.

ACTIVITY

This is a teacher demonstration.

Safety notes: Sebacoyl chloride, hexamethylenediamine and sodium hydroxide are harmful and can cause severe burns. Additionally, hexamethylenediamine and hexane can cause breathing problems. The experiment is best carried out in a fume cupboard.

The following two solutions are required for the polymerisation reaction:

● **Solution A is made by dissolving 6.0 grams of hexamethylenediamine and 2 grams of sodium hydroxide in 100 cm³ of water (this is best done in a stoppered bottle with shaking).**
● **Solution B is made by adding 2.0 grams of sebacoyl chloride to 100 cm³ of hexane (this should also be prepared in a stoppered bottle to allow shaking to dissolve the reagents).**

The method is as follows:

1 **Add 50 cm³ of solution A into a 250 cm³ beaker.**
2 **Clamp the beaker as shown in Figure 12.7, and above it clamp the roller system. Allow approximately 2 metres of drop from the roller to the receiver.**
3 **Carefully pour 50 cm³ of solution B on to solution A in the beaker.**
4 **After carefully adding solution B, use crucible tongs to pull the nylon polymer formed at the interface of the two solutions and feed it over the rollers and down towards the receiver.**
5 **When a long enough 'rope' has been formed, the process will go on of its own accord until both monomers are used up.**
6 **To obtain a dry specimen of the nylon polymer, wash it thoroughly with 50% aqueous ethanol, then with water until the washings are neutral. Dry in an oven at 110°C.**

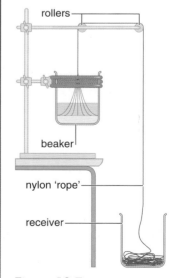

Figure 12.7
The 'nylon rope trick'

More about polymers, and their properties and uses

Polymers made from alkenes

While polythene is a very useful addition polymer, two other common and important polyalkenes are polypropene and polyvinyl chloride (PVC). The equations for formation of these polymers from their monomers are:

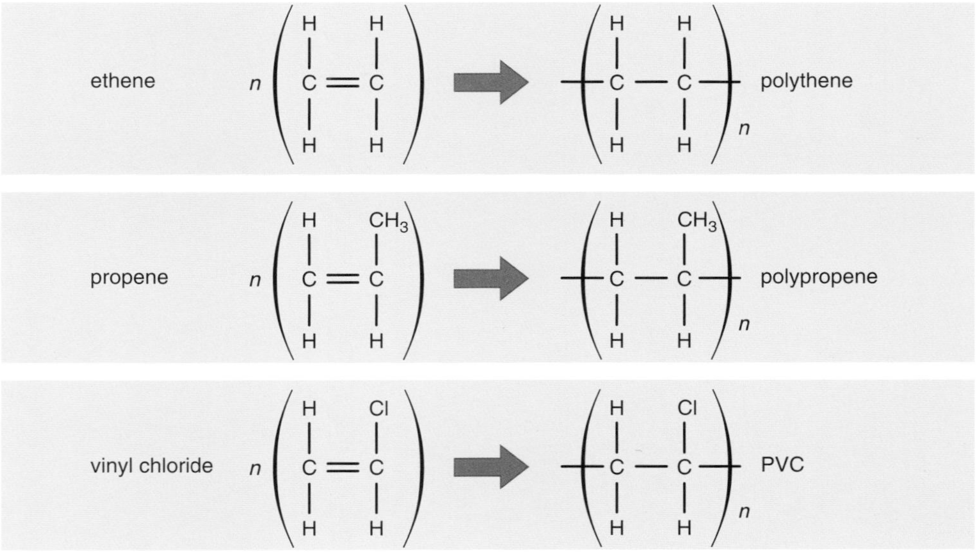

Figure 12.8 Equations for forming polythene, polypropene and PVC

Some of the uses of the polyalkenes are given in Table 12.3 on the next page and Figure 12.9 below.

Figure 12.9 Some uses of polymers in the home

Table 12.3 Properties and uses of some addition polymers

Monomer	Addition polymer	Properties	Uses
polythene	$\left(\begin{array}{cc} H & H \\ \| & \| \\ -C-C- \\ \| & \| \\ H & H \end{array}\right)_n$	light, flexible and resistant to attack by acids and alkalis	cling film, plastic bags, bottles, buckets and basins
polypropene	$\left(\begin{array}{cc} H & CH_3 \\ \| & \| \\ -C-C- \\ \| & \| \\ H & H \end{array}\right)_n$	light, flexible, durable and resistant to attack by acids and alkalis	plastic crates, ropes, carpets and packaging material
PVC	$\left(\begin{array}{cc} H & Cl \\ \| & \| \\ -C-C- \\ \| & \| \\ H & H \end{array}\right)_n$	tough, durable, waterproof and good insulator	electric cables, guttering, drain pipes and umbrellas

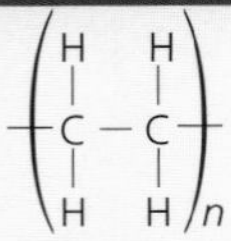

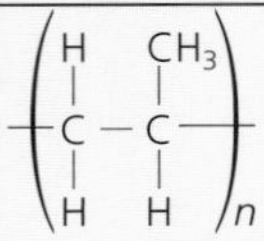

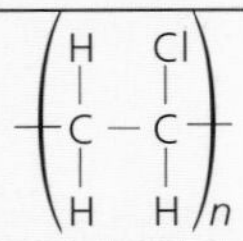

6 a Draw the structural formula of C_3H_6.
   b Give one important use of polypropene.
7 Ethene is an important monomer for making polythene.
   a Explain the meaning of:
      i   monomer
      ii polymer
      iii polymerisation.
   b Give the molecular formula and structural formula of ethene.
   c Give a symbol equation to show the formation of polythene.
   d Give two important uses of polythene.
8 Copy and complete the table, which relates the uses of some addition polymers to their physical properties.

Monomer	Addition polymer	Property	Use
ethene			plastic bags
	polypropene	light and durable	
vinyl chloride			umbrellas

Polymers made from alkenes are known as **thermoplastics** (thermoplastic polymers or thermosoftening polymers). The following sections give further information on the physical properties and uses of thermoplastics, and on the physical properties and uses of the other type of plastics: **thermosetting polymers** (or thermosets or thermosetting plastics).

Thermoplastics

Thermoplastics are flexible and can be moulded into different shapes. This is explained by the fact that the long chains in the polymer:

- can stretch easily
- soften on warming
- are flexible
- can be shaped by warming.

The structure and behaviour of this type of plastic are summarised in Figure 12.10.

Figure 12.10a Tangled chains of long, thin molecules in a thermoplastic

Figure 12.10b The effect of heat on a thermoplastic

Thermosetting polymers

Thermosetting polymers are strong, rigid materials. Once formed, they do not soften or melt and cannot be remoulded. As can be seen in Figure 12.11 the long chain molecules are joined by cross-links. When the chains are heated, the cross-links between the chains stop them from moving over each other. As a result, this type of plastic cannot be melted or remoulded and, if heated, will burn or char. The cross-linking between the chains forms a rigid network. This results in the plastic being hard. This is unlike thermoplastics, which are flexible due to their long chains which have no cross-linking.

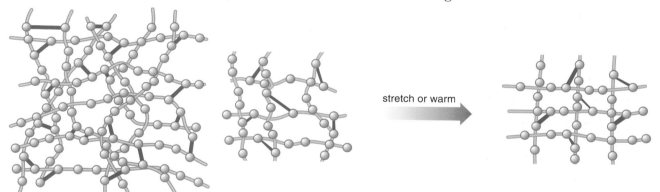

Figure 12.11a Cross-links in a thermosetting polymer

Figure 12.11b The effect of heat on a thermosetting polymer

Uses of thermoplastics and thermosetting polymers

Thermoplastics and thermosetting polymers have giant covalent molecular structures. They can act as insulators because the electrons are fixed in strong covalent bonds. Table 12.4 gives several other important physical properties of thermoplastics and thermosetting polymers.

Since the 1960s many new plastics have been discovered. These have replaced traditional materials such as wood, metal, glass, paper, ceramics, silk, wool and cotton. The properties of these new plastics make them suitable for a wide range of uses. For example, they are cheap, have a low density, are unreactive, and are easy to dye. They are used to make boats, cars, toys, packaging material, clothing, and other such items. A major disadvantage of synthetic plastics is the difficulty of their disposal, as they are non-biodegradable (are not broken down by bacteria in the soil). Recent developments have seen the introduction of new biodegradable and photodegradable plastics that could eventually replace the present ones. Cost and Government legislation on the use and disposal of plastics will determine the extent to which there is a demand for these new materials.

Table 12.4 Classes of material and their properties

Type of material	Examples	General properties
metals	iron, aluminium, lead, copper and zinc	● hard ● strong ● malleable ● good conductors of heat and electricity ● ductile ● high density ● high melting and boiling points ● can react with acids, water and air
glass	soda glass (bottles and windows) Pyrex (heat-resistant glass)	● brittle ● hard ● transparent ● very unreactive ● high melting point ● strong in compression and low tensile strength
ceramics	pottery, bricks, china, tiles and crockery	● brittle ● hard ● very unreactive ● high melting point ● strong in compression but low tensile strength
fibres	polyester, lycra, acrylics, nylon, cotton, linen and silk	● flexible ● low density ● long, thin strands of fibre ● burn on heating
plastics: thermoplastic	polythene, polypropene, PVC and polystyrene	● flexible ● low density ● insulators ● easy to melt and remould ● many burn on heating
thermosetting	melamine, bakelite and epoxy resins	● strong and stiff ● low density ● insulators ● cannot be remoulded ● decompose, burn or char when heated

Materials and their properties

There are five classes of materials: metals, glass, ceramics, fibres and plastics. Some important properties of these materials are listed in Table 12.4 and described below. These properties enable scientists to make decisions about which material is most suitable for a given purpose.

Melting point

The melting point of materials is a very important property in determining their use. For example, aluminium and steel are used to make cooking pans and utensils. This is only possible because of their high melting points. On the other hand, polythene has a low melting point. When it is heated, it softens and melts, enabling it to be moulded into different shapes such as bottles and bowls.

Conduction of heat and electricity

Metals are good conductors of heat and electricity. They are good electrical conductors because of the metallic bonding of their atoms. This allows electrical charge (electrons) to pass freely through the material. They are good conductors of heat for the same reason. Thermal energy can be rapidly transferred through the metallic structure by the free electrons.

Copper is a particularly good electrical conductor. This is why it is used to make electrical wires. Aluminium, because of its good thermal conductivity, is used to make saucepans and cooking foil. Aluminium is also important in power lines, because it is light and is a good electrical conductor.

Some materials have important uses because of their poor conductivity of heat or electricity. For example, polystyrene is used as an insulator to slow down heat losses. PVC is used to cover electrical wires so that people do not get electric shocks from live wires when they handle electrical equipment.

Figure 12.12 The uses of materials depend on their properties
Left: metals conduct heat to the food
Right: PVC provides electrical insulation, while copper is the best choice for the conducting wires

Hardness

This property of materials relates to how easy it is to scratch or dent a material. A harder material will always scratch a softer material. The Mohs scale is used to compare the relative hardness of materials and ranges from 1 for talc (very soft) to 10 for diamond (very hard).

Strength

A strong material is one that is difficult to break when a force is applied. Strength is usually associated with a stretching force (strength in tension). For example, it is possible to investigate the stretching force required to break a nylon thread. Materials that are difficult to break by stretching are said to have high tensile strength. Metals generally display high tensile strength. Strength can also be considered in terms of compression, which is the effect of crushing or squeezing a material. Glass and ceramics are strong when compressed but weak when stretched. They are said to have good compressive strength.

Uses of materials

Scientists choose a material for a particular function because the material's properties are suited to that use. For example, marble is used as a building material because it is hard and strong. Polythene is used to make washing-up bowls because it is waterproof and easy to mould. When choosing a material for a particular purpose, there are a number of questions that must be asked. Consider the problem of deciding on a suitable material for making disposable coffee cups at a football stadium. In making this decision, we are likely to ask the following questions:

- **Are the physical properties suitable?** By this we mean properties such as density, flexibility, melting point, strength and conductivity.
- **Are the chemical properties suitable?** Here we would consider chemical properties related to reactivity in air, water, acid and/or alkali.
- **Is the cost of the material suitable?** The cost of the material must not be too high or the product will be too expensive.

The following reasons could be used in deciding why polystyrene is the most suitable material for disposable cups.

- **Physical properties:** easily moulded, lightweight, insulator.
- **Chemical properties:** an unreactive material that will not react with the drink, water or air.
- **Cost of material:** readily available and cheap to manufacture.

Table 12.5 highlights some of the uses for the five types of materials. In each case we can see how the use is related to a material's properties.

Table 12.5 Some uses of materials

Material	Use	Property
iron	bridges	high strength
aluminium	saucepans	good conductor of heat
copper	electrical wiring	good conductor of electricity
lead	roofing	can be hammered into shape
ceramic tiles	flooring	very hard
soda glass	windows	transparent
Pyrex glass	glassware for cooking	resistant to changes in temperature
PVC	window frames	waterproof and strong
polythene	bottles	easy to melt and mould
polystyrene	wall insulation	good insulator
polyester	clothes	strong and flexible
melamine (thermosetting)	kitchen worktops	high heat resistance

Composite materials

It is possible to design a material that combines the desirable properties of two different materials. In sport, many tennis racquets, skateboards, fishing rods and golf club shafts are made from carbon-fibre reinforced plastic. This type of material provides the flexibility of plastics and the very high strength of carbon fibres. In most cases this material has replaced the more traditional material, wood or metal. Carbon-fibre reinforced plastic is an example of a **composite material**.

Figure 12.13 Composite materials in sport

Composite materials are those which combine the properties of more than one material and produce a more useful material for a particular purpose. In a composite material, one of the materials acts as a **matrix** while the other is used as a **filler**. This is shown in Figure 12.14 for glass-fibre reinforced plastic. Here the plastic acts as the matrix and holds the filler, glass fibre, in place.

As well as being man-made or synthetic, there are many composite materials found in nature, for example ivory, teeth and bone. Bone combines the properties of calcium phosphate with those of long chain proteins. Calcium phosphate is required to make the bones hard. The long chain protein makes it more flexible and less brittle than calcium phosphate on its own.

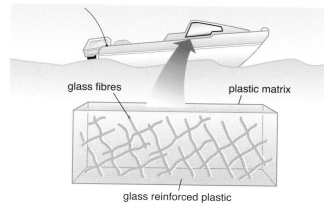

Figure 12.14 Glass-fibre reinforced plastic

Four common composite materials are shown in Figure 12.15.

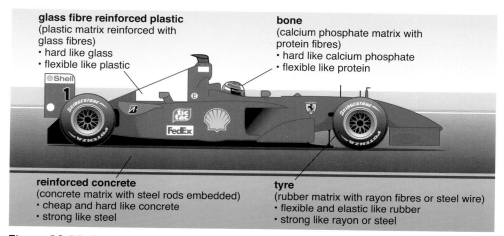

glass fibre reinforced plastic
(plastic matrix reinforced with glass fibres)
• hard like glass
• flexible like plastic

bone
(calcium phosphate matrix with protein fibres)
• hard like calcium phosphate
• flexible like protein

reinforced concrete
(concrete matrix with steel rods embedded)
• cheap and hard like concrete
• strong like steel

tyre
(rubber matrix with rayon fibres or steel wire)
• flexible and elastic like rubber
• strong like rayon or steel

Figure 12.15 Some composite materials

9 a i   Give one example of a composite material in nature.
   ii   Give one example of a man-made composite that is used in the construction industry.
   b   What are the advantages of using a composite material instead of a single material?

Decline of traditional materials

Many modern materials have replaced the traditionally used ones because of their superior properties and, in some instances, their lower cost. Some common examples are that paper bags have largely been replaced by plastic bags, and wooden windows are often replaced by PVC ones. PVC is tough, durable, waterproof and a good insulator. It does not have to be painted, is generally very low maintenance, and has a relatively low cost. So it is perhaps not surprising that many people select it to replace old wooden windows and doors.

One traditional material in Northern Ireland that has shown a marked decline in production is linen. Linen, produced from the flax plant, has traditionally had many uses, in clothing, table coverings and napkins, bed-linen and church garments. Between 1750 and 1815, the export of linen cloth from Ireland totalled 43 million yards. Its value exceeded that of any other agricultural produce. At the beginning of the 20th century, 75 000 people in Northern Ireland worked in the linen industry. Northern Ireland had become the largest linen-producing area in the world, with Lisburn as the main centre of trade. But then the industry began to change. For financial reasons, one of the main linen companies moved its production to the USA. Then during the 1920s and 1930s the demand for linen declined. This was due to the advent of new fabrics, more casual styles of dress, and the use of paper napkins and handkerchiefs. The fact that fewer families had servants to iron the wrinkle-prone linen also played a part!

Although Northern Ireland still produces linen, it is now only a fraction of the amount produced in the early 1900s.

> **10** What impact would the decline in the use of linen have had on:
> **a** the linen manufacturers
> **b** the working population of Northern Ireland?

Nanotechnology

Nanotechnology is the study of atoms and molecules. The metre is the standard SI unit of length. The term **nanometre** means 0.000 000 001 m. This is 1000 million times smaller than a metre or 10 million times smaller than a centimetre. Most molecules are smaller than one nanometre (1 nm), and this is very small. Nanotechnology refers to structures that are 1 to 100 nm in size. This is approximately the size of a few hundred atoms or molecules. Present-day scientists have the ability to see and control atoms at this dimension.

Additionally they have found out that nanoparticles show unexpected properties due to their very small size. They differ from larger particles in terms of being more sensitive to light, heat and electrical conductivity, magnetism and electrostatics. Another important property of nanoparticles is their large surface area compared to the same mass of more traditional materials. Nanoparticles with a high surface area are being investigated for use in energy storage and in separation processes, for example in the removal of water, hydrogen sulphide and carbon dioxide. Another use is to produce highly selective sensors. They are also used in coatings and as stronger and lighter construction materials, whose bonding and strength depend on the surface area and shape of the nanostructures.

Nanoparticles also have many uses in industrial catalysis. For example, in Japan chemists have found out that gold particles smaller than 5 nm catalytically convert toxic carbon monoxide to carbon dioxide at -70 °C, a reaction that usually requires a much higher temperature.

Nanotechnology is now being used to develop many new materials to replace older products. An example is ICI's latest sun creams, which use titanium dioxide nanoparticles of 50 nm in diameter. The older sun creams used titanium dioxide particles of 200 nm. It was found that they left white smears on the body. However, the newer creams with the smaller particle size leave no white smears on the skin. They absorb light and scatter much less than the larger particles.

Nanoparticles of silver have antibacterial, antiviral and antifungal properties. They are used in sterilising sprays to clean operating theatres in hospitals, and in wound dressings (Figure 12.16). There is currently much research into carbon nanotubes. It is thought that they will replace silicon in a number of smaller and faster electronic devices.

Figure 12.16 This *Acticoat* antimicrobial wound dressing uses nanocrystalline silver technology to keep harmful micro-organisms out of wounds

Smart materials

Smart materials is the name that has been given to a range of modern materials whose properties change when there is a change in the surroundings, for example, a change in temperature or light or pH. Some specific examples are as follows:

- Thermochromic paint changes colour when heated.
- Photochromic paint changes colour on exposure to light.
- Shape memory alloy (such as NiTi or nitinol, an alloy of nickel and titanium with aluminium) is easily deformed but able to regain its original shape when warmed. Some examples of its use are as staples to hold together bone fractures, as coffeepot thermostats, and as super-elastic frames for glasses (Figure 12.17).
- Polymer gels such as hydrogels have the ability to swell or shrink (up to 1000 times in volume) due to small changes in temperature or pH. They have a cross-linked polymer structure inflated with a solvent, for example water. These gels have potential uses in artificial muscles, in robot actuators or as absorbers of toxic chemicals.

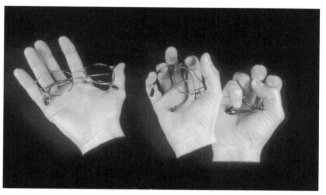

Figure 12.17 Spectacle frames made from shape memory metal can be easily misshapen but will quickly return to their original form in the warmth of the hand

websites

www.gcsechemistry.com/ukop.htm
information on oil, fractional distillation and polymers

www.bbc.co.uk/nature/programmes/tv/state_planet/pollution.shtml
information on pollution

www.moorlandschool.co.uk/earth/index.htm
relevant information on oil and polymers

www.moorlandschool.co.uk/earth/oilrefinery.htm
further information on an oil refinery and cracking

www.royalsoc.ac.uk/landing.asp?id=1210
lots of good information on nanotechnology

www.qca.org.uk/284_1500.html
good reference on smart materials

www.optics.org/articles/news/9/9/3/1
interesting article on optically smart materials

Questions

1 a The table shows how some plastics are used in many houses. Copy and complete the table by giving **two** properties of each plastic and explain why it is used in the way stated. *(8 marks)*

Plastic	Use	Properties
polystyrene	roof insulation	
PVC	plastic guttering	
polythene	plastic bucket	
melamine	kitchen work top	

b i Polymers can be classified as thermoplastic or thermosetting. Explain precisely what is meant by these two terms. *(4 marks)*

ii Using only those plastics in the table, give **one** example of a thermoplastic and **one** example of a thermosetting polymer. *(2 marks)*

c i Many plastic articles, e.g. polythene bags, create litter problems because they are non-biodegradable. What do you think the term 'non-biodegradable' means? *(2 marks)*

ii Suggest **two** methods which would help minimise the litter problems plastic articles create. *(2 marks)*

2 The table gives information about some of the hydrocarbon fuels obtained by fractional distillation of crude oil.

Fuel	Boiling range (°C)	Number of carbon atoms in each molecule
petroleum gas	below 25	1–4
petrol	40–100	4–12
paraffin	150–240	9–16
diesel	220–250	15–25

a What is a hydrocarbon? *(2 marks)*

b The fuels listed above are all fossil fuels. Give **one** other example of a fossil fuel. *(1 mark)*

c Explain how the different fuels are separated from each other by fractional distillation. *(2 marks)*

d What is the name of the process used to break up long chain molecules in order to form more useful shorter chain molecules? *(1 mark)*

CCEA GCSE Science: Double Award (Non-modular) Higher Tier 2002 (part question)

3 a Glass-fibre reinforced polymer is a composite material used to make car bodies. What is meant by a 'composite material'. *(2 marks)*

b A group of students gathered the following information about different materials to help them make decisions on the best material for using to make car bodies and bulletproof vests.

Material	Density (kg/m³)	Relative strength	Relative stiffness	Cost
steel	7800	1	210	low
polythene	960	0.02	0.6	low
Kevlar	1450	3	190	high
carbon-fibre reinforced plastic	1600	1.8	200	high
nylon	1100	0.08	3	medium

i Use the information in the table to give **two** reasons why the students selected steel to make car bodies. *(2 marks)*

ii Use the information in the table to give **two** reasons why the students selected Kevlar to make bulletproof vests. *(2 marks)*

iii Use the information in the table to give a reason why the composite material, carbon-fibre reinforced plastic, has replaced the more traditional material, wood, in tennis racquets and golf clubs. *(1 mark)*

c The students next tested the tensile strength of the different materials using the apparatus shown.

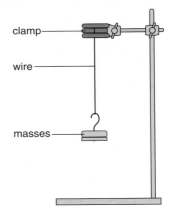

clamp
wire
masses

Give **two** ways the experiment must be carried out to make it a valid test. *(2 marks)*

CCEA GCSE Science: Single Award (Modular) Specimen Paper (Higher Tier) 2006

4 a Propane and ethene are important industrial chemicals which can be obtained from the thermal cracking of pentane as shown below:

pentane → propane + ethene
$C_5H_{12} \rightarrow C_3H_8 + C_2H_4$

i What is meant by thermal cracking? *(3 marks)*

ii Draw the structural formulae of propane and ethene. *(2 marks)*

b Propane is an important fuel. Write a balanced symbol equation to show the reaction when propane burns completely in oxygen. *(3 marks)*

CCEA GCSE Science: Single Award (Modular) Specimen Paper (Higher Tier) 2006 (part question)

Chapter 13

Water and waste management

Learning objectives

By the end of this chapter you should know and understand:

➤ What hard water is and how to test for hardness in water
➤ That compounds of calcium and magnesium cause hardness in water
➤ The word and symbol equations for hard water reacting with soap
➤ The differences between temporary and permanent hardness and the methods of softening hard water
➤ That hard water forms deposits of the carbonates of calcium and magnesium in kettles and hot water pipes
➤ The symbol equation for this formation of calcium and magnesium carbonates
➤ The word and symbol equations for the reaction when these carbonates react with hydrochloric and ethanoic acids
➤ The advantages and disadvantages of hard water
➤ The formation of stalactites and stalagmites in caves in hard water areas
➤ The problems associated with the disposal of plastic waste
➤ The difference between biodegradable and non-biodegradable waste
➤ How a biodegradable plastic can be made from starch
➤ The benefits of recycling, and explore the laws that require councils to recycle waste and reduce landfill
➤ The benefits and disadvantages in exploiting raw materials

Hard water

Water that does not lather easily with soap is called **hard water**. If the water does lather easily, it is **soft water**.

When soap is used with hard water, not only is it difficult to get a good foamy lather, but there is also a **scum** formed (Figure 13.1). The soap molecules react with dissolved salts in the water to form the scum:

$$\text{hard water} + \text{soap} \rightarrow \text{scum}$$

Hard water will produce lather eventually, but it uses more soap than a sample of soft water of the same volume.

Soapless detergents will lather well with both hard and soft water, because it is only soap that reacts to form scum.

Figure 13.1
Scum from using soap in hard water

Causes of hard water

From Table 13.1 it can be seen that dissolved calcium or magnesium ions make water hard.

Table 13.1

Salt	Behaviour with soap solution
sodium chloride	good lather
calcium chloride	no lather, scum
magnesium chloride	poor lather, scum
potassium nitrate	good lather
calcium nitrate	poor lather, scum
magnesium nitrate	no lather, scum
magnesium sulphate	no lather, scum
sodium sulphate	good lather
calcium sulphate	poor lather, scum
calcium hydrogencarbonate	no lather, scum

The calcium or magnesium ions react with soap, forming insoluble salts, which are precipitated out of the mixture as the scum:

$$Ca^{2+} + \underset{\text{sodium stearate (soap)}}{2C_{17}H_{35}COONa} \rightarrow \underset{\text{calcium stearate (scum)}}{(C_{17}H_{35}COO)_2Ca} + 2Na^+$$

For example:

$$\begin{array}{ccccccc} \text{calcium} & + & \text{sodium} & \rightarrow & \text{calcium} & + & \text{sodium} \\ \text{chloride} & & \text{stearate} & & \text{stearate} & & \text{chloride} \end{array}$$

Types of hard water

Temporary hard water

This can be softened by boiling.

Carbon dioxide in the air dissolves in rain water, forming the weak acid, carbonic acid:

$$CO_2 + H_2O \rightarrow H_2CO_3$$

When this dilute acidic solution falls on rocks containing calcium carbonate, e.g. limestone, soluble calcium hydrogencarbonate is formed. As a result, there are calcium ions dissolved in water and the water is hard:

$$H_2CO_3 + CaCO_3 \rightarrow Ca(HCO_3)_2$$

The calcium hydrogencarbonate, however, is not very stable, and is easily decomposed on heating. The calcium carbonate produced is insoluble, and is precipitated out of the solution:

$$Ca(HCO_3)_2 \rightarrow CaCO_3 + CO_2 + H_2O$$

As the calcium ions are removed, the hard water is softened. Unfortunately, the calcium carbonate is deposited in the heating vessel (Figure 13.2).

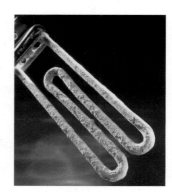

Figure 13.2 'Fur' inside a kettle is a deposit of calcium carbonate from hard water

Permanent hard water

This cannot be softened by boiling.

Carbonates are not the only calcium- or magnesium-containing compounds found in rocks. Gypsum, for example, contains calcium sulphate. When rain passes over or through these other rocks, calcium or magnesium ions can dissolve in the water and make it hard. Because these compounds do not decompose on heating, the calcium or magnesium ions remain in the water and it stays hard.

The ionic equation (with state symbols) is:

$$CaSO_4(s) \rightarrow Ca^{2+}(aq) + SO_4^{2-}(aq)$$

---

1 20 cm^3 was taken from each of five samples of water and they were shaken with soap solution. The volume of soap solution needed to get a good lather was noted.

The samples were then boiled and the test was repeated.

	Sample	A	B	C	D	E
Vol. of soap sol. (cm^3)	before boiling	10.1	6.3	12.2	1.6	8.4
	after boiling	10.1	1.9	2.3	1.6	8.4

a   Which letter represents the sample of soft water?
b   Which letter represents the sample of the hardest water?
c   Which letters represent the two samples of temporary hard water?

Reactions of calcium and magnesium carbonates with hydrochloric and ethanoic acids

Hydrochloric acid and ethanoic acid react with the insoluble carbonates of magnesium and calcium to give a metal salt, carbon dioxide and water:

calcium carbonate + hydrochloric acid → calcium chloride + carbon dioxide + water
$$CaCO_3 \quad + \quad 2HCl \quad \rightarrow \quad CaCl_2 \quad + \quad CO_2 \quad + H_2O$$

magnesium carbonate + hydrochloric acid → magnesium chloride + carbon dioxide + water
$$MgCO_3 \quad + \quad 2HCl \quad \rightarrow \quad MgCl_2 \quad + \quad CO_2 \quad + H_2O$$

calcium carbonate + ethanoic acid → calcium ethanoate + carbon dioxide + water
$$CaCO_3 \quad + 2CH_3COOH \rightarrow \quad (CH_3COO)_2Ca \quad + \quad CO_2 \quad + H_2O$$

magnesium carbonate + ethanoic acid → magnesium ethanoate + carbon dioxide + water
$$MgCO_3 \quad + 2CH_3COOH \rightarrow \quad (CH_3COO)_2Mg \quad + \quad CO_2 \quad + H_2O$$

Softening hard water

The four main methods of softening hard water are as follows:

● Boiling (only for temporary hard water), causing **thermal decomposition** of the calcium or magnesium compounds that cause the hardness, as shown for calcium hydrogencarbonate opposite.

- Adding **washing soda**, which is hydrated sodium carbonate, $Na_2CO_3 \cdot 10H_2O$.

  The symbol equation is:

  $$Na_2CO_3 \cdot 10H_2O + Ca(HCO_3)_2 \rightarrow 2NaHCO_3 + CaCO_3 + 10H_2O$$

  The insoluble calcium carbonate is precipitated out. The ionic equation is:

  $$CO_3^{2-}(aq) + Ca^{2+}(aq) \rightarrow CaCO_3(s)$$

- Using an **ion exchanger** (Figure 13.3), which removes the calcium or magnesium ions and replaces them with other suitable ions.

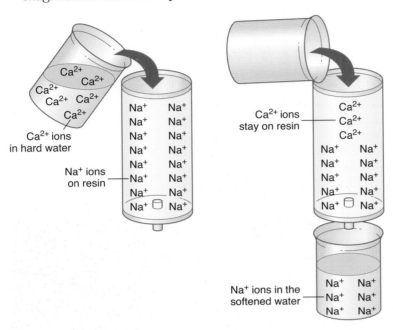

Figure 13.3 Using an ion exchange column

- Using **distillation**, in which the water is distilled off and condensed, leaving behind the calcium and magnesium compounds that cause the hardness.

Advantages and disadvantages of hard water

Advantages of hard water

- Calcium is needed for strong bones and teeth and may help to prevent heart disease. You would, however, have to drink a large amount of water in order to get a significant amount of calcium!
- Hard water is supposed to taste better, but this is presumably a matter of individual taste. Brewers find hard water is better for making beer.
- Hard water is less likely to dissolve heavy metals such as lead. So if the hard water is flowing through old lead pipes, then there is a smaller possibility of the lead dissolving in the water and damaging your health.
- In tanning leather, calcium or magnesium ions make leather cure better.

Disadvantages of hard water

- Hard water will, of course, produce a lather with soap eventually, but the amount of soap required makes it much more expensive than using soft water.

- When temporary hard water is heated in a kettle, the calcium carbonate deposited builds up on the inside and, if it is an electric kettle, on the element. This is known as 'fur'. Further use of the kettle needs more heat, as the 'fur' has to be heated before the energy gets to the water.
- When the hot water is in boilers and pipes, the deposits are known as 'scale' or 'limescale'. Again this causes problems. The pipes can become blocked and the hot water system is much less efficient.
- Stains are left on washing.

Characteristics of a hard water area

Hard water comes from areas with chalk or limestone. As the rain, containing the carbonic acid, runs through these rocks, some of the calcium carbonate is removed as the soluble calcium hydrogencarbonate (Figure 13.4).

Over very many centuries this can create caves. Inside the caves, **stalagmites** (which go up from the floor) and **stalactites** (which hang from the roof) can form (Figure 13.5). A drop of temporary hard water on the roof or floor of the cave can lose water by evaporation. As a result the calcium hydrogencarbonate decomposes leaving a solid deposit of calcium carbonate. (This is the same reaction that takes place in the softening of temporary hard water by boiling.) Very, very slowly the deposits build up to form a column of calcium carbonate.

Figure 13.4 Carbonic acid in rain water has helped to dissolve the limestone in the cracks of this limestone pavement

Figure 13.5 Stalagmites and stalactites in caves can be a big tourist attraction. These are in Marble Arch Caves, Fermanagh

Disposal and recycling of plastics

The manufacture of polymers provides us with many important man-made materials. But there are serious problems associated with their disposal. It is not unusual to see plastic litter in the countryside, towns and even on our scenic beaches. Unlike natural polymeric materials such as paper, cotton and wool, most synthetic plastics are non-biodegradable. Micro-organisms cannot break them down.

The fact that it is relatively cheap to produce plastics from crude oil further adds to the litter problem. As plastics are cheap, most people tend to dump them, rather than recycle them. Recycling plastics is costly, as it is expensive to have the waste collected and sorted. The recycling process also involves high energy costs.

Figure 13.6 Plastic waste can now be burned to produce electricity (left) or recycled into pellets of polythene (right)

The three main methods of dealing with waste are:

- dumping in a landfill site
- burning in an incinerator
- recycling (see Figure 13.6).

In recent years most of the old quarry sites available for landfill dumping have been used up. Dealing with plastics by this dumping method is now relatively expensive, especially with the recent introduction of Government landfill tax on waste.

Incineration schemes burn waste plastics. The heat generated can be made to serve a useful purpose, either directly or to generate power. The main problems associated with incineration are pollution from the products of burning and the destruction of many resources that could have been recycled. During the incineration process, poisonous gases such as hydrogen chloride, carbon monoxide and hydrogen cyanide are given off. It is very important that these compounds are controlled and removed before any waste gases are released into the atmosphere.

Recycling of plastic waste is now becoming more and more popular. Figure 13.7 shows how thermoplastics and thermosetting polymers are recycled. Recycling thermoplastics is carried out by melting the waste plastic and then remoulding it. Large quantities of the recycled plastic are used to make sheeting and plastic bags. Recycling of thermosetting polymers is much more difficult because they do not melt on heating but burn or char.

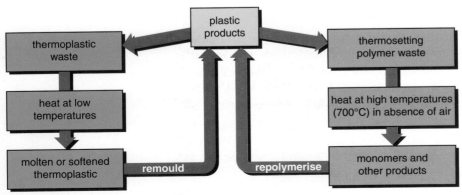

Figure 13.7 Recycling plastics

To recycle a thermosetting polymer, it is first pyrolysed (heated in the absence of air) at around 700°C. Under these conditions, the polymer partially breaks down, forming the monomers it was originally made from. The monomers are collected, and are then polymerised to give a new thermosetting polymer.

More recently, chemists have developed new **biodegradable plastics** for film, packaging and containers (Figure 13.8). In future years this could be an important method to help resolve the present environmental difficulty of the disposal of plastics.

Figure 13.8
A biodegradable plastic bag made from maize starch

Making a biodegradable plastic from potato starch

It is possible to make a biodegradable polymer by extracting starch from potatoes. Starch is made of long chains of glucose molecules joined together. When starch is dried from an aqueous solution, it forms a thin film of plastic. To make a stronger and better film, it is best to react the extracted starch with dilute hydrochloric acid. The acid causes the branches in the starch molecules to break down. This allows the chains in the starch to line up better, making a stronger film (Figure 13.9a).

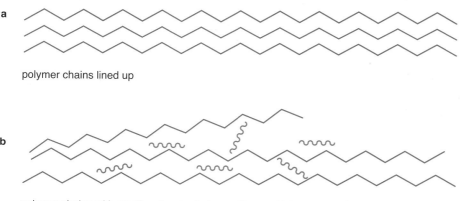

a

polymer chains lined up

b

polymer chains with small molecules between them, which prevents them lining up

Figure 13.9
a With its chains lined up, a polymer is called crystalline, and is strong but brittle
b With small molecules (called a plasticiser) in between its chains, the polymer is less strong but more flexible

Although the film is strong, it is brittle. The chains are too good at lining up. This problem can be overcome by adding a plasticiser, such as glycerol, which makes the plastic more flexible. The smaller glycerol molecules get trapped between the chains. This prevents them from lining up as well (Figure 13.9b).

- Grate 100 g of potato. The potato does not need to be peeled, but it should be clean.
- Put the potato into a mortar and add 100 cm³ of distilled water. Grind the potato carefully.
- Filter the extracted starch through a tea strainer into a beaker, leaving the used potato in the mortar. Add 100 cm³ of distilled water to the potato, grind and strain twice more.
- Leave the mixture in the beaker to settle for 5 minutes.
- Pour the water carefully from the beaker, leaving behind the white starch, which should have settled to the bottom. Put 100 g of distilled water in with the starch and stir gently. Leave the mixture to settle again. Then pour off the water, leaving the starch behind.
- Now place 25 cm³ of distilled water in a beaker. Add 2.5 g of potato starch mixture, followed by 3 cm³ of 0.1 M hydrochloric acid. (To make a more flexible plastic, 2 cm³ of glycerol can also be added.)
- Put a watch glass over the beaker. Heat the mixture with a Bunsen burner. Take care and allow the mixture to boil for 15 minutes. Do not allow it to boil dry. If it looks like boiling dry, stop heating.
- Carefully check the pH of the final solution by dipping a glass rod into the mixture and dotting it on to universal indicator paper. Add enough dilute 0.1 M sodium hydroxide to neutralise the mixture (in the region of 1 to 2 cm³).
- Now pour your mixture into a Petri dish, ensuring that it forms a thin even layer.
- Allow the mixture to dry on a warm window sill or radiator.
- After drying, observe the plastic film that you have made from starch.

Recycling of glass

For centuries, glass has been used to make containers for liquids and solids. Today, glass containers are used to store all types of substances, from jam and sauces to champagne and perfumes. Glass manufacturers and customers appreciate glass as a storage container for substances for its low cost, long-term strength, transparency, unreactivity, ease of cleaning and good looks. A great advantage of glass is the fact that it can be recycled over and over again, and at the same time retain its strength. About 90% of recycled glass is used for making food and beverage containers.

Glass recycling has grown considerably in recent years. This is due to greater collection through recycling programmes and to glass manufacturers' increased demand for recycled glass. There is no shortage of the raw materials to produce glass (sand, sodium carbonate and limestone). That is why glass is so cheap. The main cost in the production of glass is the expense of the heat energy needed to melt the raw materials together.

The main reasons for recycling glass are as follows:

- The raw materials for the production of glass are extracted from the ground. Recycling would cut down on the number of quarries.
- The production of glass depends on large amounts of energy. Recycling cuts down on the use of fossil fuels.
- Waste glass is dangerous and causes litter problems. Also, it is very unreactive and as a result it is non-biodegradable.

Today, most glass manufacturers use recycled glass, known as **cullet**, to supplement the raw materials of sand, limestone and sodium carbonate. Using cullet saves money and the environment, for the following reasons:

- The cost of cullet is less than the cost of the raw materials.
- Cullet prolongs the lifetime of the furnace, as it melts at a lower temperature.
- As cullet cuts down on energy costs, it also cuts down on the emissions of greenhouse gases such as nitrogen dioxide and carbon dioxide.

Figure 13.10 shows a typical process for the recycling of glass.

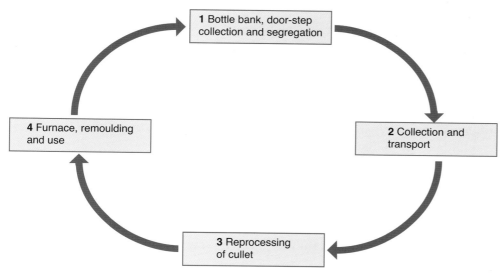

Figure 13.10 Flow chart for glass recycling

1 **Bottle bank, door-step collection and segregation.** You take different glass bottles to a bottle bank. The bottles are separated by colour and they smash into smaller fragments, called cullet.
2 **Collection and transport.** When the bottle banks are full, they are collected and transported to the reprocessing facility. Glass may be transported from other sources by a collector who provides kerb-side collection for homes and business.
3 **Reprocessing of cullet.** This is needed for a number of reasons. Various steps may be taken:
   - crushing to reduce the size of the cullet
   - removal of contaminants mixed with the cullet
   - washing and drying the cullet.
4 **Furnace, remoulding and use.** After the cullet has been purified, washed and dried, it can now be melted down and remoulded into new glass containers.

Landfill directive and waste strategy

Each year in the UK there is in the region of 30 million tonnes of municipal waste. This waste is under the control of local authorities. Almost 80% of this waste goes to landfill sites (see page 81). Almost 60% of it is biodegradable. The majority of the biodegradable waste is food, paper and garden waste. In the landfill sites this waste decays anaerobically to produce methane. Unfortunately, methane is a greenhouse gas, and this adds to the problems of global warming. Other problems associated with landfill sites are leaching of poisonous chemicals into the ground water and soil, unsightly litter, pests and the wastage of recyclable materials.

Recycling reduces energy-intensive mining, transportation and production of goods from raw materials. It also offers the opportunity of creating many new jobs. At present, councils are encouraging recycling by:

- use of several bins for household refuse
- separation of metal/iron and steel from general waste
- production of mulch from garden waste
- providing household recycling centres
- charging businesses for placing waste in landfill sites.

You can read more about recycling in Northern Ireland on pages 90–91.

Chemistry at work

All human activity has an influence on our environment and especially on our use of the natural resources found on Earth. Since they first evolved, humans have made use of natural materials. Early humans used plant and animal material for food, coverings and building shelters. They also made use of minerals for tools.

Today we continue to exploit the raw materials found on Earth to satisfy our needs. Some needs are more important than others! They range from basics such as food to luxuries such as diamonds, and they include the raw materials required by industry.

The extraction of metals from their ores, the processing of food and the manufacture of pharmaceuticals, dyes, pigments, plastics and fertilisers are only a few examples of 'chemistry at work'.

Limestone quarrying

Limestone, calcium carbonate, has many uses and is a very important raw material for industry (Figure 13.11). Limestone is an abundant raw material and as it is relatively easily obtained it is fairly cheap. The business of quarrying provides jobs at the quarry and in transporting the limestone.

Unfortunately, quarries destroy natural habitats. The traffic associated with them contributes to noise and dust pollution, as does the blasting that is part of the process. If a new quarry is to be dug, consideration must be given to the balance between the demands of industry and care for the environment.

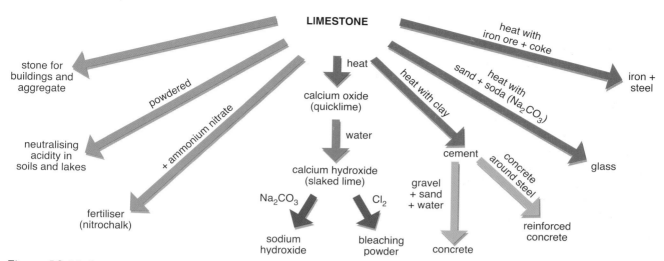

Figure 13.11 Important uses and products of limestone

---

2 Why is limestone considered to be a cheap raw material?
3 Give two advantages and two disadvantages of setting up a quarry.

Peat cutting

Peat has been used as a fuel for centuries. In Ireland families had rights to remove the turf from a certain, usually quite small, strip of the local peat bog. Once industry became involved, however, the removal of peat from the bog speeded up considerably. Not only was it being taken for use as a fuel, it was also being used in treating soils and making gardening composts.

Peat bogs are very special habitats. Many of the plants found in them are not found anywhere else. Large-scale peat cutting was destroying these habitats too rapidly. Concern about the loss of the peat bogs prompted many gardeners to stop using peat-based products.

Lignite mining

Lignite, a soft brown coal, can be found around Lough Neagh. The Crumlin area was estimated to have reserves of about 200 million tonnes that could be obtained by open-cast mining. During the energy crisis of the 1960s, interest was shown in these reserves. Three possibly commercial seams were identified. They could have been very important for Northern Ireland. It was suggested that the lignite could be extracted and burned to provide 40% of the electricity needs of the country. This would have been of economic value, as we would have needed to import less oil. The project in opening and running the mine would have provided employment. The forecast was for about 400 new jobs. The lignite found in Northern Ireland is low in sulphur. So it would result in relatively little atmospheric pollution when it was burnt.

There were many factors against the project. Not only would the mining destroy the habitat of local wildlife, it could also be unsightly. The area had a thriving fishing industry and productive agricultural land. It included five listed buildings. There was thought to be a possible problem with underground water supplies. In the end the project was shelved (the disadvantages outweighed the possible advantages). But who knows what may happen in the future?

ACTIVITY

Imagine you want to open a lignite mine near Crumlin. Write a letter to the Department of the Environment trying to persuade them to give you permission to open the mine.

Or

Imagine you are part of a group that is against lignite mining in the area near Lough Neagh. Design a leaflet that could be distributed to local people to encourage them to object to the mine.

Environmental problems arising from 'chemistry at work'

The effect of human activity can result in chemicals being found where they cause harm. Such chemicals are called **pollutants**. In many places on Earth, our air and water are polluted.

As more has been learned about pollution, efforts have been made to deal with the problems. Once sewage went straight into the local river or the sea, but now it is dealt with in sewage works. The Clean Air Act, which allowed local authorities to set up smokeless zones, has greatly reduced air pollution.

Pollution is not, however, a local matter. Oceans, seas and many rivers do not touch only one country. A factory in Basle in Switzerland had a fire. When it was being put out, pollutants were washed into the river Rhine. The pollution was carried down the river, causing problems as it passed through France, Germany and The Netherlands (Holland).

The air is definitely international, and acid rain is an international problem. The sulphur dioxide may be produced in one country, but it is carried away by the wind. Lakes in Scandinavia have been badly affected by acid rain formed in Britain. Greenhouse gases are another matter for international concern.

Governments meet at summits to discuss the environment and the harm we are causing it. Unfortunately, getting them all to agree about what has to be done to put matters right seems to be impossible!

websites

http://recycling-guided.com/topics/kids-recycling.html
www.recyclenow.com/
www.recyclingconsortium.org.uk/schools/index.htm
www.recyclezone.org.uk/
these four sites all give good information on recycling, reusing and reducing waste

www.recyclingglass.co.uk/
information on recycling glass

www.ch4.org.uk/eduarticle.php/Rotten+Landfills
a good article on landfill sites and the production of methane

http://news.bbc.co.uk/1/hi/magazine/3116318.stm
a good article on the recycling of plastics

Questions

1 Many plastic articles, e.g. polythene bags, create serious disposal problems in landfill sites, as they are non-biodegradable.

  a What do you understand by the term 'non-biodegradable'. *(2 marks)*

  b Give **two** ways which would help to overcome the disposal problem of plastics. *(2 marks)*

CCEA GCSE Science: Single Award (Modular) Specimen Paper (Higher Tier) 2006 (part question)

2 a A developer has plans for a quarry to be built close to an existing housing development. Some residents welcome this development while others oppose it. Give **four** arguments that could be used by the residents to back up their support or opposition to the development. *(4 marks)*

  b Glass bottles can be collected, crushed into fine powder called cullet and used to make new glass containers. Complete the diagram below showing how this is done in practice. *(1 mark)*

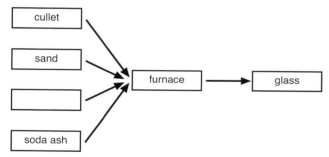

CCEA GCSE Science: Single Award (Modular) Specimen Paper (Higher Tier) 2006

3 A student tested five samples of water (each 20 cm³) from different areas in Northern Ireland. The samples were shaken with soap solution and the volume of soap solution required to get a good lather was noted in the table below. The samples were then boiled and the test repeated.

Sample	A	B	C	D	E
Volume of soap solution before boiling (cm³)	10.1	8.2	12.2	1.6	8.4
Volume of soap solution after boiling (cm³)	10.1	1.9	2.3	1.6	8.4

  a i Which letter represents the sample of softest water? *(1 mark)*

    ii Which letters represent the two samples of temporary hard water? *(2 marks)*

  b i Complete the word equation to show how temporary hardness in water can be removed by boiling:

calcium hydrogencarbonate
→ .... + ... + carbon dioxide
(2 marks)

    ii Give **one** advantage and **one** disadvantage of hard water. *(2 marks)*

CCEA GCSE Science: Single Award (Modular) Specimen Paper (Higher Tier) 2006

4 Four samples of water A, B, C and D were obtained from four different water supplies and tested for 'hardness'. 50 cm³ of each sample was shaken with soap solution, and the volume of soap solution needed to make a good lather was recorded as shown in the table below. The experiment was repeated but this time each sample was boiled and then tested with soap solution.

Sample	A	B	C	D
Volume of soap solution before boiling (cm³)	22	27	23	14
Volume of soap solution after boiling (cm³)	12	12	23	6

  a From the results above, which sample is the hardest? *(1 mark)*

  b Which sample represents water that is permanently hard? *(1 mark)*

  c How can you tell from the readings that area B will have the greatest problem with temporary hardness? *(1 mark)*

Chapter 14

Using materials to fight crime

By the end of this chapter you should know and understand:

➤ How fingerprints can be taken in a variety of situations and from different surfaces
➤ The different properties of materials that make them suitable for taking fingerprints
➤ How fingerprint types are used for identification, and how fingerprint evidence is treated in Court
➤ How to protect valuables in the house, and the individual's responsibility in crime prevention
➤ How retail outlets check for forged bank notes
➤ That altered cheques can be tested for forgery using chromatography
➤ That fibres have different properties that can be used to identify them
➤ That different metal ions produce different colours when heated in a flame
➤ That these colours can be used to identify their presence in a given sample from a crime scene
➤ What genetic fingerprinting is and how it is used to identify criminals
➤ The dangers of driving with alcohol or drugs in the body, and that there is a legal limit of alcohol in blood above which it is illegal to drive

Forensic science

Forensic science can be described as the application of science to law. When a crime takes place, forensic scientists are quite often called in. They carry out scientific tests to detect materials that may indicate whether or not someone was involved in the crime. This could involve very small (trace) amounts of materials like blood and other body fluids (Figure 14.1), hair and fibres. It could also involve analysing building materials, paint, glass, footwear, tyre marks, bullets, petrol and explosives, which may all be associated with the scene of a crime.

Many forensic scientists are involved with testing for suspected drug abuse. This could be analysing a drug find or specimens from people who are thought to have taken them. They could also be involved in testing specimens from people who have been drinking too much alcohol. Other forensic scientists could be involved in checking the authenticity of documents.

Figure 14.1 Forensic scientists collecting DNA evidence from a crime scene

Fingerprints

The ridges on the surfaces of the fingers and thumbs are present at birth. They remain unchanged for life, except for size as growth occurs. Their appearance can be obscured by scarring. But the scars can also be helpful points of identification. No two people have the same fingerprints. This allows them to be used for identification purposes.

Everyone's fingerprints have general ridge patterns. This allows them to be classified into four types (Figure 14.2): **arch**, **loop**, **whorl** and **composite**. This classification system was put forward by Sir Edward Henry in 1897 and adopted by Scotland Yard in 1901.

Figure 14.2 The four fingerprint pattern types

Classifying fingerprints has allowed them to be stored in a filing system and subsequently retrieved for comparison. Fingerprints are still the primary method for the identification of criminals. Modern developments include:

- improved detection techniques, which include the use of lasers and luminescence
- improved storage, searching, retrieval and matching of prints using computers, known as the **automated fingerprint identification system** (**AFIS**).

Detection of fingerprints

The most commonly used method of detecting fingerprints is to dust the print using a fine powder that sticks to the traces of oil and sweat in the print. There are a number of powders suitable for hard and/or non-absorbent surfaces:

- Aluminium dust is suitable on dark and mirrored surfaces, as it is grey and highly visible.
- Carbon black is excellent for white surfaces.
- Luminescent powders can also be used, because they fluoresce under ultraviolet light and show up the print.

Dusting is not always a suitable method for detecting fingerprints. It is not suitable for porous surfaces or surfaces like paper or cloth. Here the forensic scientist uses chemical treatments. This involves treating the sample with iodine vapour or superglue vapour to show up the prints.

Getting fingerprints from powder

Several surfaces may be used to obtain prints, for example, black paper, glossy paper, a flat plastic surface, a white tile or a crucible lid. Talcum powder can be used for dark surfaces, while carbon powder is used for lighter surfaces. The following shows the method that can be used.

- Gently press your finger on one of the surfaces so that a good fingerprint is made.
- Sprinkle some powder over the fingerprint: use carbon powder for a print on a light surface and talcum powder for one on a dark surface.
- Now use a soft paintbrush to gently rub off the excess powder. Your fingerprint should now be visible.
- Place a piece of sticky tape over the fingerprint. Lift off the tape. If the print was on a dark surface, stick the tape onto a dark surface. If it was on a light surface, stick it on a light surface. At this stage you should have a copy of your fingerprint.
- Carry out the same procedure for all the different surfaces.
- From the prints, identify what type of fingerprint you have. Gather information from students in your class and compare the different types of fingerprints.

ACTIVITY

Present arguments for and against the idea that all suspects in a crime should have to provide their fingerprints to the police to assist in solving the case.

Or:

Present your ideas as to whether you think it is right that there should be national and international files that contain everyone's fingerprints.

Fingerprints and the law

As fingerprints are so variable, there are no two people with the same prints. Thus fingerprints are unique to an individual. If fingerprints obtained at the scene of a crime are the same as those of a suspect, then it is certain that the suspect was there. It is important to ensure that the suspect's fingerprints and the prints found at the scene of the crime are identical. In Court, the police will get the opinion of an expert witness, and use a 16-point standard to ensure complete matching of the fingerprints. There can then be no question of another person having made the print. The odds against being incorrect when 16 similar features are compared for two fingerprints is 4000 000 000 to 1.

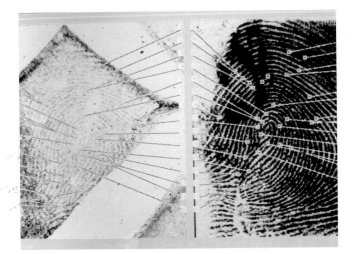

Figure 14.3 The points indicated show that these two fingerprints were made by the same finger

The different law enforcement agencies around the world (for example, the Metropolitan Police or the FBI) have built up vast files of fingerprints. When a fingerprint has been found at the scene of a crime, it is classified. Similar fingerprints are taken from the files and compared with the one from the scene of the crime. A suspect may be identified from this comparison.

The comparison of fingerprints was initially done manually. Now it is all done by computer technology (Figure 14.4). Using the AFIS equipment, a photograph of the fingerprint from the scene of the crime is scanned in. This

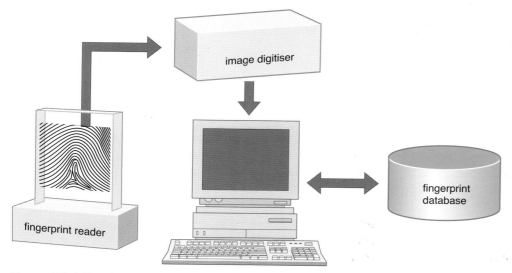

Figure 14.4 The AFIS computerised fingerprint system

print is then compared with the database of prints. A list of suspects and their prints are drawn up. An expert then makes the final decision as to whether the prints match or not.

There is little doubt that this computer technology has revolutionised the criminal investigative method of fingerprinting. Computers can compare thousands of fingerprints in a second. This has resulted in catching criminals much faster than when it was done manually. When it was first brought out, it helped Los Angeles police to bring to justice the multiple killer known as the Nightstalker.

---

1 a Name the four types of fingerprints.
   b Give the names of the three common powders used to detect fingerprints.
   c Explain how fingerprints can be used to help solve a crime.

It pays to be careful

It is very important that individuals and communities take responsibility for crime prevention in their areas. There are a number of simple things that people can do to reduce crime in their area. For example, while on holidays, do not leave behind the tell-tale signs of an empty house:

- Ensure that there are no unlocked gates or doors.
- Cancel all the newspapers and milk.
- Check that no windows have been left open.
- Get a friend to check your house each day and store any mail that arrives.

Additionally it is important to be observant in our communities. If we see someone acting suspiciously around a house or a car, then we should contact the owner or the police. This could mean a simple phone call to the owner to make them aware of what is happening. If the owner is away, then it would be best to give the police a call to have them check it out. Everyone would agree that taking a responsibility for crime prevention is extremely important if we want to make our communities safer places to live in. Some communities that have a 'Home Watch' or 'Neighbourhood Watch' can obtain lower-cost house insurance. The insurance companies recognise that when people are involved in crime prevention then it is likely to have a major effect on reducing crime.

ACTIVITY

Write to the Crime Prevention Officer in your area, asking for advice on what young people can do to help reduce crime in the local community. You could put forward your own ideas.

2 List four different ways that you could protect your home while away on holiday.

Protecting against counterfeit products

In recent years the problem of counterfeit goods has dramatically increased. However, forensic scientists have developed technologies that are helping to reduce these problems. One classic example of counterfeit is that of bank notes. Currently there are about 16 billion pounds worth of bank notes issued by the Bank of England and banks in Northern Ireland and Scotland.

The different banks design and print their own bank notes or else use security printers. The lifetime of a bank note is generally around two years. In designing bank notes, there are several ways of protecting the new notes against counterfeit. These include:

- quality of the paper
- watermarks
- windowed metal strip
- bar coding
- holograms.

Paper bank notes are now printed on paper that is of high quality and is impossible to economically mass produce.

Ultraviolet (UV) light is one method of testing for counterfeit bank notes (Figure 14.5). The UV light tests the paper in the bank note. If it is a genuine note, then the cotton paper on which the note is printed will not itself fluoresce (that is, it is UV-dull), but various security features will. The paper that counterfeiters use will contain 'brightening agents' and these give the paper a characteristic glow.

Figure 14.5 A 50 euro note viewed under UV

Using chromatography to overcome forgery

An example of personal forgery is when someone writes a signature on a cheque which is not their own. It could also be where someone changes the figures or wording on a cheque or on another document. In many instances this is so well done that a forensic scientist is called in to provide evidence that a forgery has been committed. For example, the forensic scientist can show that the word 'seven' on a cheque has been changed to 'seventy' and the number '7' has been changed to '70'. To do this, the forensic scientist analyses the inks that appear on the cheque. They can tell it is a forgery when the inks on the cheque are different for different parts of the cheque.

To show that the inks are different, forensic scientists use the separation technique of **chromatography**. As discussed in Chapter 9, chromatography is a way of separating the different coloured dyes in ink. As different inks will contain different dyes, it is easy for the forensic scientist to tell when more than one pen has been used to write a cheque. When the ink in the print is analysed, it will be seen that the different inks are made up of different coloured dyes.

Using chromatography to separate the dyes in different black inks

The following shows the method that can be used (Figure 14.6).

- Take a piece of rectangular chromatography paper.
- Using a pencil, draw a base line in pencil 3 cm from the bottom of the paper.
- Using one of two different black inks, make a small spot on the base line.
- Make another small spot with the other black ink.
- Add a small amount of solvent to the beaker.
- Place the chromatogram in the beaker and allow it to develop.
- Note down how many dyes are in each and if the distance they move is the same.
- Explain why the two inks are different.

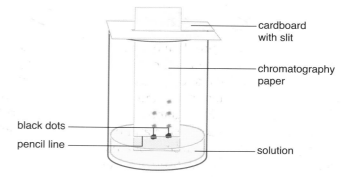

Figure 14.6 Paper chromatography can distinguish between two black inks

3 a How can paper chromatography be used to help solve crimes? Give an example.
  b How is UV light used to detect counterfeit bank notes?

Detecting crime through fibres

Most people are aware of the wide range of fibres used in the clothing industry today. When a crime is committed, it is most likely that the criminal will leave traces of hair or clothing fibre at the scene of the crime. Forensic scientists use these clothing fibres and hair to help prove who carried out the crime. When the police have a clear suspect for a crime, they will examine the hair and the clothing of that suspect. Clothing that matches the description given by any witnesses will be sent for examination to the

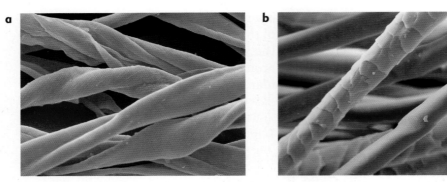

Figure 14.7 How various fibres look under a scanning electron microscope: **a** cotton, and **b** wool (pale) mixed with a synthetic fibre (red)

forensic science laboratories. Loose fibres are obtained from the suspect's clothing using strips of sticky tape. The fibres are then examined under the microscope and compared with those found at the scene of the crime. Figure 14.7 shows what some different fibres look like under a very high-power microscope.

Looking at fibres

You can look at a number of known natural and synthetic fibres under a microscope. You can then identify unknown fibres. It is important to note the colour, twist and weave pattern of each fibre. The following shows the method that can be used.

- Set up the microscope with good illumination.
- Take a few fibres from each known fabric and tape them onto microscope slides. Ensure that you have labelled each sample.
- Carefully examine each fibre sample in turn (use low magnification). Make notes about each sample, include a sketch of each sample.
- Using the information you have gained about the known fibres, try to identify the unknown samples.
- Give reasons for the conclusions you reach about the unknown fibres.

ACTIVITY

A local businessman in your town arrived home from work one evening with a large sum of money in his briefcase. As he went in the back door, he was suddenly grabbed and assaulted by a robber. Determined not to have his money stolen, he struggled with the robber. Unfortunately he was overcome and the robber escaped with the money. As a forensic scientist, how would you suggest that evidence could be gathered to help identify the person who committed the crime?

Using flame colours to identify metal ions

Forensic scientists use their knowledge of colour chemistry to identify a number of unknown metal ions present in certain substances found at the scene of a crime. Two everyday examples of colour chemistry that we are familiar with are street lamps and fireworks. Both of these examples contain sodium compounds, and it is the sodium ion that produces the unique orange–yellow colour when heated. Table 14.1 shows that different metal ions produce different colours when heated in a Bunsen flame.

Table 14.1 Flame colours produced by metal ions

Metal ion	Flame colour
barium	light green
calcium	brick red
copper	blue–green
lead	blue–white
potassium	lilac
sodium	orange–yellow

Flame tests

The flame tests for known metal salts can be examined and recorded, and unknown metal ions identified by comparison. The following shows the method that can be used.

- Check that the flame test rod is clean. Do this by placing the flame test rod in the hottest part of the Bunsen burner flame (Figure 14.8). If clean, there should be no change in the colour of the flame when the rod is placed in the flame. If the flame test rod is not clean, dip it into concentrated hydrochloric acid (**take care!**), and then heat it in the Bunsen burner flame. This is repeated until there is no change in the colour of the flame.
- Next dip the flame test rod into a known metal salt solution and then place it in the hot Bunsen burner flame. Note the colour of the flame and record it in a table. Clean the flame test rod as before and repeat for other known test samples.
- Now carry out flame tests on the unknown sample. Identify the unknown metal ion from the characteristic flame colour (see Table 14.1).

In a forensic science laboratory unknown metal ions are detected by a technique known as emission spectroscopy.

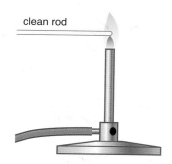

clean rod

Figure 14.8 Flame test

Genetic fingerprinting

Cells are the building blocks for all living things. Your body is made up of cells. Not all cells are the same. Cells from different parts of the body have different functions. For example, nerve cells are very different from blood cells. From the study of cells, you will remember that all cells contain a nucleus. In the nucleus there is DNA, which is the chemical molecule that carries the genetic information on the genes.

Over the last 15 years a successful method for looking at DNA has been developed. Just like a person's fingerprint, each individual's DNA is unique to that person. Figure 14.9 shows how the DNA 'fingerprints' for different people are all different, although some bands in the pattern are shared by members of a family. Only identical twins can have exactly the same DNA sequence.

The technique (see Figure 14.10 on the next page) requires only very small samples and can be carried out on a single cell. Additionally, the cell can come from any part of a person, for example, blood, hair, skin or semen. The extracted DNA fragments are placed on a gel. They are separated by passing an electric current through the gel, a process known as **electrophoresis**. As the DNA fragments have a negative charge, they will move towards the positively charged electrode at the end of the gel. The lighter and shorter DNA fragments travel faster and further than the longer and heavier fragments. This separates the DNA fragments according to their size. The DNA band pattern is then transferred to a nylon membrane, and a DNA fingerprint is produced.

When a crime has taken place, the forensic scientist takes samples from the suspects and compares the DNA pattern of these to DNA samples found at the scene of the crime (Figure 14.11). DNA or genetic fingerprinting has been a really successful method in solving crime. One speck of blood or one hair can provide the evidence that police require.

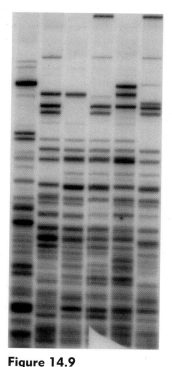

Figure 14.9
DNA fingerprints from a mother (lane 2), her children (lanes 3–6) and an unrelated person (lane 1)

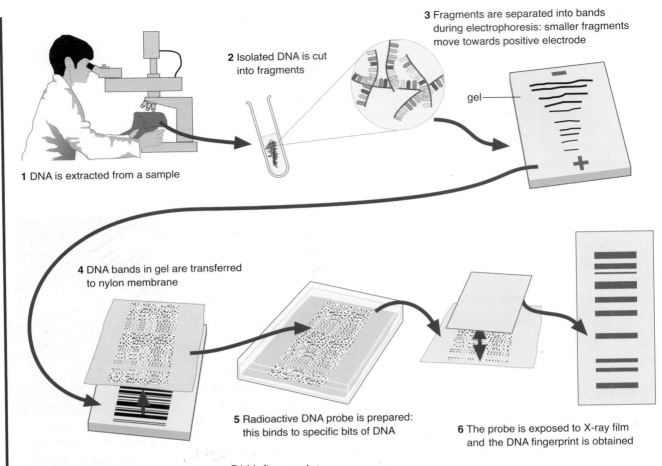

3 Fragments are separated into bands during electrophoresis: smaller fragments move towards positive electrode

2 Isolated DNA is cut into fragments

gel

1 DNA is extracted from a sample

4 DNA bands in gel are transferred to nylon membrane

5 Radioactive DNA probe is prepared: this binds to specific bits of DNA

6 The probe is exposed to X-ray film and the DNA fingerprint is obtained

Figure 14.10 The steps in getting a DNA fingerprint

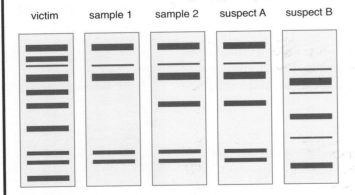

victim   sample 1   sample 2   suspect A   suspect B

Figure 14.11 The forensic scientist can identify the guilty person from the DNA fingerprint match

Alcohol and drink driving

Small amounts of alcohol can affect people's judgement and hence their ability to drive. So it is important that people do not drive after consuming alcoholic drinks. Each week we read about drivers who are charged with drunken driving, and also how these drivers are involved in fatal road accidents. When a person is caught by the police for drinking alcohol before driving, that person will normally be disqualified from driving for a period of time. He or she may have to pay a fine for their offence and, if serious enough, may even go to prison. Around 30% of accidents on the road are caused by alcohol, and many of these are by young drivers. The legal limit for driving a car is 80 milligrams of alcohol per 100 cubic centimetres of blood (80 mg/100 cm^3).

Drinking in excess is also harmful to our health. It can cause serious illness such as heart disease (see page 11), liver damage, brain damage and alcoholism (addiction). Experts agree that, to reduce health problems and the adverse social effects caused by alcohol, people should stick to safe drinking limits, and in particular avoid 'binge drinking' (see page 74).

Testing for alcohol

When alcoholic drink is consumed, the alcohol from the drink is absorbed from the stomach and intestines into the blood. The bloodstream carries it around all parts of the body, including the brain. It has an effect on the nervous system of the body, producing effects that are bad for safe driving. Alcohol in the blood is detected using a technique that involves a chemical reaction between an orange crystalline solid called potassium dichromate and exhaled air from the suspected offender. If the person has been drinking alcohol, the crystals turn green. The greater the amount of alcohol consumed, then the more crystals will turn green. A more accurate determination of the level of alcohol can be made using an infrared (IR) spectroscopic method, based on absorption of infrared radiation by alcohol molecules. The level of infrared absorption indicates the level of alcohol.

Alcohol is not the only drug that affects motorists. Other illegal ones such as LSD produce mental effects and sometimes result in permanent personality changes. Marijuana can cause a user to be apathetic and sluggish. Young people, especially, do not understand the dangers of driving with alcohol or any illegal drug. At present there is much discussion on a total ban on alcohol while driving.

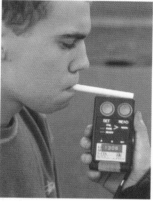

Figure 14.12 A driver undergoing a breathalyser test to check for alcohol consumption

ACTIVITY

Have a class debate, putting forward the arguments for and against a complete ban on the consumption of alcohol before driving.

ACTIVITY

Describe how you could make a breathalyser in the laboratory to test for alcohol using potassium dichromate crystals.

websites

www.innocent.org.uk/misc/fingerprints.html
good site about the reliability of fingerprints

http://en.wikipedia.org/wiki/DNA_fingerprinting
information on genetic fingerprinting

www.howstuffworks.com/breathalyzer
explains the test for alcohol

Questions

1 When a crime is committed police look for fingerprints at the scene of the crime.

  a Name the **four** types of common fingerprints. *(4 marks)*

  b Why are fingerprints good evidence for police? *(1 mark)*

  c What two people have the same fingerprints? *(1 mark)*

  d Why do some criminals deliberately injure their fingertips? *(1 mark)*

  e Give **three** ways that forensic scientists can obtain fingerprints on hard or non-absorbent surfaces. *(3 marks)*

  f When are chemical treatments used to obtain fingerprints? *(1 mark)*

2 **a** What is the '16-point standard' in fingerprinting? *(1 mark)*

  b Why has the automated fingerprinting system, AFIS, revolutionised fingerprinting? *(2 marks)*

3 Counterfeiting of bank notes has risen dramatically in the last 16 years.

  a Give **three** ways in which bank notes are protected from counterfeiting. *(3 marks)*

  b What was the main reason for the increase in counterfeiting of bank notes in 1989? *(1 mark)*

  c Outline **one** method for testing for counterfeit bank notes. *(1 mark)*

4 **a** What is chromatography? *(2 marks)*

  b Explain how you could use chromatography to distinguish between two different black inks to check out which was used in a forged cheque. Give clearly labelled diagrams to show the different steps carried out in your method. *(5 marks)*

  c Give another example where chromatography could be used to solve a case involving personal forgery? *(1 mark)*

5 **a** Describe **two** types of crime in which it would be common for hair and fibres to be left at the scene of the crime. *(2 marks)*

  b Why would police remove the contents of a suspect's vacuum cleaner for forensic examination? *(1 mark)*

  c Give **two** reasons why genetic fingerprinting has been so successful in solving crime. *(2 marks)*

6 Genetic or DNA fingerprinting has been a really successful method in helping police to resolve crime.

  a **i** What do you understand by the term 'genetic or DNA fingerprinting'? *(2 marks)*

    ii What is the name of the process used in this technique to separate the different fragments of DNA in a blood sample? *(1 mark)*

    iii What **two** properties of the DNA fragments make it possible to separate them? *(1 mark)*

  b Use your understanding of genetic fingerprinting to analyse the following DNA fingerprints of a blood sample with several suspects.

    i Determine who committed the crime. *(1 mark)*

    ii Give a reason for your answer. *(1 mark)*

CCEA GCSE Science: Single Award (Modular)
Specimen Paper (Higher Tier) 2006

Chapter 15
Electricity

By the end of this chapter you should know and understand:

➤ How to draw circuit diagrams using the appropriate circuit symbols
➤ How to use ammeters and voltmeters in simple series and parallel circuits
➤ How to apply the rules for currents and voltages in circuits
➤ The way that variable resistors control current
➤ The heating effect of a current
➤ How to apply the formula

$$power = voltage \times current$$

to choose the correct size of fuse
➤ The use of meter readings to calculate the cost of using appliances
➤ The location of Northern Ireland's power stations and the types of fossil fuel used
➤ The energy transfers that take place within power stations
➤ The advantages and disadvantages of using renewable energy resources for generating electricity and the placing of such generators
➤ The concerns of using nuclear power including disposal and decommissioning

Electrical circuits

An electric cell (commonly called a battery) can make electrons move, but only if there is a **conductor** between its two terminals making a **complete circuit**. Inside the cell chemical reactions take place, which push electrons out from the negative terminal and pull electrons in at the positive terminal. The cell is therefore a **source of electrical energy**.

In the 19th century there was an agreement (a 'convention') among physicists that current flowed from the positive terminal of a battery to the negative terminal. It was not until the **structure of the atom** was understood in the first part of the 20th century that physicists realised what was really happening when current flowed in a circuit. Negatively charged **electrons** were being injected into the circuit from the negative terminal of the battery and flowed towards the positive terminal, where they were removed from the circuit. For more information about atomic structure, see Chapter 11.

Although the initial idea about current flow was wrong, the convention of current flowing from positive to negative remained. Today we say that:

conventional current flows from positive to negative

electrons flow from negative to positive

How can we tell which materials are conductors and which are insulators (non-conductors)? The easiest way is to build a **continuity tester** like the one shown in Figure 15.1. If the material between the crocodile clips is a conductor, the lamp will light up. If it is an insulator, the lamp will stay off. You should try to get some practice setting up apparatus like this.

You need to know the most common conductors and insulators (see Table 15.1). They are easy to remember:

- **all the metals and graphite are conductors**
- **almost everything else is an insulator**.

Circuit diagrams and symbols

An electrical circuit is often represented by a circuit diagram, with symbols for the components connected in the circuit. Clearly drawn circuit diagrams are easy to understand and are universally understood. Table 15.2 shows the most commonly used symbols.

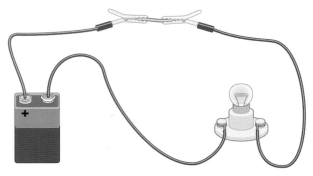

Figure 15.1 A continuity tester

Table 15.1 Some common conductors and insulators

Conductors	Insulators
aluminium	air
brass	cork
graphite (pencil 'lead')	glass
copper	plastic
iron	rubber
steel	wood

Table 15.2 Circuit symbols

Component	Circuit symbol	Function of component
cell	—┤├—	Supplies electrical energy. (A single cell is often wrongly called a battery: strictly a battery is two or more joined together
battery	—┤├··┤├—	Supplies electrical energy. A battery is more than one cell joined together
DC supply	—○ ○— (+ −)	Supplies electrical energy. DC = direct current, always flowing in one direction. A battery provides DC
AC supply	—○~○—	Supplies electrical energy. AC = alternating current, continually changing direction. The mains supply is AC
fuse	—▭—	A safety device that 'blows' (melts) if the current flowing through it exceeds a specified value
heater	—▭▭▭▭—	Converts electrical energy to heat
motor	—(M)—	Converts electrical energy to kinetic energy (motion)
voltmeter	—(V)—	Used to measure voltage
ammeter	—(A)—	Used to measure current
ohmmeter	—(Ω)—	Used to measure resistance
resistor	—▭—	Restricts the flow of current in a circuit, for example to limit the current flowing through a component
variable resistor (rheostat)	—▭⟋—	Used to control current, for example to adjust lamp brightness or motor speed
buzzer	—◁—	Converts electrical energy to sound
lamp	—⊗—	Converts electrical energy to light
on–off switch	—○╱○—	Allows current to flow only when it is in the closed (on) position

Simple circuits

Two things are important for a component (such as a lamp) to work:

- there must be **a complete circuit**
- there must be **no short circuit**.

To check for a complete circuit, follow a wire coming out of the positive terminal of battery with your finger. You should be able to go:

- out of the positive battery terminal
- through the lamp (or other component)
- back to the negative battery terminal.

To check for a short circuit, see if you can find a way from one terminal of the battery to the other *without* passing through the lamp (or other component). If you can, you have a short circuit and the lamp will not light.

We can describe what happens to the lamps in Figure 15.2 with a **truth table** – see Table 15.3.

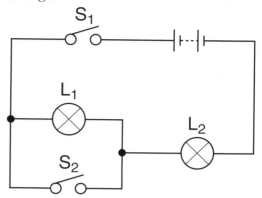

Figure 15.2 A simple circuit with lamps

Table 15.3 Example of a truth table

| State of switches | | State of lamps | | |
S_1	S_2	L_1	L_2	Reason
open	open	OFF	OFF	S_1 open means incomplete circuit
open	closed	OFF	OFF	S_1 open means incomplete circuit
closed	open	ON	ON	There is a complete circuit, two lamps in series, no short circuit
closed	closed	OFF	ON	S_2 closed **short circuits** lamp L_1. L_2 is now very bright as it is the only lamp taking a current

Short circuits are **potentially very dangerous**. Shorting out lamp L_1, for example, allows twice as much current to flow through lamp L_2. With batteries and lamps, the lamp may 'blow'. But with mains voltages and heating elements, a short circuit can make the current so large as to cause a fire.

Measuring current

The simple series circuit shown in Figure 15.3a is represented in Figure 15.3b as a circuit diagram using the symbols for the components.

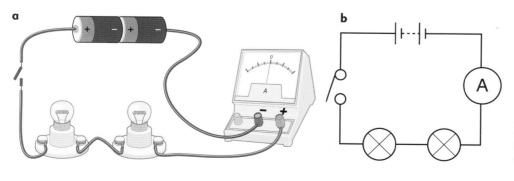

Figure 15.3 A simple series circuit including an ammeter

Note that, in a series circuit like that in Figure 15.3, if one lamp blows, there is no longer a complete circuit so the other lamp(s) will also go out.

To measure the current in a circuit we must place the ammeter **in series** at the point where we want to find the current.

The ammeter must be connected the right way round. The red (+) terminal must be on the same side as the positive (+) terminal of the battery. If an analogue meter is connected the wrong way round the mechanism may be broken. Digital meters are much more robust. If a digital meter is connected incorrectly the reading is simply a negative value.

Figure 15.4 An analogue ammeter (left) and a digital ammeter (right)

Current in parallel circuits

In a parallel circuit, the current always splits and then combines again before it goes back into the battery. Suppose that in the circuit of Figure 15.5 both switches are closed and the current flowing at X is 0.4 A. Then the current reading on ammeter A_1 is 0.4 A. But what happens at junction Y?

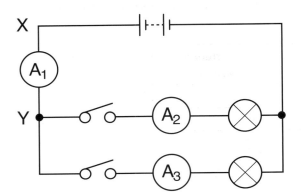

Figure 15.5 A simple parallel circuit with ammeters

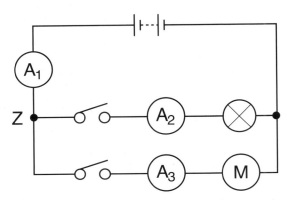

Figure 15.6 A parallel circuit with a lamp and a motor

If the two lamps in Figure 15.5 are identical, then the current splits equally at Y. So, 0.2 A flows in ammeter A_2 and 0.2 A flows in ammeter A_3.

If one of the switches is then opened, then no current flows in that ammeter, but the current in *both* the other ammeters is 0.2 A.

In Figure 15.6, a lamp is in parallel with a motor. Suppose now the current reading on ammeter A_1 is 0.9 A. At Z the current splits, but this time it will not split equally because the parallel components are different. Some of the current (say 0.2 A) will flow though the lamp and the remainder (0.7 A) will flow through the motor.

This current splitting is summarised in Figure 15.7. The current flowing into the junction is i_1. The currents flowing out of the junction are i_2 and i_3. Then:

$$i_1 = i_2 + i_3$$

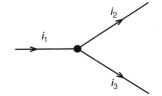

Figure 15.7 Currents at a junction

1 a Draw a circuit diagram of the circuit in Figure 15.8.

The bulbs are identical. Ammeters 2 and 3 both read 1.0 A.

   b What does ammeter 4 read?
   c What does ammeter 1 read?

Figure 15.8

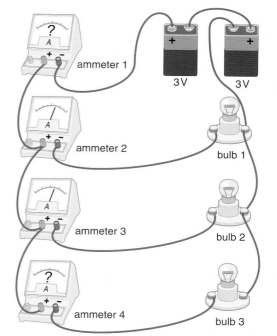

ammeter 1

3 V   3 V

ammeter 2   bulb 1

ammeter 3   bulb 2

ammeter 4   bulb 3

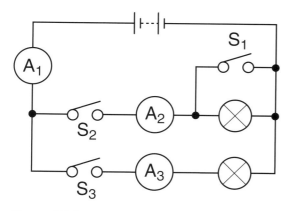

Figure 15.9

2 Copy and complete the table below to show the current reading on each ammeter in Figure 15.9 for the various states of the three switches. The lamps are identical.

Position of switches			Current in A_1 in A	Current in A_2 in A	Current in A_2 in A
S_1	S_2	S_3			
open	open	open		0	
open	closed	closed			0.5
open	closed	open			
open	open	closed			

Measuring voltage

To measure voltage, we must connect a voltmeter **in parallel** with the component we are interested in.

Voltage in series circuits

In a series circuit, the voltages across different components will be different, but **the sum of the voltages will always be equal to the battery voltage**. Look at Figure 15.10 on the next page. In this series circuit:

$$\begin{array}{ccccccc}
\text{voltage} & = & \text{voltage} & + & \text{voltage} & + & \text{voltage} \\
\text{across battery} & & \text{across resistor} & & \text{across motor} & & \text{across lamp} \\
V_b & & V_1 & & V_2 & & V_3
\end{array}$$

The voltage across individual components will be the same only if those components are identical.

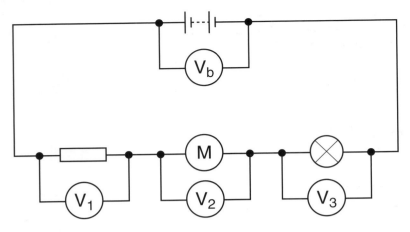

Figure 15.10 A series circuit with voltmeters

Problem
Suppose that in the circuit of Figure 15.11 the voltage across the battery, V_b, is 12 V and the voltage across the lamp, V_3, is 2 V. If the motors are identical, calculate V_1 and V_2.

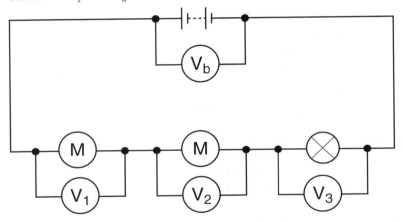

Figure 15.11

Solution

$$V_b = V_1 + V_2 + V_3$$

so substituting gives

$$12 = V_1 + V_2 + 2$$
$$V_1 + V_2 = 10$$

and, since the motors are identical,

$$V_1 = V_2 = \textbf{5 volts}$$

Voltage in parallel circuits
In parallel circuits, **the voltages across the components will always be the same**, whether the components are identical or different.

In the circuit of Figure 15.12, the resistor, motor and lamp are all in parallel across the battery. All four voltmeters will give the same reading. If the battery voltage was 12 volts, all four voltmeters would read 12 V.

Remember, however, that the current through each device would, in general, be different.

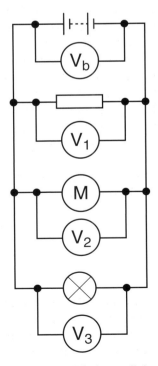

Figure 15.12 A parallel circuit with voltmeters

3 Four identical lamps are placed in series across a 24 volt battery (Figure 15.13). What voltage would be shown on each of the three voltmeters?

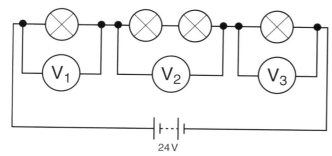

Figure 15.13

4 a How can four identical 1.5 V cells be arranged to give a 6 V battery?
  b Suggest what has happened if Maya arranges four such 1.5 V cells but finds the battery voltage is only 3 V.

Resistance

We already know that two lamps in series will be dimmer than one lamp on its own. This is because with two (identical) lamps we get half the current that we do with one lamp. In other words, it is twice as hard for the electrons to pass through two lamps as one.

Physicists call this property of the lamp filament **resistance**. Two lamps offer twice the electrical resistance of a single lamp.

Whenever a current flows through a resistance there is a heating effect. The heating occurs because electrons collide with the atoms as they pass along the conductor. The electrons lose some kinetic (movement) energy to the vibrating atoms. The faster vibrations of the atoms mean that the wire's temperature rises.

Usually the heating effect in electrical wires is a nuisance: the heat produced is wasted energy. Sometimes it can be a serious problem. Computer manufacturers, for example, go to great lengths to ensure that the heat produced does not cause damage to valuable computer chips. However, sometimes the heating effect is exactly what is needed – such as in filament lamps, electric fires, toasters, ovens and hairdryers.

How do we measure resistance?

Resistance is defined by the equation:

$$\text{resistance of any device (in ohms)} = \frac{\text{voltage across device (in volts)}}{\text{current through device (in amps)}}$$

$$R \text{ (in } \Omega) = \frac{V \text{ (in V)}}{I \text{ (in A)}}$$

To measure the resistance of a component, we pass various values of current through it and measure the corresponding voltage across it. This is referred to as the ammeter–voltmeter method and is illustrated in Figure 15.14a. The **variable resistor** is used to control the current through the component under test. The bigger the resistance of the variable resistor, the smaller will be the current in the component under test.

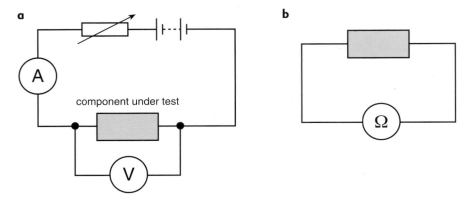

Figure 15.14 Measuring resistance: **a** ammeter–voltmeter method, and **b** ohmmeter method

However, it is easier to use a device called an **ohmmeter**, connected directly across the ends of the device (Figure 15.14b). This measures the resistance directly.

Table 15.4 shows typical results using the ammeter–voltmeter method for a metal wire at constant temperature. Notice that, whatever the voltage, the resistance remains the same.

Table 15.4 Current and voltage readings for a metal wire

Current I in A	Voltage V in V	Ratio of V/I in Ω
0.25	1	0.25
0.50	2	0.25
0.75	3	0.25
1.00	4	0.25

ACTIVITY

Connect a datalogging ammeter in series with a torch bulb, a rheostat and a 6 V power supply. Connect a datalogging voltmeter across the torch bulb. Slowly decrease the resistance of the rheostat and capture corresponding values of voltage and current.

Transfer (or record) the captured data to a spreadsheet and use the graphing software to plot the graph of voltage against current. Examine the curve and suggest what has become of the bulb's resistance with increasing current.

Why do some wires have a large resistance and others have a small resistance?

It turns out that the resistance of a wire is:

- directly proportional to its length
- inversely proportional to its cross-section area.

This means that if we double the length of a wire, we also double its resistance. If we treble its length, we treble its resistance, and so on. On the other hand, if we double the cross-section area, we *halve* the resistance. If we treble the cross-section area, the resistance is reduced to one-third of its previous value, and so on.

The easiest way to investigate these ideas is with an ohmmeter. To keep the tests fair we must use the same material at all times. Copper is too good a conductor – its resistance would be too small to measure accurately. For these purposes, it is best to use wires made of an alloy of nickel and chromium, called **nichrome** wire.

The first investigation involves using an ohmmeter to measure the resistance of different lengths of nichrome wire of the same cross-section area. In the second investigation the resistances of the same lengths of nichrome wire with different cross-section areas are measured. Table 15.5 shows typical results.

Table 15.5 Typical experimental results

| Investigation 1 (constant area) | | Investigation 2 (constant length) | |
Length of wire in cm	Resistance in Ω	Area of cross section in mm^2	Resistance in Ω
25	0.5	0.02	6.0
50	1.0	0.04	3.0
75	1.5	0.06	2.0
100	2.0	0.08	1.5

5 a From the results of Investigation 1 in Table 15.5, plot the graph of resistance against length. You should obtain a straight line through the origin, showing that resistance is directly proportional to length.

b From the results of Investigation 2, plot the graph of resistance against 1/area. You should obtain a straight line through the origin, showing that resistance is inversely proportional to cross-section area.

How a wire-wound variable resistor (rheostat) works

We can now understand how a wire-wound variable resistor controls the amount of current in an electrical circuit. A diagram of such a rheostat is shown in Figure 15.15.

As the slider moves to the right, the length of resistance wire in the circuit increases. This increases the resistance of the circuit containing the rheostat and so reduces the amount of current flowing.

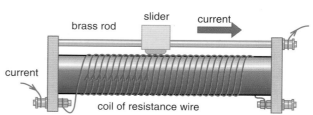

Figure 15.15 A rheostat

How heating elements work

For heating elements, such as in a hairdryer, a kettle or an iron, we need a wire of **high resistance**. To achieve this we need the wire to be **long and thin**. It cannot be too thin or it will melt when it becomes hot. We therefore have to make a compromise – the wire must be thin enough to keep the resistance high, but not too thin or it will melt. It must be long enough to have a high resistance, but short enough to fit into the container holding it.

The wire filament in an ordinary bulb is extremely thin. It is made of a very high melting-point metal – tungsten – so that it does not melt even when white-hot. But why does it not burn out? In this case the reason is that the gas surrounding the filament is so unreactive. Often, argon gas is used because it is totally inert. This means it is so unreactive that it does not allow the wire to burn, even though the wire becomes white-hot. If you look at an unlit clear glass bulb you can see that the filament is very thin and is coiled – this is because it is so very long. See Figure 15.16.

Electrical safety

Voltages of 50 V and currents as low as 50 mA may be fatal so electrical safety is vitally important.

The three-pin plug

Figure 15.16
A filament bulb

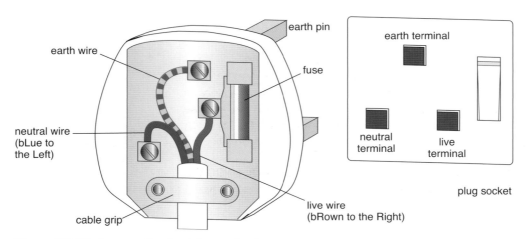

Figure 15.17 A correctly wired three-pin plug

To wire a three-pin plug:

- Hold the three-core cable tightly with the cord grip.
- The wire with the blue insulation is the neutral wire; connect this to the left-hand pin.
- The brown insulated wire is the live wire; connect this to the right-hand pin. This pin has a fuse attached because it is connected to the live wire.
- The wire with the yellow and green insulation is the earth wire; connect this to the top pin.
- Each of these wires should be wrapped around its securing screw so that it is tightened as the screw tightens.

Each pin in the plug fits into a corresponding hole in the socket. The earth pin is longer than the others so that it goes into the socket first and pushes aside safety covers which cover the rear of the neutral and live holes in the socket.

If an appliance becomes live, a current flows through the earth wire, and from the socket earth connection to the earth via a water pipe. During the process the **fuse** in the plug will blow. Before it is replaced, the appliance should be checked by a qualified electrician.

Fuses

Fuses are safety devices. They are short lengths of resistance wire, which burn out when the current flowing is too high. In the UK the most common fuses used in plugs are rated at 1 A, 2 A, 3 A, 5 A and 13 A.

We can find out the maximum safe current through an appliance from looking at the rating plate, which is usually found as a label at the back. We can calculate the maximum current from the power rating, using the equation:

$$\text{current (in amps)} = \frac{\text{power (in watts)}}{\text{voltage (in volts)}}$$

$$I \text{ (in A)} = \frac{P \text{ (in W)}}{V \text{ (in V)}}$$

Problem

What fuse should be used in the plug of a toaster with a power rating of 1000 W running off a 220 volt mains supply?

Solution

$$\text{Current} = \frac{\text{power}}{\text{voltage}} = \frac{1000}{220} = 4.55 \text{ A}$$

A 13 A fuse would allow a dangerously high current to flow through the toaster and still not blow. A fuse rated 4 A or less would blow immediately the toaster was switched on and the normal current of 4.55 A started to flow. So we need the fuse *just above* the maximum expected current of 4.55 A. In this case we should select a **5 A fuse**.

> 6   The power of a CD player is 100 W and it is designed to be used with a 220 V mains supply. Which of the following fuses would you put in the plug of this CD player?
> 1 A,   2 A,   3 A,   5 A,   13 A

Other safety features

The **earth wire** prevents serious shock to the user, should a fault develop in an appliance. Suppose a fault occurs in an electric fire and the element comes into contact with the outer metal casing. The casing will be live and if someone were to touch it they would get a possibly fatal electric shock as the current rushed through their body to the earth. The earth connection prevents this. It

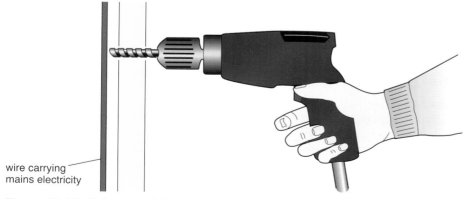

wire carrying
mains electricity

Figure 15.18 If the user drills through the electric cable in the wall, serious shock could result if the drill had no earth connection or double insulation

offers a low resistance route of escape for the current to the earth, by a wire rather than through a human body. The large current would soon blow the fuse. Any appliance with metal outer parts could become live in this way.

In fact many hand-held appliances such as electric drills and hairdryers are often **double insulated**. You can recognise this from the symbol on the casing (see Figure 15.19). If you opened the plug for such a product, you would notice immediately that there was no earth wire. Instead, all metal parts of the appliance are enclosed in an insulating plastic case so that no live part can ever come in contact with the user and cause an electric shock.

Double insulation is almost always used with appliances that have no earth connection point because the case or handle is made entirely of plastic. The symbol for double insulation is shown opposite.

Fuses, similar to those in plugs but of thicker wire, used to be connected in house circuits to prevent overload of the circuit. But nowadays most circuits for domestic appliances are protected by **trip switches**, rather than fuses. Figure 15.20 shows a row of trip switches on a distribution board (this is close to the electricity meter, where the electricity supply enters the house); Figure 15.21 shows how they work. If the current is small, the electromagnet (current-carrying coil) is not strong enough to pull down the steel cylinder. When the current reaches a critical value, the steel cylinder is pulled into the coil of the electromagnet and the spring-loaded switch is opened. This immediately cuts off the current, making the circuit safe. The cause of the overload can then be investigated and put right before re-setting the spring-loaded switch. The important idea is that a trip switch prevents damage to equipment by cutting off the current if it becomes greater than the maximum safe current.

The disadvantage of a trip switch is that it can take a second or so to operate, so it is unsuitable for protecting the user from electric shock. This problem is overcome in a second type of circuit breaker, discussed below.

Figure 15.19 The symbol to indicate double insulation

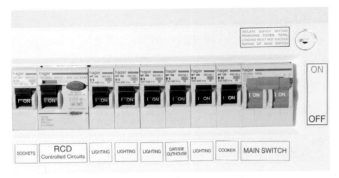

Figure 15.20 Trip switches in household circuits

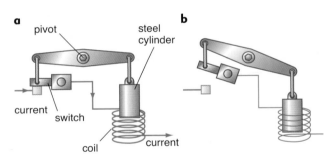

Figure 15.21 How a trip switch works
a Normal operation **b** Broken circuit

---

7 a Explain why some electrical appliances cannot be earthed.
   b What does double insulation mean and how does it protect the user?

Residual current circuit breakers

A **residual current circuit breaker** or **RCCB** is an extremely fast switch. Normally the current in the live and neutral wires is the same. If a fault develops, the current in the live and neutral wires will be different. An RCCB senses this (see Figure 15.22) and causes internal switches to open very, very quickly. This stops the current flowing and prevents any harm to the user.

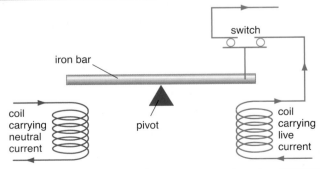

Figure 15.22 A residual current circuit breaker (RCCB)

RCCBs (sometimes called RCDs or 'residual current devices') break the current much more rapidly than fuses or trip switches and are becoming more common in people's homes. Like trip switches, they can be reset quickly and easily by pushing a button, rather than having to replace a fuse wire. However, they are much more expensive than fuse systems.

If RCCBs are not fitted, a portable plug-in RCCB should be used when operating a lawnmower or a hedge trimmer. Here the main danger is in cutting through the electric cable, which could cause death or very serious injury by electric shock. An RCCB prevents this by cutting off the current rapidly.

Figure 15.23 Using a plug-in RCCB

> 8 Explain how the RCCB shown in Figure 15.22 works.

Paying for electricity

Electricity companies bill customers for electrical energy in special units known as **kilowatt hours** (kWh), sometimes referred to as the 'unit' of electricity. One kilowatt hour is the amount of energy transferred when 1000 W is delivered for one hour. You should prove for yourself that

$$1 \text{ kWh} = 3\,600\,000 \text{ joules}$$

There are two important numbers on an electricity bill:

kWh				
5	7	1	3	9

Present meter reading

kWh				
5	5	6	5	2

Previous meter reading

Northern Electricity Board   Customer account no:

3427 364

Present meter reading	Previous meter reading	Units used	Cost per unit (incl. VAT)	£
57139	55652	1487	11.0p	163.57

The difference between the present and previous readings is the number of units used. In this particular example

$$57139 - 55652 = 1487 \text{ units (kWh)}$$

So 1487 units have been used. If the cost of a unit is known, then the cost of the electricity used may be determined.

Different appliances have different power ratings. The following two formulae are very useful in calculating the cost of using a particular appliance for a given amount of time.

Number of units used = power rating (in kilowatts) × time (in hours)

Total cost = number of units used × cost per unit

Problem 1

Calculate the cost of using a 100 W study lamp for 8 hours (assume that the price of a unit is 9p).

Solution

Power = 100 W = 0.1 kW
 Time = 8 hours

No. of units used= 0.1 × 8 = 0.8 units

Cost = 0.8 × 9

= **7.2p**

Problem 2

Calculate the cost of using a 3000 W immersion heater for 8 hours.

Solution

Power = 3000 W = 3.0 kW
 Time = 8 hours

No. of units used= 3.0 × 8 = 24 units

Cost = 24 × 9

= **£2.16**

Clearly, studying is much cheaper than having a bath!

ACTIVITY

Examine the rating plates of various household appliances (for example toaster, CD player, coffee maker, and so on) and record in a spreadsheet (or database) the appliance and its power. Use the spreadsheet to determine the relative cost of running each appliance for 1 hour continuously. Produce a bar chart to compare the cost of each.

9 A 3 kW immersion heater is switched on for 3 hours.
   a   How much electrical energy is transferred by the heater? Give your answer in kWh.
   b   The electricity costs 11p per kWh. How much does this energy cost?
   c   Suggest why the kWh is used by electricity companies as the unit for energy, rather than the joule. (Remember 1 watt is 1 joule per second.)

Reducing energy bills

The only way to reduce energy bills is to use less energy. We can do this by:

● reducing the temperature setting of the thermostat on the boiler (or on individual radiators)
● draught-proofing windows and doors
● fitting cavity wall insulation to reduce heat loss through walls
● fitting an insulation jacket on the hot water tank

- laying down mineral fibre insulation in the loft space
- blocking up unused chimneys
- drawing curtains at night to reduce heat loss through windows
- turning off electrical equipment, rather than leaving it on 'standby', when it is not being used
- replacing ordinary light bulbs with fluorescent tubes or low energy bulbs
- using only the quantity of water that is needed in the kettle
- using the washing machine and dishwasher on 'economy' cycles and only when there is a full load to wash
- using less water in the bath or having a shower instead.

Double glazing is very popular in Northern Ireland. But, although it reduces draughts and heat loss (and noise) through the windows, in financial terms it is not worth the initial cost. The savings gained are so small that, at current energy prices, it would take about 40 years to repay the cost of installation in an average house!

Making electricity

The first attempts to make electricity without the use of batteries involved moving magnets into and out of coils of wire. Figure 15.24 illustrates the idea.

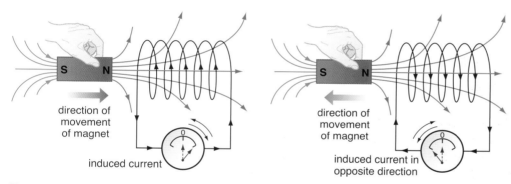

Figure 15.24 Inducing a current by relative motion of a magnetic field and a coil of wire

When the magnet moves into or out of the coil, a current is made to flow in the ammeter. We call the process **electromagnetic induction**. The size of the induced current can be increased by:

- **using a stronger magnet**
- **moving the magnet into (or out of) the coil faster**
- **using a coil with more turns of wire**.

ACTIVITY

You are provided with a strong horseshoe magnet, some connecting wire and a sensitive ammeter. How could you demonstrate that an electric current can be produced and measured using only this apparatus?

In general, we can induce an electric current in a coil when a magnet moves near it, or in a conductor when the conductor moves near a magnet.

Electromagnetic induction is put to use in a bicycle dynamo. Here the motion of the bicycle wheel makes a magnet spin inside a coil of wire; see Figure 15.25.

But the exciting question is, how do we make electricity in a power station? In this case a coil is made to move inside a magnetic field. The coil is turned by a turbine, which is usually powered by steam. Figure 15.26 shows the main steps in the process:

Step 1 Burning fuel (oil, coal or gas) produces heat

Step 2 Heat turns water to steam

Step 3 Steam turns a turbine (a gigantic fan)

Step 4 The turbine spins the generator coil

Step 5 The generator produces electricity

Step 6 The electricity is fed (via a transformer) to the National Grid

Step 7 The steam is then condensed by cool water drawn from a nearby source (such as a river, or sea water). Some of the hot water (condensed steam) is recycled to step 2

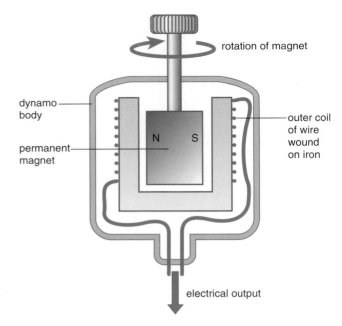

Figure 15.25 A bicycle dynamo

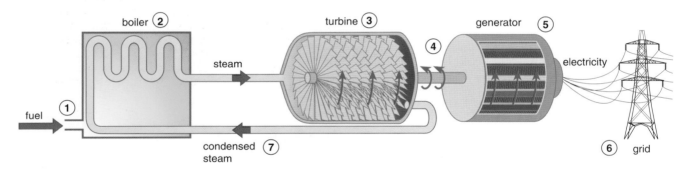

Figure 15.26 Steps in the generation of electricity

The cooling water is returned to its source at a temperature around 30 °C. Since this is a much higher temperature than the surroundings, it is an example of **thermal pollution**.

The whole process can be represented in an energy-flow diagram:

chemical energy → heat energy → kinetic energy → electrical energy

In Ireland, the steam used in power stations is produced mainly by burning **fossil fuels**: mostly coal, oil or gas. In Great Britain, **nuclear energy** from uranium is also used. In a nuclear power station, heat is generated when uranium nuclei split (fission) in a reactor. This heat is then used to produce steam (Figure 15.27) and the rest of the process is exactly the same as in a fossil fuel power station. There are major problems with both of these fuel resources, as summarised in Table 15.6.

In hydroelectric, wave or tidal power generation, the turbines are driven directly by moving water, while on a wind farm the turbine blades are driven by the kinetic energy of the moving air.

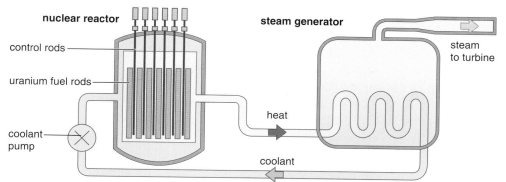

Figure 15.27
Generating steam in a nuclear power station

Table 15.6 Advantages and disadvantages of using the different energy resources to generate electricity

Energy resource	Advantages	Disadvantages	Other comments
fossil fuels – coal, oil, natural gas, lignite, turf	• Relatively cheap to start up • Moderately expensive to run • Large world reserves of fossil fuels	• All fossil fuels release carbon dioxide on burning and so contribute to greenhouse emissions • Burning coal and oil also releases sulphur dioxide gas, which causes acid rain. To combat this the sulphur can be removed from fuels before they are burned, or the sulphur dioxide can be removed from the waste gases (scrubbing) before they enter the atmosphere • All fossil fuels are non-renewable • As most fossil fuels are burned to produce steam (a slow process), the system responds only very slowly to changes in electrical demand	• Coal releases the most carbon dioxide and natural gas the least per unit of electricity produced • Removing sulphur or sulphur dioxide is very expensive and adds greatly to the cost of electricity production • Coal- and oil-fired power stations must be kept running all the time. The furnaces are seriously damaged if they cool down • Some gas-powered stations can be switched on and off as required • The process is about 30% efficient
nuclear fuels – mainly uranium	• Do not produce greenhouse gases like carbon dioxide • Do not emit gases which cause acid rain • Usually emit very few radioactive materials into the environment	• The waste products will remain dangerously radioactive for tens of thousands of years. As yet, no one has found an acceptable method to store these materials cheaply, safely and securely for such a long time • An accident could release dangerous radioactive material which would contaminate a very wide area • Nuclear fission fuels are non-renewable • As nuclear fuels are all used to produce steam (a slow process), the system responds only very slowly to changes in electrical demand	• Nuclear fuel is relatively cheap on world markets • Nuclear power station construction costs are much higher than fossil fuel stations, because of the need to take expensive safety precautions • Decommissioning – shutting down the power station at the end of its useful life, safely removing the dangerous radioactive waste and returning the site to its former state – is extremely expensive • Nuclear power stations must be kept running all the time • The process is about 30% efficient

Where do you build a power station?

In Northern Ireland, all our power stations are located on the coast. There are good reasons for this. Northern Ireland has no nuclear power stations and needs to import all its fossil fuel. It makes sense therefore to locate power stations on the coast so that imported fuels can be off-loaded directly from the large ships used to bring them here. Power stations on the coast mean it is not necessary to transport fuels long distances by road or rail. There is another advantage. Having a power station on the coast provides a ready supply of water for steam production and for cooling water.

The main Northern Ireland power stations are indicated in Table 15.7.

Table 15.7 Northern Ireland's power stations

Power station	Location	Fuel burned
Belfast West	Belfast Harbour Estate	coal
Kilroot	shore of Belfast Lough	oil/gas
Coolkeeragh	Lough Foyle	gas

Gas is the cleanest fossil fuel for electricity production. In the 1990s, gas was relatively cheap on world markets. These two facts were of significant importance when the decision was made to convert the station at Coolkeeragh from oil to gas. Belfast West is the oldest power station in Northern Ireland; this explains why it burns coal.

> **10** Find out what it means to decommission a power station, and why decommissioning a nuclear power station is so expensive.

Renewable energy resources

There is great interest today in replacing fossil fuels in electricity generation by **renewable energy resources**. Renewable energy resources are continuously supplied by nature as they are used by people. The main 'renewables' are **wind**, **waves**, **tides**, **solar energy** and **hydroelectric energy**. Why are technologies being developed to harness these energy sources?

The major waste product from burning all fossil fuels is carbon dioxide (CO_2). Research suggests that the spread of industrialisation throughout the world has increased the number of sources of CO_2 while the reduction of the tropical rainforests has decreased the total amount of photosynthesis taking place. Together these changes have caused a significant increase in the amount of CO_2 in our atmosphere, and this is still rising. This, in turn, is leading to **global warming** as a result of the **greenhouse effect**. You can read more about this on pages 82–86.

Most scientists agree that global warming is potentially disastrous for humankind. Climate patterns around the world are already changing, with greater incidences of flooding in some areas and drought and desertification in others. There is also some evidence that the polar ice caps are starting to melt, which will cause even more catastrophic changes.

What can be done to minimise these effects? One obvious task is to reduce the amount of CO_2 being produced. We could do this by replacing the fossil fuels we burn with renewable energy resources, which do not produce

CO_2. However, renewables such as wind, wave and solar energy are very **unreliable**. So we cannot depend totally on these resources, although we are likely to see much greater use of them in the future. Hydroelectric energy is a more reliable renewable resource, but it requires enough rainfall in a hilly area where a huge dam can be made. Reliable tidal energy is possible; for example a tidal barrage could be constructed across Strangford Lough – but this would be very, very expensive and it would destroy the mudflat habitat on which so many wading birds depend.

Figure 15.28 This habitat would be lost if a tidal barrage were built

websites

www.crocodile-clips.com/crocodile/physics
general-purpose website useful for teaching all aspects of physics at GCSE

www.darvill.clara.net/worksheets/ElectricalSafety2.ppt
PowerPoint slide show on electrical safety devices

www.gcsescience.com/pme9.htm
good explanation of how an RCCB works

www.howstuffworks.com
excellent general site for information on science – follow the link to ScienceStuff and then to Physical Science

http://home.howstuffworks.com/circuit-breaker3.htm
includes a good video showing a circuit breaker in operation

www.nirex.co.uk/educate/educate.htm
helpful information about everything to do with the commercial exploitation of nuclear energy and its associated problems

Questions

1   Below is part of an electricity bill.

NI ELECTRIC CO

Bill for quarter ended 31 December 2006

Meter readings

Previous	Current	Units used	Cost per unit	Total cost
12082	12832		11 pence (incl. VAT)	£

a   Copy and complete the table of meter readings, entering the figures for 'Units used' and 'Total cost'. *(2 marks)*

b   What is the scientific name for the 'unit' in the 'Units used' column? *(1 mark)*

c   What type of fuel do most Northern Ireland electricity companies use to produce electricity? *(1 mark)*

d   Give **two** reasons why all the major Northern Ireland power stations are built on the coast. *(2 marks)*

e   Suggest **two** reasons why we are likely to see greater use of renewable energy resources in the future. *(2 marks)*

2 Julie sets up the circuit below to investigate how to control the brightness of a bulb.

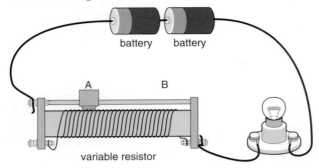

battery   battery

A   B

variable resistor

a Explain carefully why the bulb is dimmer when the slider of the variable resistor is at position B than when it is at position A. *(3 marks)*

b i If 1 m of copper wire has a resistance of 3 Ω, calculate the resistance of 3 m of copper wire. *(1 mark)*

ii Explain your answer to part **i**. *(1 mark)*

iii A wire of length 1 m has twice the area as the wire in **i**. Find its resistance. *(1 mark)*

CCEA GCSE Science: Single Award (Modular) Specimen Paper (Higher Tier) 2006

3 The ACME Fuse Company makes cartridge fuses for use in electrical plugs.

Its biggest customer is Duck & Swann Ltd, which makes different sorts of domestic electrical equipment. Duck & Swann recently sent back 5000 fuses, all 13 A, with a complaint that the last batch of fuses did not work properly.

Most of the fuses were fitted in 13 A electric fires. ACME told its Physics Team to investigate and submit a report. Below is the report the team submitted.

Report of Physics Team on Fuses Returned by Duck & Swann

We tested a sample of the fuses returned from Duck & Swann using the test circuit shown below:

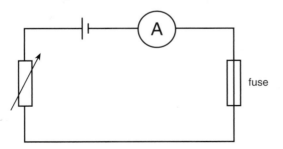

fuse

We quickly increased the current by increasing the resistance of the rheostat until the fuse blew. We then recorded for each fuse the maximum current it could take before it blew. Our results are shown in Table 1.

Table 1: Fuses returned by Duck & Swann

Maximum current in A	below 12.8	12.8	12.9	13.0	13.1	above 13.1
% of fuses which blew at this current	30	56	2	2	5	5

We also tested a sample of 13 A fuses taken at random from the current production in our factory. Our results for these fuses are shown below:

Table 2: Random sample of fuses from current production

Maximum current in A	below 12.8	12.8	12.9	13.0	13.1	above 13.1
% of fuses which blew at this current	0	0	0	53	46	1

a One of the ACME managers asked the Physics Team if it was quite sure the test method described would give reliable results. What made the manager think there might be something wrong with the way the testing was carried out? *(2 marks)*

b The fuses were all contained within an opaque cartridge, so the fuse wire could not be seen. What would be observed in the circuit when the fuse blows? *(1 mark)*

c With one of the fuses the Physics Team found that the fuse did not blow no matter what they did to the rheostat. Suggest why this might have occurred and how the team might have changed the apparatus to measure the fusing current. *(2 marks)*

d The ACME manager told the Physics Team he had additional questions to ask concerning the results in Table 1. State **one** of the questions he might reasonably ask. *(1 mark)*

e The Physics Team tested the fuses from current production (Table 2). Do you think the information gained from these tests would reassure the Duck & Swann management? Give a reason for your answer. *(1 mark)*

f Assume the Duck & Swann fuses tested by the Physics Team are a fair sample. What do you think would have happened when Duck & Swann first switched on the electric fires to test them? *(1 mark)*

g Do you think the complaint made by Duck & Swann is justified? Give a reason for your answer. *(1 mark)*

The Quality Assurance Manager told the Physics Team that after the Duck & Swann order was processed, they knew that they had to obtain a very thin fuse wire, but they could find no suppliers.

h What else might ACME have done to obtain suitable fuse wire? *(1 mark)*

CCEA GCSE Science: Single Award (Modular) Specimen Paper (Higher Tier) 2006

Chapter 16

Waves and communication

By the end of this chapter you should know and understand:

➤ That waves are caused by vibrations, and transport energy
➤ The difference between transverse and longitudinal waves
➤ The main features of a transverse wave (wavelength, amplitude and frequency), and how the wave propagates in terms of particle movement
➤ How to measure the speed of sound
➤ That sound can be reflected to produce an echo, and what steps are taken in auditoriums to counteract this problem
➤ How to carry out simple calculations, involving the echo method, on the speed of sound
➤ The audible range of humans
➤ How ultrasound is used for depth measurement, locating fish, and in medicine
➤ The make up of the electromagnetic spectrum, from gamma rays to radio waves
➤ The dangers associated with electromagnetic radiation
➤ The microwave heating effect, in terms of energy absorption and molecular behaviour
➤ The use of microwaves in mobile phone communications
➤ The difference between analogue and digital signals
➤ What is meant by critical angle and total internal reflection
➤ The ways that converging and diverging lenses refract rays of light parallel to their principal axis
➤ The formation of an image on the retina
➤ The difference between long sight and short sight in terms of the converging power of the eye lens
➤ How sight defects are corrected by lenses
➤ What astigmatism is

Types of waves

All waves **transfer energy** from one point to another but, in general, they do not transfer matter. Microwaves, for example, transfer energy into the food in a microwave oven, but no matter moves into the food as a result.

Waves are produced as a result of **vibrations** and can be classified as **longitudinal** or **transverse**. A vibration is a regular repeated movement first in one direction and then in the opposite direction.

Both types of wave can be shown on a slinky spring. A longitudinal wave can be produced by moving the hand back and forth parallel to the axis of the spring. When we do this we see places where the coils are bunched together (compressions) and between them places where the coils are further apart (rarefactions). As the hand moves back and forth, so the compressions move along the spring. The only common longitudinal waves in nature are sound (and ultrasound) waves and some types of seismic wave (which travel through the Earth as a result of an earthquake – see Chapter 10).

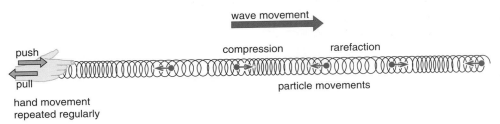

Figure 16.1 Modelling a longitudinal wave

A transverse wave can be produced on a slinky spring by moving the hand back and forth perpendicular to the axis of the spring. When we do this we see wave crests (humps) advancing along the spring.

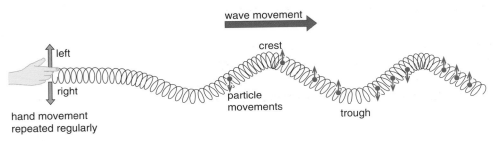

Figure 16.2 Modelling a transverse wave

You are probably familiar with the up-and-down movement of water waves. These are transverse waves. If you look carefully at a floating cork you can see how the cork bobs up and down as the waves pass it.

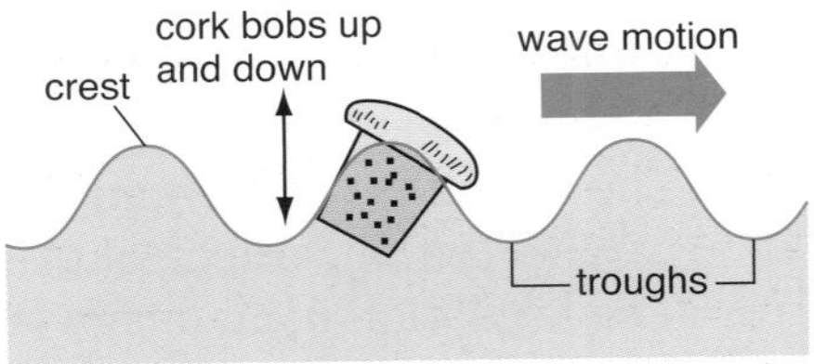

We can summarise this by saying:

Figure 16.3 Ripples on water are transverse waves

- a **longitudinal wave** is one in which the particles of the material **vibrate parallel** to the direction in which the wave is moving
- a **transverse wave** is one in which the particles of the material **vibrate perpendicular** to the direction in which the wave is moving.

Most waves in nature are transverse. Some common examples are:

- water waves
- waves on strings and ropes
- light
- infra-red radiation
- microwaves
- radio waves
- X-rays.

Describing waves

There are three important quantities relating to waves, which we will define for a transverse wave:

1 The **wavelength** of a wave is the distance between two successive crests or troughs (see Figure 16.4). Wavelength is given the symbol λ, and is measured in metres. λ is the Greek letter l and is pronounced *lambda*.
2 The **amplitude** of a wave is the greatest displacement of the wave from the rest position (see Figure 16.4). Amplitude is measured in metres.
3 The **frequency** of a wave is the number of complete waves passing a fixed point in a second. Frequency is given the symbol f, and is measured in units called **hertz** (abbreviation Hz), equivalent to 1/second.

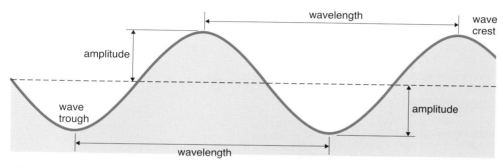

Figure 16.4 A transverse water wave showing the wavelength and amplitude

---

1 The vertical distance between the peaks and the troughs of a water wave is 30 cm. The horizontal distance between a peak and the next trough is 80 cm.
   a   Illustrate this wave with a diagram.
   b   Calculate (i) the amplitude of the waves and (ii) the wavelength of the waves.

Sound and ultrasound

Longitudinal waves are produced in the air when an object vibrates. We call these sound waves if the vibration is at a frequency that the human ear can detect. The range of human hearing is from around 20 Hz to around 20 000 Hz (20 kHz). This is called the **audible frequency range**. Sound of frequencies above 20 kHz cannot be heard by humans and is called **ultrasound**. Generally, the upper frequency limit of hearing gets smaller as we get older, and it is not uncommon for middle-aged people to be unable to hear sound above 14 000 Hz.

There are several other factors that might affect a person's hearing. These include:

● a birth defect
● ear drum damage
● prolonged exposure to a noisy environment (for example at work, or in clubs and discos).

Interestingly, many clubs now issue their customers with ear plugs for protection against the very loud music from their loudspeakers. Similar precautions must be taken where there is any prolonged, loud noise such as in quarries, on building sites and in other heavy industry.

You can get a rough idea of someone's audible frequency range using an oscillator connected to a set of headphones. The person whose hearing is being tested wears the headphones, while someone else slowly increases the frequency from about 3000 Hz until the sound from the headphones is no longer heard. The reading on the dial of the oscillator then indicates the upper frequency limit. In the same way the lower limit can be found by decreasing the oscillator frequency from about 3000 Hz to around 20 Hz.

ACTIVITY

Sound waves are produced by stretched strings when they are plucked and made to vibrate. You can study vibrations of strings using a signal generator and a stroboscope, set up as in Figure 16.5.

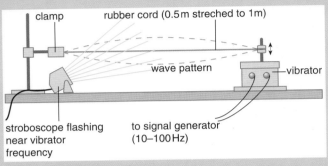

clamp   rubber cord (0.5 m streched to 1 m)

wave pattern   vibrator

stroboscope flashing
near vibrator
frequency

to signal generator
(10–100 Hz)

Figure 16.5 Observing vibrations

The vibrator moves vertically up and down at a frequency set by the signal generator. At a certain frequency, called the resonant frequency, the wire vibrates with a large amplitude. If you adjust the frequency of the flashing stroboscope so that it is close to that of the vibrating wire, the wave pattern of the vibrating wire appears to be standing still.

Investigate the effect on the resonant frequency of:

● **using a string of longer length**
● **using a string of greater thickness.**

ACTIVITY

Play the same note (e.g. middle C) on a violin, a recorder, a xylophone and a flute. Identify what is vibrating to generate the sound.

Your teacher will connect a microphone to a cathode ray oscilloscope (CRO) for you and adjust the knobs so that waveforms of the sounds are shown. Play the note on each instrument in turn and draw a diagram of each waveform.

Identify what is similar about the waveforms and what is different.
What happens when the notes are played louder?
What happens if a higher note is played?

How fast do sound waves travel?

There are two common ways of measuring the speed of sound in air. They are sometimes called the **flash–bang method** and the **two microphones method**.

Flash–bang method

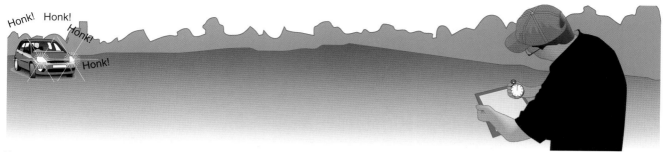

Figure 16.6 The flash–bang method of measuring the speed of sound

This involves two people being about a kilometre or so apart. Typically, one person stands with a stop watch at one end of a large field. The other person sets the distance meter to zero and drives a kilometre away. With the two people facing each other, the person with the car simultaneously flashes the car headlights and sounds the horn. Immediately the headlights are seen, the person with the stop watch starts the watch, and then stops it when the sound is heard. This is repeated several times and the average time for the sound to travel the known distance is calculated. This reduces the effect of human error. To reduce possible error due to the wind, the two people reverse positions and measure the time of travel of the sound in the opposite direction. The speed of sound is then taken as the average of the two calculated speeds. Typical results are shown in Table 16.1.

Table 16.1 Typical results

	Distance travelled by sound in m	Average time taken in s	Speed in m/s	Average speed in m/s
With the wind	990	2.9	341	330
Against the wind	990	3.1	319	

Two microphones method

This method involves two microphones placed a known distance, say 6 metres, apart (Figure 16.7). Each microphone is connected to the input of a cathode ray oscilloscope (CRO), an instrument that can display a sound waveform as a visible trace. A student stands in a straight line with the two microphones and makes a short, loud noise. The CRO is set up to trigger when a loud sound reaches the first microphone. When the sound reaches the second microphone the signal is detected and two peaks are displayed on the CRO screen. By reading the time setting and measuring the distance between the peaks on the screen, a figure can be found for the time taken for the sound to travel the known distance between the microphones. A typical set of results might be:

Distance between peaks on CRO screen = 4.5 cm
Time setting on CRO = 0.004 s/cm
Time between spikes = 0.018 s
Distance between microphones = 6 m

$$\text{Speed of sound in air} = \frac{\text{distance between microphones}}{\text{time taken}}$$

$$= \frac{6 \text{ m}}{0.018 \text{ s}} = 330 \text{ m/s}$$

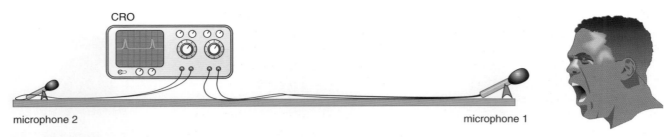

CRO

microphone 2   microphone 1

Figure 16.7 The two microphones method of measuring the speed of sound

The following questions are examples of the type of question on 'How science works' that you will get in your GCSE exam. You may not be able to find the answers in the text. You need to think carefully about the experiment.

2 Why is it necessary for the two microphones and the person making the loud sound all to be in a straight line?

3 What difference, if any, would it make to the separation of the spikes on the CRO screen if the time setting on the CRO was 0.0001 s/cm, rather than 0.001 s/cm?

4 The experiment works best when the distance between the microphones is at least 1 metre. Why will the experiment be less successful if the distance between the microphones is 30 cm?

5 We always repeat measurements and average the results. This is because it is likely that some results will be a bit bigger while others will be a bit smaller than the true speed of sound. And we need to recognise 'rogues' (false results) and ignore them. Identify the 'rogues' in the list of results given here, and then calculate the average speed of sound:

Speed of sound in m/s: 335, 340, 330, 385, 390, 335, 330, 340, 335

6 Why is it not important to measure the speed of sound in both directions in the two microphones experiment, but it is very important to do so in the flash–bang method?

7 Which of the two methods is likely to give you the more reliable result? Why?

Echoes

Like all waves, sound waves can reflect off a surface. A reflected sound is called an **echo**. The best reflectors of sound are hard, like steel. Soft surfaces tend to absorb sound. Actors on stage are aware of this as they stand behind the curtain – they can hear only a little of the sound from the front of the theatre.

Sound reflection occurs in a similar way to the reflection of light off a flat mirror. When sound reflects, the angle of incidence at the surface is equal to the angle of reflection. This is easily tested using two cardboard tubes and a wooden board. Sound waves from a ticking watch pass down one tube and are reflected from the board. The loudness of the sound reaching the ear is a maximum when the board is adjusted so that the angles of incidence and reflection are equal.

At times echoes can be very useful. At other times they are a real nuisance.

Echoes and building design

Suppose you are in a theatre listening to an artiste on stage. Sound reaches you directly from the loudspeakers and also as a result of echoes from the walls and ceiling. If the echoes follow so closely behind the direct sound that the sounds cannot be identified separately, you get the impression that the original sound has been slightly prolonged. The effect is called **reverberation**. In some cases it is a nuisance and destroys the pleasure of hearing the performance. In Saint Paul's cathedral, for example, it used to take about six seconds for the sound of the organ to die away after the organist stopped playing.

Reverberation is reduced by using sound-absorbing materials on the walls and ceiling. Often wall panels padded with mineral fibre are used. Nowadays reverberation is always considered by architects when designing concert halls.

> 8 Why is the sound in a theatre different when it is full of people and when it is empty?
> 9 How might you reduce the amount of sound that can pass from one floor to another in a block of flats?

Making use of echoes

Ultrasound reflections are used to:

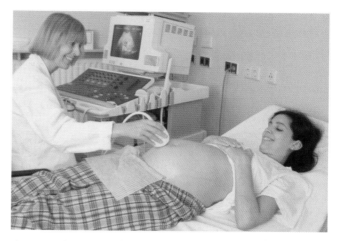

Figure 16.8 Ultrasound scans of unborn babies are safe for the mother and the baby

- scan metal castings for faults or cracks (e.g. in rail tracks)
- scan a pregnant woman's womb to check the development of the unborn baby
- scan soft tissues to diagnose cancers
- locate fish deep below the surface of the sea
- map the surface of the ocean floor
- measure the distance from one wall of a room to another (e.g. by estate agents).

Problem 1

A ship emits a pulse of ultrasound and after 0.4 seconds an echo from the sea bed is detected. If the average speed of sound in sea water is 1500 m/s, calculate the depth of the sea.

Solution

Total distance travelled by ultrasound = speed of ultrasound × time
$$= 1500 \text{ m/s} \times 0.4 \text{ s} = 600 \text{ m}$$
But the ultrasound travels to the sea bed and back again to the ship, so depth of the sea $= \frac{1}{2} \times 600 \text{ m} = \textbf{300 m}$

Problem 2

A doctor examining an unborn baby finds that it takes 50 microseconds (0.000 05 s) for an ultrasound pulse to travel from one side of the baby's head to the other and back again. The baby's head is 4 cm wide. Calculate the average speed of the ultrasound in the baby's head.

Solution

Total distance travelled by ultrasound = distance across the head and back again
$$= 2 \times 4 = 8 \text{ cm} = 0.08 \text{ m}$$

Average speed $= \dfrac{\text{total distance}}{\text{total time}} = \dfrac{0.08}{0.000\ 05} = \textbf{1600 m/s}$

(Why is it not surprising that the speed of ultrasound in tissue is so close to that in water?)

10 A girl stands 99 m from a high wall and claps her hands at a regular rate. All the sounds are reflected from the wall. A friend notices that when she makes 100 claps per minute the sound of an echo coincides exactly with the sound of the clap that follows.

   a What time passes between one clap and the next?

   b What distance does the sound travel in the time calculated in part a?

Electromagnetic waves

Electromagnetic radiation travels as waves. All electromagnetic waves:

- are **transverse** waves
- are able to travel through a **vacuum**
- travel at the **same speed** in a vacuum
- **transfer energy**.

There are seven types of electromagnetic wave, or members of the electromagnetic 'family', called the **electromagnetic spectrum**. Their properties depend very much on their wavelength. They are listed in Table 16.2 in order of increasing wavelength.

Table 16.2 Electromagnetic waves

Electromagnetic wave	Typical wavelength		Typical frequency in Hz
gamma (γ) rays	0.000 000 000 01m	(0.01 nm)	3×10^{19}
X-rays	0.000 000 000 1 m	(0.1 nm)	3×10^{18}
ultra-violet (UV)	0.000 000 010 m	(10 nm)	3×10^{16}
visible light	0.000 005 m	(500 nm)	6×10^{14}
infra-red	0.000 01 m	(10 μm)	3×10^{13}
microwaves	0.03 m	(30 mm)	1×10^{10}
radio waves	1000 m		3×10^{5}

1 m = 1000 mm = 1000 000 μm = 1000 000 000 nm
The mathematical expression 3×10^{5} means 3 followed by 5 zeros, or 300 000;
6×10^{14} means 6 followed by 14 zeros, or 600 000 000 000 000; and so on

One interesting feature about the table is the enormous range of the wavelengths, from a hundredth of a billionth of a metre (gamma rays) to about a thousand metres (radio waves). Note that as the wavelength increases, so the frequency decreases.

Effects of electromagnetic waves on living cells

Different electromagnetic waves affect living cells in different ways. This makes some of them much more dangerous than others. It also means that different waves can be used in different ways, as shown in Table 16.3.

You can see from the table that gamma rays and X-rays can be **very harmful to human tissues**.

Table 16.3 Uses of electromagnetic waves

Wave	Effect on living cells	Main applications
gamma (γ) rays	● Can kill cells ● Can cause cancer by disrupting cell DNA	● Cancer treatment (radiotherapy to kill cancer cells) ● Sterilisation of equipment (kills bacteria) ● Preservation of food (kills surface fungi)
X-rays	● Can kill cells ● Can cause cancer by disrupting cell DNA	● Cancer treatment (radiotherapy to kill cancer cells) ● Medical diagnosis (broken bones, tumours) and dental investigations ● Testing metal components for metal fatigue
ultra-violet (UV)	● Causes a sun tan ● Can cause skin cancers	● Sun-beds ● Detecting bank note forgeries ● Security marking (labelling only shows up in UV) ● Causing certain fabrics to fluoresce (glow) in clubs/discos and in stage performances
visible light	● Produces a response in the cells of the retina, enabling us to 'see' ● Used by skin cells to produce vitamin D_3	● Lamps ● Photography ● Photosynthesis
infra-red	● Produces a sensation of warmth ● Can cause burns	● Heaters ● Night-time photography ● PIR (passive infra-red security detectors) ● Oven-hardening of cellulose paint on cars ● Remote controls (for TVs and other electronic equipment) ● Communications via optical cables
microwaves	● Can cause heating and even burning under the skin if dose is high	● Fast food defrosting and cooking ● Radar for planes and ships ● Communications via satellites ● Mobile phone communications ● Speed cameras
radio waves	● Little effect on human body	● Long range communications ● Radio and TV broadcasting

We can explain some of the harmful effects of gamma rays and X-rays in terms of the **high frequency** of the radiation. High-frequency electromagnetic waves carry very much more energy than lower-frequency waves. They can therefore cause much more damage to a cell, and especially to the cell's nucleus. These high-frequency waves are also very penetrating – they can pass through skin, flesh and even bone. This explains why gamma rays and X-rays readily cause cancers within the body and can kill cells. Ultra-violet has a lower frequency so is less penetrating, and its damaging effects are restricted to the skin.

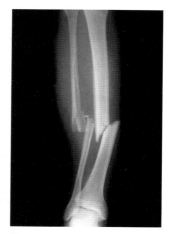

Figure 16.9 X-ray diagnosis is very useful but too many X-rays should be avoided

ACTIVITY

Plan a debate on the motion: 'Children under the age of 10 years should not be allowed to use mobile phones'. Mobile phones work by transmitting and receiving microwaves. You will need to do some internet research on the possible risks associated with these.

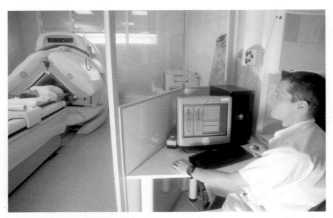

Figure 16.10 Medical staff operating X-ray or gamma scanners need to be well shielded from the harmful rays

The danger from over-exposure to sunlight

Ultra-violet light comes to us from the Sun. Much of it is absorbed in the ozone layer, which extends from 15 to 40 km above the surface of the Earth. Even so, enough of it reaches the Earth's surface to cause problems for careless sunbathers. Ultra-violet light can disrupt cell DNA in skin cells and so cause skin cancers. A sun tan is a change in the pigment of our skin and is itself caused by ultra-violet light. The change in the pigment is a defence mechanism against the damage that can be caused by the ultra-violet.

How do microwave ovens work?

Microwaves are really short-wavelength radio waves. In a microwave oven, microwaves of a particular wavelength are produced. This particular wavelength is the one that is best absorbed by water molecules. The absorbed microwave energy causes the water molecules in the food to vibrate more rapidly. We observe this as an increase in the temperature of the food. Microwave cooking is particularly fast because microwaves can penetrate right to the middle of the food, whereas conventional ovens rely on heat being slowly conducted through the food from the outside to the centre. Microwave ovens are generally encased in a metal box, which prevents microwaves escaping. The grid of metal wires in the glass window at the front also prevents microwaves escaping through the oven door.

> **11** Explain why it is important that microwave energy does not escape from a microwave oven.

How do mobile phones work?

Your mobile phone is a small microwave transceiver. This means it can transmit and receive messages carried by a microwave beam. In the USA they are called 'cell phones' because the country where they work is divided into thousands of geographical areas called cells. Each cell has its own microwave mast. Apparatus on the mast receives communications from one cell and passes them on to the next until the messages finally reach their destination. In this way each cell acts as a 'repeater station'. Without these repeater stations the signal transmitted by the mobile phone would have to be much stronger and the handset would be much bigger.

Carry out some research on the way mobile phones are used in both short distance and international communications.

Long distance calls

If a telephone call is long distance, for example from Ireland to the USA, then it may be sent by microwave link or through fibre optic cable (see page 221) to the nearest International Telecom tower. Here the signal is boosted and transmitted to an Earth Station such as that at Goonhilly in Cornwall. A powerful **dish transmitter** there then sends the signal to a **geostationary satellite**. This type of satellite orbits the Earth at a height of about 36 000 km above the equator and makes one Earth orbit in exactly 24 hours. Since the satellite orbits the Earth in exactly the same time as the Earth spins on its axis, it is always above the same part of the Earth. The receiving satellite boosts the signal again and transmits it to the receiving dish in the destination country. With only three such satellites it is possible to communicate by satellite with all parts of the world.

Figure 16.11
Dish transmitter at
Goonhilly Earth Station

Analogue and digital signals

The electrical signal produced by a microphone in a telephone is **analogue**. This means it changes continually and the voltage can take any value, depending on the loudness and frequency of the sound. Before the signal can be transmitted via a microwave or fibre optic link, it must be converted into a **digital** signal. A digital signal consists of a series of pulses, in a code rather like Morse Code. In telecommunications the code used is **binary code**, which is the same as that used by computers. This consists simply of on–off pulses.

What are the advantages of a digital signal over an analogue signal? There are two:

● Digital signals are less likely to be affected by interference (noise). Stray voltages distort analogue signals, but they have much less effect on digital signals. This is because with a digital signal it is only necessary to detect a pulse or the absence of a pulse (see Figure 16.12).
● Digital signals can be processed more readily by computers.

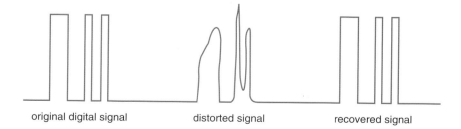

original digital signal   distorted signal   recovered signal

Figure 16.12 A distorted digital signal can usually be fully recovered, as it is still possible to detect the on–off pulses

Observe the CRO traces of a low-frequency digital signal (a rectangular waveform from an oscillator) and an analogue signal (from a microphone picking up music from a radio station). Make diagrams to illustrate your observations.

Refraction of light

Refraction is the change in direction of a beam of light as it travels from one material into another. It occurs because light travels at different speeds in different materials. Table 16.4 shows the speed of light in air, water and glass.

Table 16.4 Speed of light in different materials

Material	Speed of light in m/s
air (or vacuum)	300 000 000
water	225 000 000
glass	200 000 000

Experiments show that when a ray of light passes **obliquely** (at an angle) **from air into glass**, it slows down and **bends towards the normal** (the imaginary line at 90° to the surface). As the light leaves the glass and re-enters the air it speeds up again and bends away from the normal. If the block is rectangular, the incident ray and the emergent ray are parallel to each other (see Figure 16.13). However, when light is refracted in this way, some light is always reflected as well. The angle of reflection is always equal to the angle of incidence.

When light entering a glass block strikes it at 90° to the surface (we call this normal incidence) it passes straight through without changing direction.

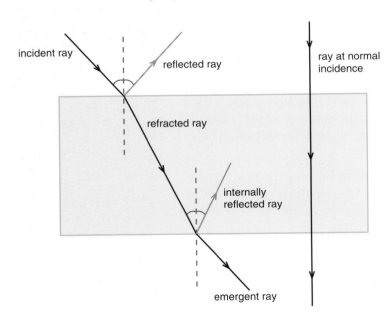

Figure 16.13 Refraction and reflection of a ray of light incident on a glass block

Suppose now the ray box producing the light ray is moved so as to make the angle of incidence at the air–glass boundary larger. The angle of incidence at the glass–air boundary inside the block will also become larger. This causes the emergent refracted ray in the air to become weaker and the internally reflected ray to become stronger. As the angle of incidence in the glass increases further, there comes a point where the angle of refraction is 90°. The angle of incidence in the glass for which the angle of refraction in air is 90° is called the **critical angle**. At angles of incidence greater than the critical angle the light is **totally internally reflected** and no refraction occurs at all. For glass the critical angle is about 42°.

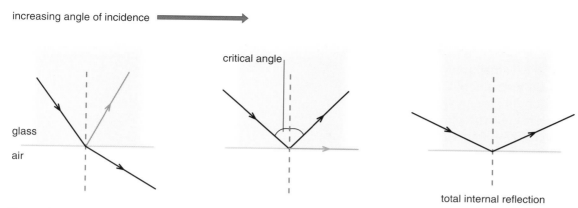

increasing angle of incidence

critical angle

glass

air

total internal reflection

Figure 16.14 How total internal reflection occurs

ACTIVITY

Direct a ray of light from a ray box into a semi-circular glass block, along a radius towards the centre. Rotate so that the angle of incidence at the flat edge inside the block gradually increases. Measure the critical angle. Is the critical angle different for blocks made of different materials?

Applying total internal reflection in optical fibres

Total internal reflection allows light to pass through a solid glass fibre with almost no energy loss. It does this by repeated total internal reflections – see Figure 16.15. You have probably seen bundles of these glass fibres, called **optical fibres**, in ornamental Christmas trees and other decorations. But their uses are far from only decorative. Today optical fibres are used extensively for communications and to assist surgery.

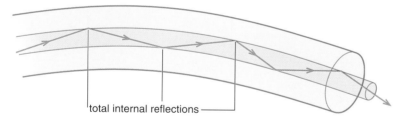

total internal reflections

Figure 16.15 Transmission of light through an optical fibre

Figure 16.16
Two bundles of optical fibres

Optical fibres in communications

Telephone land lines were once made from copper wire, but nowadays telephone companies are increasingly using optical fibres. Also, the cable used by companies providing cable TV services is almost always made up of optical fibres. We call it **fibre optic cable**. Signals are sent through the cable as digital pulses of light – usually infra-red light.

Optical communications have several advantages over electrical signals in copper wires:

- The signal does not need boosting as often.
- An optical cable of the same diameter can **carry much more information** than a copper cable.
- The signal is much **more secure** – it is more difficult to tap into.
- The signal is much **less likely to suffer interference** from electrical sources.

Optical fibres in surgery

Light transmission through optical fibres makes it possible to look inside people and carry out **keyhole surgery**. Two small bundles of optical fibres are used, in an instrument called an **endoscope**. One bundle carries light into the body; the other carries out the picture (image) of the inside of the body. See Figures 16.17 and 16.18. The full colour, moving image is displayed on a monitor. This allows surgeons to carry out operations with only a tiny hole cut in the patient's body.

Before optical fibres were developed, keyhole surgery was impossible. An internal operation would require a large opening – a much more risky procedure – and would leave a large wound to heal.

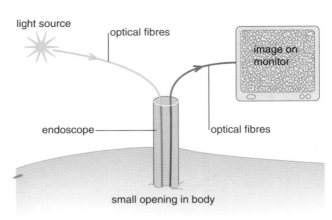

Figure 16.17 The use of optical fibres in an endoscope

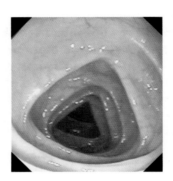

Figure 16.18 Image of the interior of part of the large intestine, produced by an endoscope

> 12 Explain how the light travels through an endoscope.

Other applications of total internal reflection

In car and bicycle rear reflectors there are tiny **air prisms** (triangular shapes). Light is totally internally reflected so that the incident light is sent back parallel to the way it came in (Figure 16.19). This means that the driver of the vehicle behind, whose headlamps shine on the reflectors, gets a strong reflection, making for maximum visibility.

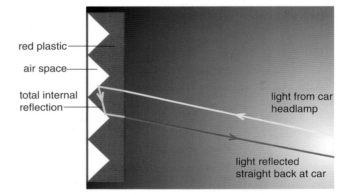

Figure 16.19 Total internal reflection of light in a rear reflector

Lenses

When light passes through a triangular glass prism it refracts at two surfaces. The way in which the light bends depends on whether the prism has its corner at the top or bottom (Figure 16.20).

Suppose we could place parts of prisms on top of each other, each bending the light by a slightly different amount. Then we could create a **converging lens**. See Figure 16.21. Each part of the converging lens bends the light by a slightly different amount, but together they focus a parallel beam to a single spot. For an incident beam parallel to the axis of the lens (normal incidence), the spot is known as the **principal focus**, F (or focal point). The type of lens that does this is called a **convex** lens – it is fatter in the middle.

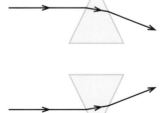

Figure 16.20 Refraction of light by triangular prisms

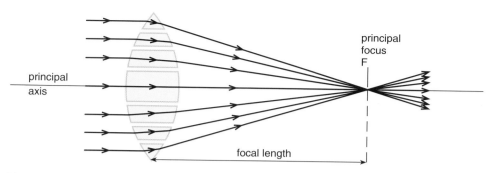

Figure 16.21 Refraction of light by a converging (convex) lens

It is possible to build up a lens from prisms in a different way, so that each part bends the light so as to make the beam diverge (spread out). This **diverging lens** is **concave** – thinner in the middle. Now the parallel beam of light spreads out so that it appears to come from the principal focus, F (or focal point). See Figure 16.22.

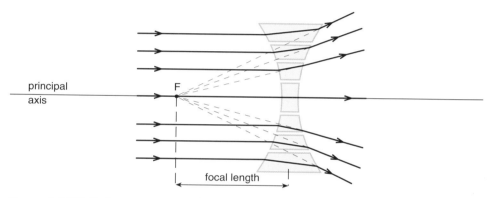

Figure 16.22 Refraction of light by a diverging (concave) lens

For both types of lens, the distance between the centre of the lens and its focal point is called the **focal length**, and the line joining the centre of the lens to its principal focus is called the **principal axis**.

13 Inside each of the boxes A, B and C in Figure 16.23 is a piece of glass. A parallel beam of light enters the glass and leaves in the directions shown. Use your knowledge of refraction to identify the shape of the glass object inside each box.

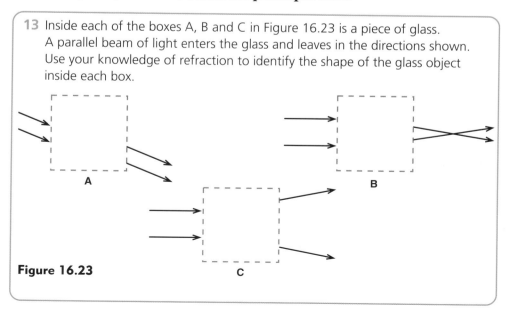

Figure 16.23

The human eye

Figure 16.24 shows three main features of the human eye. A sharp inverted image of any object viewed by the eye is formed on the **retina**. This image is formed by refraction. Most refraction occurs in the **cornea**. However, to obtain a sharp image on the retina, the light must be focused by the **eye lens**. The lens is a flexible bag of clear liquid. Unlike the sort of solid, glass spectacle lens we are familiar with, the lens of the eye can be pulled into different shapes by the eye's muscles.

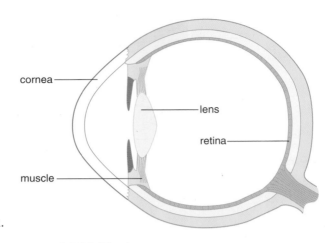

Figure 16.24 The human eye

- When the eye lens is thin it has a long focal length.
- When the eye lens is thick it has a short focal length.

This adjustment allows the eye to focus on objects at a great range of distances.

The human eye has a normal **near point** of about 25 cm. This simply means that a person with normal sight can see clearly objects 25 cm or further from his/her eye. If the object is closer than 25 cm it will be seen, but it might be blurred and looking at it might cause the eye to become strained. To see an object as close as 25 cm from the eye, the lens must become quite thick to converge the light as much as possible.

The normal **far point** of the human eye is infinity. This means that a person with normal sight can see clearly objects that are very, very far away – such as the stars. To focus on objects that are very far away, the eye lens must become very thin.

Vision problems

There are three common problems that occur with human vision:

- long sight
- short sight
- astigmatism.

Long sight

In a long-sighted person the eye lens is not converging enough. Rays from an object at the normal near point (N, at 25 cm) are brought to a focus behind the retina.

An object must be further way than 25 cm for the eye lens to bring the light to a sharp focus on the retina. Objects closer than the eye's own near point (O) appear blurred.

A converging spectacle lens reduces the divergence of the light entering the eye. The rays then appear to come from the eye's own near point and can be focused on the retina. See Figure 16.25.

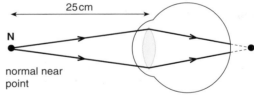

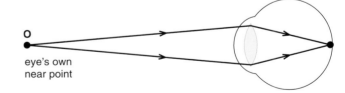

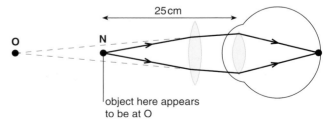

Figure 16.25 Long sight and how it is corrected

Short sight

In a short-sighted person the eye lens is too converging. Rays from an object at the normal far point (infinity) are brought to a focus in front of the retina.

An object must be quite close for the eye lens to bring the light to a sharp focus on the retina. Objects further than the eye's own far point (P) appear blurred.

A diverging spectacle lens makes parallel incident rays appear to come from the eye's own far point, so that they can be focused on the retina. See Figure 16.26.

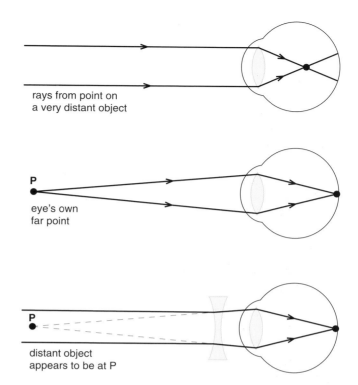

> **14** Describe, with the help of diagrams, what is meant by
> a   long sight
> b   short sight.

Figure 16.26 Short sight and how it is corrected

Astigmatism

Most of the refraction in the eye takes place in the cornea, the clear curved outer part of the front of the eye. If the cornea's surface is not spherical, that is if it has a different curvature in different directions, then objects seen in some directions will be in sharper focus than others. This is called **astigmatism**. The optician normally tests for this by asking the patient to look at a chart with lines drawn on it at different angles, like that in Figure 16.27. The lines all have the same thickness. But if the patient suffers from astigmatism, he/she will say that some lines are thicker (more blurred) than others. When the optician knows which lines are blurred, a cylindrical spectacle lens can be prescribed, to correct the effect. This can be combined with a curvature so that long or short sight can be corrected with the same lens.

Figure 16.27 Do the lines in the diagram all appear to you to be equally thick?

websites

http://imagine.gsfc.nasa.gov/docs/science/know_l1/emspectrum.html
excellent website, full of first-class graphics on electromagnetic radiations and their applications

www.bbc.co.uk/science/hottopics/sunshine/dangers.shtml
article on the dangers of sunshine and the need to take sensible precautions

http://news.bbc.co.uk/2/hi/health/4113989.stm
article about the possible health risks associated with the use of mobile phones

www.longman.co.uk/higherscience/docs/phyws36.doc
early ideas about X-rays

www.timesonline.co.uk/article/0,,8122-983239,00.html
article linking medical X-rays with cancers

www.smgaels.org/physics/gamm_1.htm
short article on the uses of gamma radiation in science, medicine and industry and the associated dangers

http://electronics.howstuffworks.com/cell-phone2.htm
excellent text and graphics on how cell phones work

www.glenbrook.k12.il.us/gbssci/phys/Class/refrn/u14l3b.html
the principles of total internal reflection in water and glass

www.gcse.com/waves/tir.htm
excellent treatment of total internal reflection using colourful ray diagrams

http://science.howstuffworks.com/eye.htm
introduction to vision and the anatomy of the eye

www.eyelaser.co.za/refractive_errors.php
simple explanation of vision defects

www.allaboutvision.com/conditions/astigmatism.htm
further explanation of astigmatism

Questions

1 The electromagnetic spectrum consists of a family of waves.

a The incomplete table below shows some of the electromagnetic spectrum in order of increasing wavelength. Copy and complete the table.

Gamma waves		Ultra-violet light			Micro-waves	

(4 marks)

b Holiday-makers are advised to use a high-factor sun-cream when sunbathing.

 i What is the main purpose of such sun-creams? *(1 mark)*

 ii Against what type of radiation do these creams give protection? *(1 mark)*

 iii What is the long-term danger linked with over-exposure to radiation from the sun? *(1 mark)*

c Jane is making notes on the uses of gamma rays and X-rays in medicine. Her notebook contains the following entry:

	Uses in medicine
X-rays	1. Detect broken bones 2.
Gamma rays	1. Radiotherapy to kill cancer cells 2.

Copy and complete the table by adding another use for X-rays and another use for gamma rays.

(2 marks)

d Gamma rays are much more penetrating than X-rays and have a shorter wavelength.

 i Give **one** other way in which gamma rays and X-rays are different. *(1 mark)*

 ii Give **one** property of gamma rays which is identical to that of X-rays. *(1 mark)*

2 a The diagram shows two buoys, 60 m apart floating on the sea.

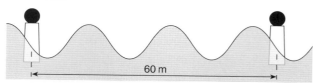

i Use the diagram to calculate the wavelength of the sea waves. *(1 mark)*

ii The buoys are found to move up and down a total distance of 50 cm as the waves pass them. Calculate the amplitude of the water waves. *(1 mark)*

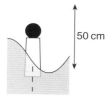

iii What type of waves are these sea waves? *(1 mark)*

b Three different sounds are made, and the waveform produced by each is displayed on the screen of an oscilloscope as shown below. The oscilloscope settings are the same for each note.

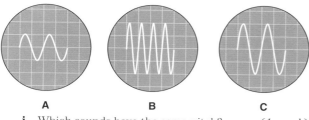

i Which sounds have the same pitch? *(1 mark)*
ii Which sounds have the same loudness? *(1 mark)*

CCEA GCSE Science: Single Award (Modular) Specimen Paper (Higher Tier) 2006

3 a In a large concert hall, sound can reach a girl sitting in the back by a number of different paths. One path is drawn on the diagram below.

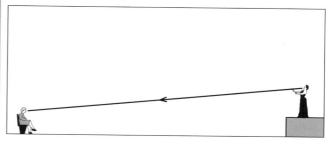

i Sketch the diagram and draw a different path for the sound to travel from the singer to the girl *(1 mark)*

ii The speed of sound in air is 340 m/s. It takes the sound from the singer 0.25 seconds to reach the girl. Calculate how far the girl is from the singer. *(3 marks)*

b Ultrasound is used often in medicine to obtain an image of a baby in the womb.

The diagram below shows an ultrasound scan being performed on a baby in the womb. Signals from the ultrasound scanner are processed by a computer to display an image on the screen.

Describe what happens at the ultrasound scanner to produce the signals that are sent to the computer. *(3 marks)*

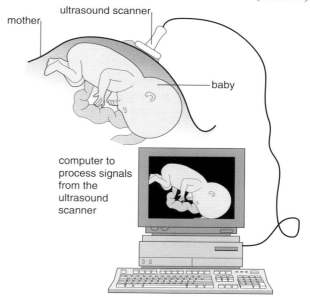

CCEA GCSE Science: Single Award (Modular) Specimen Paper (Higher Tier) 2006 (part question)

Chapter 17

Energy, transport and road safety

By the end of this chapter you should know and understand:

➤ That fossil fuels are the remains of dead plant and animal matter
➤ Why the most useful energy resources for transport are oil derivatives: petrol and diesel
➤ The consequences of the increasing use of fossil fuels, including global warming
➤ Strategies to reduce reliance on oil, such as the use of biofuels, hydrogen fuel cells and hybrid systems
➤ The use of fuel cells based on methanol
➤ The arguments for and against the use of taxes to control the consumption of fossil fuels, particularly petrol and diesel
➤ How to calculate the efficiency of a device using the equation

$$\text{efficiency} = \frac{\text{useful work output}}{\text{total energy input}}$$

➤ The terms thinking distance, braking distance and stopping distance
➤ The meaning of reaction time, and be able to describe a simple experiment to measure reaction time
➤ How thinking distance changes with speed, and appreciate that thinking distance may increase when the driver has taken alcohol or drugs
➤ That braking distance increases with speed, and investigate other factors that affect braking distance
➤ Friction as the force that opposes motion, and its role when a vehicle brakes
➤ How the use of seatbelts, airbags and crumple zones reduce the risk of serious injury in car accidents
➤ Methods of speed control imposed to reduce the risk of accidents on the road
➤ The ethical issues raised by speed cameras

Fossil fuels

The most common fuels used in the world today are fossil fuels. Of these, the most important are **oil**, **coal** and **natural gas**. Other fossil fuels include **peat** (turf) and **lignite** (brown coal), but these are not used in such large quantities as oil, coal and natural gas.

What are fossil fuels? They are all formed from the dead remains of plant and animal matter buried in the Earth for millions of years. In general, plant remains have produced coal, while animal remains have produced oil and natural gas.

Over the last two centuries, the use of fossil fuels in the UK has increased dramatically. The initial increase was at the time of the Industrial Revolution in the early 1800s, a period of tremendous growth in the number of industries and factories. Table 17.1 shows the main users of fossil fuels in the world today. Some countries in the Developing World are now going through rapid industrialisation, so the growth in the use of fossil fuels is set to continue over the next few decades.

Table 17.1 Main consumers of fossil fuels in 2004

Country	Oil-based fuels used per year in millions of barrels*	Coal used per year in millions of kg	Natural gas used per year in millions of cubic metres
USA	5700	934 930	710 290
Russia	4330	462 800	753 370
Japan	1670	74 300	66 500
China	1330	1 563 400	unknown
Germany	780	175 900	103 580
UK	690	83 760	67 330

*1 barrel of oil averages 159 litres

The figures in the table hide the fact that different countries have different populations.

1 Find out the population of each of the countries in Table 17.1 by visiting the website

www.census.gov/ipc/www/idbsum.html

Then work out the fossil fuel use per person. How do the figures compare for the different countries?

If you research data comparing different countries' use of fossil fuels, you may find that all use has been converted into kg (or tonnes) of oil (or 'oil equivalent') for easier comparison, as shown in Table 17.2.

Table 17.2 Fossil fuel use per person in 2004

	Average use per person in kg oil per year
World population	1422
USA	8360
UK	3185
Burundi (in southern Africa)	8

2 Why can we not present the data in Table 17.2 as a bar chart? What do the figures make clear?

Research the trend in fossil fuel use (i) in Western Europe and (ii) in Asia, from about 1980 to 2004 or later. Can you put forward any explanation for these trends, particularly the increase in fossil fuel use in China and India?

Fossil fuels in Ireland

Ireland has **very few fossil fuel resources** and continues to import increasing quantities of fuel, particularly oil. In recent years it has exploited natural gas reserves discovered in the Celtic Sea.

Northern Ireland has **substantial deposits of lignite** around Crumlin and Ballycastle, but as yet these deposits have not been exploited commercially. To do so would involve open-cast mining with significant visual, dust and noise pollution, and so would spoil areas considered to have much natural beauty. Those who favour the commercial development of these sites point out that it would also bring much needed employment to Northern Ireland and that it would contribute much to the local economy.

Oil – a special fuel

The middle of the 19th century saw the first vehicles that did not need animals to pull them. These were generally steam driven, and required fossil fuel – usually coal – to be fed regularly into a furnace to produce steam in a boiler. We call this an **external combustion engine**. For over a hundred years this was the way in which most trains were driven, but the technology was very labour intensive and dirty.

In 1885 Karl Benz built the first vehicle to use an **internal combustion engine**. The fuel needed to be a fluid – a material that could flow down a pipe – that is, a gas or a liquid. Benz used petrol as the fuel. The petrol was mixed in the right proportions with air in a carburettor and then **burned inside the engine**. This was much more convenient than a steam engine because:

- the engine could be switched on and off instantly
- there was no need to burn fuel except when the engine was being used
- it was much more efficient (less wasteful of energy – see page 233) than an external combustion engine.

Figure 17.1 A steam traction engine, which worked by external combustion of coal

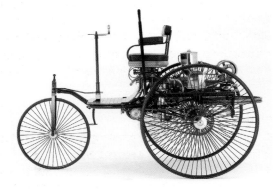

Figure 17.2 One of the first motor vehicles, designed by Karl Benz in 1886, which worked on internal combustion of petrol

Table 17.3 Comparison of the energy density of fuels

	Diesel	Petrol	Auto gas (liquefied petroleum gas)	Coal	Car battery
Approximate energy from 1 kg fuel in millions of joules	38	28	24	20	0.2

Oil-based fuels have a further advantage over other fossil fuels. They have much **higher energy density**. This means there is more energy available from 1 kg of oil-based fuel than there is from any other type of fossil fuel. In transport, a higher energy density fuel means that it possible to travel further without refuelling. Table 17.3 shows the energy density of different energy resources. Note the very low energy density of a car battery. This is the reason why, so far, few car engines have been designed to run on battery power alone. A battery provides so little energy for its mass, that any car using only a battery would only be able to travel about 50 miles before the battery would have to be recharged.

> 3 Describe briefly the difference between an internal combustion engine and an external combustion engine. Give an example of a machine that uses an external combustion engine.

The problem with oil

The 20th century saw a dramatic rise in the number of cars. In 1885 there were less than 1000 petrol-driven cars in the world; by the year 2000 there were more than 400 million cars, nearly all of which used oil-based fuels. In the same period, industry was also increasing its use of oil, both as a fuel and as a raw material for manufacturing chemicals such as plastics. The problems that many scientists are becoming increasingly concerned about today are:

- the limited world reserves of fossil fuels, especially oil
- global warming caused by the carbon dioxide emissions from burning fossil fuels.

The governments of many countries have been advised by their scientists that global warming and decreasing reserves of fossil fuels are real problems and that action needs to be taken to avoid catastrophe. Many countries of the world have entered into an agreement, called the **Kyoto Protocol**, that limits carbon dioxide emissions and so should reduce use of fossil fuels. (See page 90 for more details of this.) All of us need to be conscious of conserving fossil fuels by using energy as efficiently as possible.

How can we reduce our reliance on oil?

In Brazil it has been common for many years for oil companies to add alcohol to petrol for use by cars. The product is called **gasohol**. This is done to extend the country's oil supplies. In Germany, there has been much research on the use of oils obtained from seeds, such as maize and rapeseed (Figure 17.3). These oils can be processed into **biodiesel** fuel that can be bought in many petrol stations in Germany (Figure 17.4). Biodiesel fuels (or biofuels) are **carbon neutral**, that is they do not contribute to the greenhouse effect.

Figure 17.3 Biodiesel can be produced from the vegetable oil extracted from the seeds of oilseed rape

Figure 17.4 Biodiesel fuel is a viable alternative to conventional diesel

This is because the plants from which they are made take exactly the same amount of carbon dioxide out of the atmosphere as the oils put back into the atmosphere when they are burned. All petrol and diesel on sale in the UK from 2010 will contain 5% biofuel.

ACTIVITY

Find out what a biodigester is and how it can be used to produce fuel gases.

Alternative fuels under test by car manufacturers include **hydrogen fuel cells**. Fuel cells are like batteries – they produce electrical energy to drive an electric motor – but, unlike batteries, they can be recharged by adding hydrogen at a filling station.

The German car industry is also researching **methanol fuel cells**. Methanol is a liquid, similar to alcohol, used in many industrial processes.

For many years, London buses used **regenerative braking systems**. Normally when a bus brakes, a lot of wasted heat is produced. In these buses the wheel was attached to an electrical generator and as it braked its kinetic energy was converted into electricity. This electrical energy recharged the battery and extended its life. Some car makers have now gone one stage further and developed **hybrid propulsion**. The Toyota Prius, for example, has an ordinary petrol engine and a high voltage rechargeable battery. As far as possible, energy which would otherwise be wasted is used to recharge the battery. This battery is used at times to drive the vehicle. A computer management system selects whether it is more efficient at any given time to use the normal petrol engine or the high voltage electric motor powered by the rechargeable battery. This greatly **increases the fuel efficiency** of the vehicle.

Controlling the demand for fuel for transport

Normally when prices rise, people buy less of that product. So a rise in the price of petrol and diesel should limit the demand.

In the late 1990s, the British Government decided that it would **gradually increase the price of petrol and diesel year by year**, by increasing the taxes to be paid on these fuels. There were two reasons for doing this:

1 By increasing taxes the Government could raise more money for schools, hospitals and so on.

2 By raising the price of petrol and diesel, the Government hoped that people would use less of these fuels.

However, in the early years of the following decade there was strike action against these increasing taxes, because people thought it was unfair that British petrol prices were so much higher than those in France or Germany, and that foreign companies were able to take advantage of lower fuel prices in their countries. Outside the big cities, there were complaints that public transport was so poor that people had no choice but to use private cars. So, the Government was forced to change its policy.

What is likely to happen in the years to come? Almost all fuel for transport comes from oil, and as the world's supply of oil gets less and less, **the cost of petrol and diesel is almost certain to rise**. The challenge for science is to develop alternative, inexpensive forms of transport. Until that happens, we all have a responsibility to **use fossil fuels as sparingly as we can**.

Efficiency

The **efficiency** of a device is a way of describing how good the device is at transferring energy from one form to another, in the way it was designed to.

Suppose a light bulb takes in 100 joules of electrical energy and gives out 5 joules of light energy and 95 joules of heat energy. Then only $\frac{5}{100}$ (or 5%) of the input electrical energy is converted to useful light energy. The rest of the input energy is wasted as heat. We say the efficiency of the bulb is 5% or 0.05.

But if the same light bulb were used as a heater to keep a pet snake warm, then the intended output energy form would be heat, so the efficiency of the bulb would be $\frac{95}{100}$ or 95% or 0.95.

Efficiency can be calculated by the equation:

$$\textbf{efficiency} = \frac{\textbf{useful work (or energy) output}}{\textbf{total energy input}}$$

If all energy forms are considered, the **total energy output is equal to the total energy input**.

Problem 1
An electric kettle uses 400 000 joules of electrical energy to boil some water. If 80 000 joules of this energy is wasted, calculate the kettle's efficiency.

Solution
Here the useful energy output is heat energy.
Useful energy output = 400 000 − 80 000 = 320 000 joules

$$\text{Efficiency} = \frac{\text{useful energy output}}{\text{total energy input}} = \frac{320\ 000}{400\ 000} = \textbf{0.8}$$

Problem 2
A car does 560 000 joules of useful work in climbing a hill. The efficiency of its petrol engine is 28% (0.28). How much petrol energy does it use?

Solution

$$\text{Efficiency} = \frac{\text{useful work output}}{\text{total energy input}}$$

$$\text{Total energy input} = \frac{\text{useful work output}}{\text{efficiency}} = \frac{560\ 000\ \text{J}}{0.28} = \mathbf{2\ 000\ 000\ J}$$

4   A car's energy use is summarised in the table.

Input energy		Output energy	
Form	Amount in kJ	Form	Amount in kJ
chemical (fuel)	300	heat	190
		sound	
		kinetic	96
		other	12

a   How much sound energy does the car produce?
b   What is the *useful* output energy form?
c   Calculate the efficiency of the engine.

Road safety

One cause of road accidents is that some drivers do not keep a big enough gap between themselves and the vehicle ahead. If the car ahead brakes suddenly, the car behind crashes into it. What is the safe distance to keep from the car ahead? When a driver has to apply the brakes, two things happen.

- The driver's brain must consider what is happening before he/she makes a decision to apply the brakes. The distance the car travels during this thinking time is called the **thinking distance**.
- Once the brakes are applied, the car takes time to decelerate. The distance travelled after the brakes are applied but before the car comes to rest is the **braking distance**.

The **stopping distance** is the sum of the thinking distance and the braking distance. All these three distances depend on the speed of the car: they are greater at higher speeds. Research by the Road Traffic Laboratory for a typical family car is shown in Table 17.4.

Table 17.4 Stopping distances at different speeds for a typical family car

Speed in miles per hour (and m/s)	Thinking distance in metres	Braking distance* in metres	Stopping distance in metres
20 mph (9 m/s)	6	6	12
30 mph (13 m/s)	9	14	23
40 mph (18 m/s)	12	24	36
50 mph (22 m/s)	15	38	53
60 mph (27 m/s)	18	55	73
70 mph (31 m/s)	21	75	96

*on dry roads, with good tyres and brakes

What affects the thinking distance?

The thinking *time* depends mainly on the ability of the driver's brain to judge that it is necessary to stop. Anything that slows down the brain or affects the driver's judgement will increase the thinking time and hence increase the thinking distance. The major factors that increase thinking time are:

- alcohol
- some drugs prescribed by a doctor or bought from a chemist's shop
- illegal drugs.

Problem

a Use Table 17.4 to calculate the average thinking time of a driver travelling at 40 miles per hour.

b As a result of taking cough medicine, this driver's thinking time is increased to 0.95 s. What effect would this have on his thinking *distance* if he was travelling at **i** 40 mph (18 m/s) and **ii** 70 mph (31 m/s)?

Solution

a From the table we see that at 40 mph (18 m/s), the thinking distance is 12 m.

$$\text{Since time} = \frac{\text{distance}}{\text{speed}}, \text{time} = \frac{12 \text{ m}}{18 \text{ m/s}}$$

So, thinking time = **0.67 seconds**

b i Normal thinking distance at 40 mph (18 m/s) is 12 m.
After taking the medicine,
thinking distance = speed × thinking time
$$= 18 \times 0.95 = 17.1 \text{ m}$$
which is an increase of $17.1 - 12 = $ **5.1 m**

ii Normal thinking distance at 70 mph (31 m/s) is 21 m.
After taking the medicine,
thinking distance = speed × thinking time
$$= 31 \times 0.95 = 29.45 \text{ m}$$
which is an increase of $29.45 - 21 = $ **8.45 m**

> **5** Check using Table 17.4 that the thinking time does not depend on the car's speed.

The thinking distance is increased with increased speed of the car – the car travels further during the thinking time.

What affects the braking distance?

The following all tend to increase the braking distance:

- increased speed
- bald tyres
- wet or icy roads
- poor brakes
- poor road surface.

The police take the location of the road and its condition into account when advising local authorities about speed limits. Older cars must be tested at least once a year (the MOT test) to find out if they are roadworthy. But we still all rely on the driver leaving enough space between himself and the car in front, especially on poor roads or in wet or icy conditions.

The Police Service (**www.psni.police.uk/**) publishes the causes of road accidents. Find out the percentage of road accidents where (i) high speed or (ii) alcohol has contributed to the cause of the accident.

Measuring reaction time

Reaction time is the time that passes between an observation and the start of the body's response to it. Reaction times can be measured roughly using a metre stick. A metre stick is held vertically by one person (A), against the fingers of another person's (B) outstretched palm, with the zero mark on the stick at the index finger. Person B is told to grasp the metre stick when it is let go by person A. The distance the stick falls before it is grasped is a good measure of the reaction time of person B. The experiment needs to be repeated several times and an average taken, to be confident of a reliable result.

Since the metre stick falls freely from rest, the reaction time, t, can be found from the equation

$$t = \sqrt{\frac{4.9}{d}}$$

where d is the distance the stick falls before it is grasped by person B. Typical results are shown in Table 17.5.

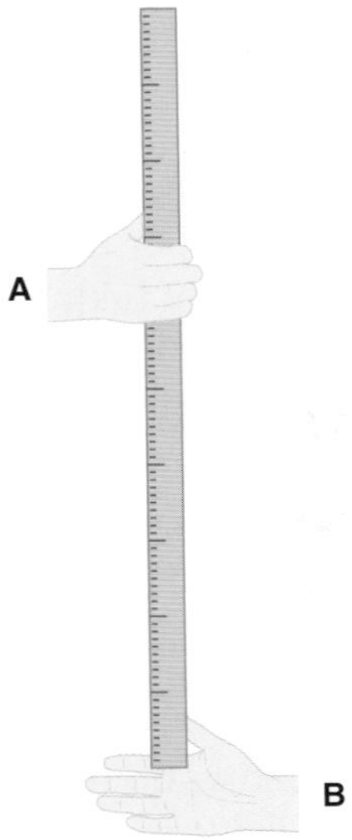

A

B

Figure 17.5 Measuring reaction time using a metre stick

Table 17.5 Typical results

Distance d in m	0.82	0.82	0.86	0.99	0.86	0.91
Reaction time t in s	0.41	0.41	0.42	0.45	0.42	0.43

Average reaction time (excluding the 'rogue' at 0.45 s) = 0.42 s

Carry out a series of experiments to find a friend's reaction time. Then ask your friend to count down out loud backwards from 100 to zero, while you measure his/her reaction time again.

Does this provide evidence that reaction time changes when our minds are not on the task? Discuss whether or not motorists should be prevented from using a mobile phone when driving.

Friction

Friction is the name given to the **force that opposes motion**. The friction force:

- slows a vehicle down when the brakes are applied
- brings a moving car to a standstill when the engine is switched off
- prevents tyres from slipping as they turn.

We can readily investigate the factors that determine the size of the friction force. We do this by pulling a rectangular block of wood with a metal eye at one end along a runway called a 'friction plane'. The eye on the block is attached by a cord to a spring balance, which acts as a newtonmeter to measure the pulling force. If we gradually increase the pulling force on the block until the block *just* begins to slide, the pulling force on the newtonmeter represents the maximum or **static friction** between the block and the runway.

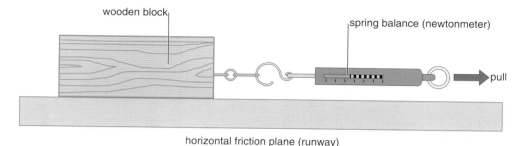

Figure 17.6 Investigating friction

There are three questions which require an answer:

1 Does the friction force increase with the weight of the block, if the area in contact with the runway is kept constant?
2 Does the friction force change if the roughness of the rubbing surfaces changes?
3 Does the friction force change if the area in contact with the runway changes, assuming the weight of the block and the nature of the surfaces rubbing together remain the same?

To answer the first question we use a single block of known weight and measure the static friction by the method described above. We increase the weight by adding additional known weights on top of the block. This keeps the area in contact with the runway and the surface between the runway and block unchanged, so that the test is fair. Typical results are shown in Table 17.6.

Table 17.6 Typical experimental results

Weight of wooden block = 2.5 N

Added weight in N	0	2.0	4.0	6.0	8.0	10.0
Total weight of block and added weights in N	2.5	4.5	6.5	8.5	10.5	12.5
Friction force in N	0.6	1.1	1.6	2.1	2.6	3.1

Repeated experiments show that the **static friction force is directly proportional to the weight of the moving object**.

We can tackle the second question above by changing the nature of the rubbing surfaces. The easiest way to do this is to glue sandpaper of different grades (roughness) to the lower surface of the moving block. By doing so we keep the weight (nearly) constant and do not change the area of contact. The experimental evidence suggests that **the rougher the surfaces rubbing together, the greater the friction force**.

The third question requires us to change the area in contact with the runway while keeping the total weight of the block and the nature of the surface constant. To do this we use blocks of different area, each with sandpaper of the same grade glued to the lower surface. We keep the total weight constant by adding weights as required to the block. The experimental evidence suggests that the **friction force is entirely independent of the area of contact** with the runway.

6 a Give two situations where friction is helpful and two where it is a nuisance.
  b If you do not know what a lubricant is, find out. Why are lubricants used in car engines?
  c In rural areas, sand bunkers can sometimes be seen at the side of the road. The bunkers are most often seen at the bottom of a steep hill. What is the sand used for?
7 In a certain experiment the friction force between a wooden block and a surface is measured for different block weights. The purpose of the experiment is to find out if the weight of the block is related to the static friction force.
  a Describe briefly how the friction force could be measured.
  b What factors would have to stay constant if the test was to be fair?
  The experimental results are in the table below:

Total weight of block in N	2.5	4.5	6.5	8.5	10.5	12.5
Friction force in N	0.6	1.1	1.6	2.1	2.6	3.1

  c Plot a suitable graph and discuss what the data show.

ACTIVITY

Is the size of the friction force between a block of wood and the bench the same when the block is moving as when it is stationary? Plan an experiment to find out.

Collisions

Moving objects have kinetic energy. When collisions occur, the speed of the objects involved generally changes as kinetic energy transfers from one object to another. Sound and heat energy are produced too. There will be less kinetic energy after the collision than there was before.

If the colliding objects are cars, some of the lost kinetic energy is used in deforming the car bodies. Car designers these days use their knowledge of physics to make modern cars safer than ever before. One method is to design **crumple zones** at the front and rear of the vehicle. These **absorb most of the lost kinetic energy in a direct collision** by crumpling – this leaves less energy to harm the people inside the car, who are protected by a rigid (non-crumpling) steel shell.

In a collision, passengers tend to be thrown forwards. To reduce the risk of serious injury, car drivers and all passengers must, by law, wear seatbelts. These provide a **restraining force**, preventing, for example, the front seat occupants being thrown out through the front windscreen.

Figure 17.7 The car's crumple zone absorbs the energy of the collision

More recently, **airbags** have been fitted to the front and sometimes the side of the driver and front seat passenger. In a serious collision, a small explosive charge is detonated, the airbag inflates in about 1/10th of a second and deflates shortly afterwards. The airbag reduces the risk of crush injuries against the steering wheel, for example, or collision injuries caused by fast-moving objects inside the vehicle.

Crash barriers

On dual carriageways and motorways you often see steel barriers. The design of these crash barriers is constantly being developed. They must be strong enough to prevent vehicles travelling from one carriageway to another, but weak enough to deform and absorb energy in a collision. Designers must take into account the probable speeds and masses of vehicles colliding with the barrier. They also consider the number and positions of the pillars to which the barrier is attached – the closer the pillars, the stronger the barrier is likely to be.

Speed control

In the UK and in Ireland there are **speed limits on all roads**. They depend on the type of vehicle and the type of road. Table 17.7 summarises them.

Table 17.7 Normal speed limits (in miles per hour), except where road signs show otherwise

Type of vehicle	In built-up area	On single carriageway	On dual carriageway	On motorway
cars and motorcycles	30	60	70	70
cars towing caravans or trailers	30	50	60	60
buses and coaches	30	50	60	70
goods vehicles	30	50	60	70
heavy goods vehicles (more than 7500 kg)	30	40	50	60

There are two main reasons for speed limits. They:

- make accidents less likely
- reduce the risk of fatal injury if an accident occurs.

Police reports indicate that in nearly every fatal accident the speed of the vehicles involved has contributed to the cause. Since occasional speed traps did not succeed in getting drivers to slow down, the Government allowed the police to install **speed cameras** in many parts of the country. These photograph cars randomly, so catching on camera speeding cars and those 'jumping' traffic lights. Later the owner of the offending vehicle is identified from the photograph of the registration number, and the motorist is penalised.

ACTIVITY

Hold a class debate on one of these motions:
   'Northern Ireland should have many more speed cameras to encourage better driving'; or
   'In the interests of safety, cars should be fitted with a device to limit their maximum speed to 70 miles per hour'.

Speed cameras play an important part in road safety, but not everyone is in favour of them. Some believe they are an **infringement against personal liberty** when people are doing nothing against the law. Others complain that they **prevent the policeman exercising his discretion** as to whether the case should involve penalties or not. A third group believes that the Government is simply using these cameras to **raise more money** by way of fines. Whatever the truth, there is no doubt that these cameras have caused many motorists to be more aware of their speed and so reduced the number and seriousness of accidents caused. That may have saved lives.

Traffic calming

There are other ways to get motorists to slow down. These are called 'traffic calming' measures. The most common are **speed bumps** and **road narrowing schemes**. They are often installed in residential areas and on private property where other methods are too expensive or impracticable. Drivers are forced to slow down or risk a bumpy ride with possible damage to their vehicles. However, these measures also have their critics, as they **increase the time taken to provide emergency services** – police, fire brigade or ambulance.

ACTIVITY

Do some research to find out the number of deaths per year on Northern Ireland's roads and their main causes. Which motorists are most at risk?

Accidents involving pedestrians

Road accidents involving pedestrians are often very serious. Pedestrians have much smaller mass than road vehicles, so they always come off worse. To minimise risk to themselves and others, pedestrians should follow **The Highway Code**:

- stay on the footpath where there is one
- walk on the right-hand side of the road where no footpath is provided
- wear light-coloured, reflective or fluorescent items such as armbands at night or in foggy conditions
- always use the Green Cross Code when crossing the road
- wherever possible use a Zebra crossing, Pelican crossing or Puffin crossing.

ACTIVITY

Use your favourite search engine to investigate the following:
i   the increase in the number of cars on Northern Ireland's roads in the last 40 years;
ii   the increase in the number of car accidents over the past 10 years;
iii the increase in the number of deaths on Northern Ireland's roads.

websites

www.eia.doe.gov/pub/international/iealf/tablee1.xls
tables of world fossil fuel consumption from 1980 to 2003 – a good resource, but students may need some help in extracting the information they need

http://en.wikipedia.org/wiki/Internal_combustion_engine
useful enrichment material on the history of the internal combustion engine, with some excellent graphics

http://inventors.about.com/library/inventors/blsteamengine.htm
useful enrichment material on early external combustion engines, especially those of Savery, Newcomen and Watt

www.foe.co.uk
home page of Friends of the Earth, providing useful information on nearly all environmental issues

www.commuterpage.com/afv-hev.htm
information about alternative, non-fossil fuels and hybrid vehicles

www.thinkroadsafety.gov.uk/campaigns/seatbelts/seatbelts.htm
Department of Transport website, providing useful information about seatbelts, crumple zones, use of alcohol and other drugs

www.rospa.com/roadsafety/advice/motorvehicles/airbags.htm
information about how airbags work

www.corusautomotive.com/en/news
Go to the 2004 press release archives and scroll down to 'Corus helps advance Road Safety' for an article dealing with the design and positioning of steel crash barriers

www.science-projects.com/Crumple.htm
ideas for science investigations of crash barrier design using confined, crumpled paper

http://news.bbc.co.uk/1/hi/magazine/4587629.stm
information about 'bendy road signs' and their application to road safety

www.rospa.com/roadsafety/citizenship/teachers_notes.pdf
ideas for activities and discussions about the rights and responsibilities of citizens in relation to road safety

http://ireland.iop.org/videos.html
website of the Irish Institute of Physics, giving details of videos and other resources available to teachers

Questions

1 a The table shows a list of energy resources. Copy the table and place a tick (✓) in the second column if the resource named is a fossil fuel, or in the third column if it is renewable.

Energy resource	Fossil fuel	Renewable
gas		
biomass		
wood		
oil		

(4 marks)

b Name the main greenhouse gas produced by burning fossil fuels. *(1 mark)*

c Increased greenhouse gases in our atmosphere are causing global warming. Give **two** specific results that are likely to be experienced in N. Ireland as a result of global warming. *(2 marks)*

2 a Copy and complete the table giving information about the stopping distances for a car.

Speed of car in m/s	Thinking distance in m	Braking distance in m	Stopping distance in m
10		5	10
20	10		30
40	20	80	

(2 marks)

b Explain what is meant by **thinking distance**. *(2 marks)*

c Give **two** factors that can affect **thinking distance**. *(2 marks)*

d Higher speed causes the **braking distance** to increase. Write down **two** other factors that can make the braking distance longer. *(2 marks)*

CCEA GCSE Science: Single Award (Modular) Specimen Paper (Foundation Tier) 2006

3 The most common energy resources used in Europe today are:

oil, natural gas, coal, nuclear energy, hydroelectric energy and wind energy

a Choose **one** non-renewable energy resource from the list above and say why it is non-renewable. *(1 mark)*

b Choose **one** renewable energy resource from the list and say why it is renewable. *(1 mark)*

c Give **one** advantage that renewable energy resources have over non-renewable resources. *(1 mark)*

4 A small, portable television has an efficiency of 0.4. Every second it gives out 18 joules of useful light energy (the picture) and 10 joules of useful sound energy. The rest of the output energy is wasted as heat. Calculate

a the total useful energy given out every second; *(1 mark)*

b the total wasted heat energy produced per second; *(3 marks)*

c the total electrical energy input per second. *(1 mark)*

5 Traffic calming is designed to make drivers slow down in built-up areas.

a Describe briefly **one** traffic calming method. *(1 mark)*

b Give a reason why the local authorities might think traffic calming is a good idea. *(1 mark)*

c Give a reason why emergency services (police, fire brigade and ambulance services) might think traffic calming is sometimes a bad idea. *(1 mark)*

6 Read the following passage and then answer the questions.

Hybrid cars

A hybrid vehicle has two power sources. A mo-ped is a **mo**torised **ped**al bike. It is a hybrid because it has a motor and pedals. A petrol-electric car is another type of hybrid vehicle.

The pie chart shows the fuel used for personal transport in Europe.

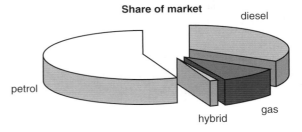

Share of market

a Suggest **two** reasons why hybrid cars have a small percentage of the market. *(2 marks)*

b Many cars in Brazil run on alcofuel. Alcofuel is a mixture of alcohol and petrol. Give **one** advantage of using this type of fuel. *(1 mark)*

c Name a suitable substitute for diesel fuel. What is this diesel substitute made from? *(1 mark)*

CCEA GCSE Science: Single Award (Modular) Specimen Paper (Foundation Tier) 2006 (part question)

Chapter 18

Motion

By the end of this chapter you should know and understand:

➤ The effects of balanced and unbalanced forces on motion
➤ The Newtonian model for constant motion
➤ The difference between instantaneous speed and average speed
➤ How to apply the equation for average speed
➤ The interpretation of straight line graphs of distance against time
➤ How to investigate speed using a datalogger
➤ The meaning of acceleration and how to apply the equation for acceleration
➤ How to investigate acceleration using a datalogger
➤ That momentum is the product of mass and velocity
➤ That momentum transfer in a collision means a force is acting

Balanced and unbalanced forces

A **force** has both size and direction. The size of the force is measured in **newtons** (N). When drawing forces in diagrams it is usual to represent the direction of the force by an arrow and the size of the force by the length of the arrow drawn to scale.

A horizontal force of 50 N acting to the right may be represented by

A horizontal force of 150 N acting to the left may be represented by

$\longrightarrow$ 50 N

150 N $\longleftarrow$

If the forces are equal in size and opposite in direction, then the forces are balanced. **Balanced forces do not change the velocity** of an object.

Figure 18.1 shows a car travelling at a steady speed of 30 km/h in a straight line under the action of two equal and opposite forces: the driving force (or thrust) exerted by the engine and drag.

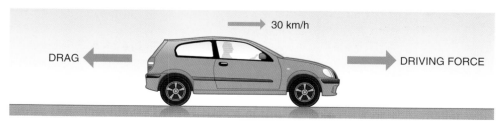

DRAG

30 km/h

DRIVING FORCE

Figure 18.1 Balanced forces mean a steady speed

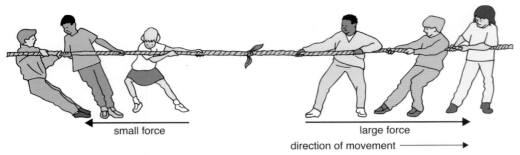

small force

large force

direction of movement ⟶

Figure 18.2 The forces in this tug of war are unbalanced, as the team on the right is pulling with a larger force

If an object is stationary (not moving), it will remain stationary if balanced forces act on it.

In a tug of war like that in Figure 18.2, two teams pull against each other. When both teams pull equally hard, the forces are balanced and the rope does not move. But when one team starts to pull with a larger force, the rope moves. When this happens the two forces are no longer balanced.

Unbalanced forces will change the velocity of an object. Since velocity involves both speed and direction, unbalanced forces can make an object speed up, slow down or change direction.

Unbalanced forces applied to the handlebars will make the cyclist in Figure 18.3 change direction. This means the velocity of the cyclist will change even though the speed may stay the same.

An object will only accelerate when an unbalanced (or **resultant**) force acts on it. It then accelerates in the direction of the unbalanced force. If the driving force on a car is greater than the drag force, the car will accelerate or speed up.

pushing force

pulling force

Figure 18.3 The cyclist changes direction by applying unbalanced forces to the handlebars

DRAG

DRIVING FORCE

Figure 18.4 This car is accelerating

If the driver then decides to apply the brakes, the driving force will be smaller than the braking force and the car will decelerate or slow down.

BRAKING FORCE

DRIVING FORCE

Figure 18.5 This car is decelerating

Imagine a car travelling in a straight line along a motorway. Table 18.1 shows in which situations there is an unbalanced force on the car.

Table 18.1

Situation	Unbalanced force acting
The car's speed is increasing	✓
The car's speed is decreasing	✓
The car's speed is constant	
The car starts going round a bend	✓

Newton's Law of Uniform Motion

All that has been said so far about balanced forces can be summarised by Newton's Law of Uniform Motion:

> **A body stays at rest or continues to move with a constant speed in a straight line unless an unbalanced force makes it behave differently.**

This law is by no means obvious. The ancient Greeks, for example, believed that a force was needed to keep an object moving. Aristotle, who lived in Athens about 2400 years ago, taught this. But Aristotle was wrong! Before Newton, scientists knew little about the force of friction, which slows down moving objects. We now know that forward forces are needed to balance friction if constant motion is to continue. However, deep in space there is almost no friction. Far away from the Earth therefore, a spacecraft can simply switch off its engines and coast at a constant speed in a straight line. And this motion will continue until another force causes the spacecraft to change its speed or its direction.

ACTIVITY

Imagine you are Isaac Newton and your friend is Aristotle. How could Newton convince Aristotle that when the forces on a moving object are balanced the object moves in a straight line with constant speed?

Speed

If a car travels between two points on a road, its **average speed** can be calculated using the formula

$$\text{average speed} = \frac{\text{total distance moved}}{\text{total time taken}}$$

If the distance is measured in metres (m) and the time in seconds (s), then the speed is measured in metres per second (m/s).

For example, the distance between Belfast and Coleraine is 100 km. Suppose a car travels from Belfast to Coleraine in 2 hours. Then the average speed can be found as follows:

$$\text{average speed} = \frac{100 \text{ km}}{2 \text{ hours}} = 50 \text{ km/h}$$

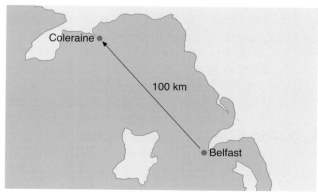

Figure 18.6

The speedometer of the car would certainly not read 50 km/h for the whole journey but would vary considerably from this value. The driver might stop for a rest or slow down because of a traffic jam, and he might speed up to overtake another car. The speed of the car at any instant in time is called the **instantaneous speed**. The car's speedometer tells us the instantaneous speed, but we need the car's on-board computer (or a simple calculator) to find the average speed.

1 A newspaper reports that the world's fastest passenger airliner is the Russian Tupolev Tu-144. One statement in the report reads: 'On one particular flight it reached a maximum speed of 1600 m/s or Mach 2.4.' Does 1600 m/s represent an instantaneous speed or an average speed?

Problem

Find the average speed of a car if it accelerates from rest and travels 60 m in 3 s.

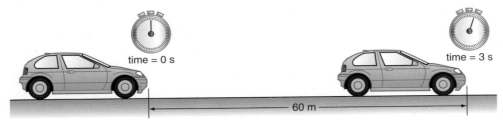

time = 0 s   time = 3 s

60 m

Figure 18.7

Solution

$$\text{Average speed} = \frac{\text{total distance moved}}{\text{total time taken}}$$

$$= \frac{60 \text{ m}}{3 \text{ s}}$$

$$= \textbf{20 m/s}$$

2 A car travels 800 m in 40 s. Calculate its average speed.
3 A car has a steady speed of 10 m/s.
   a How far does the car go in 9 s?
   b How long does it take the car to travel 220 m?
4 Calculate the average speed of:
   a an athlete who runs 400 m in 50 s
   b a car which travels 175 miles in 5 hours
   c a space shuttle which travels 70 000 km in 2.5 hours.
5 A cyclist travels 50 km at a steady speed of 25 km/h. He then takes a rest for half an hour before cycling home again at a steady speed. His average speed for the 100 km round trip is 20 km/h. Calculate:
   a the time taken for the outward 50 km part of the journey
   b the total time taken for the 100 km round trip
   c the time taken for the return leg of the journey.

Distance–time graphs

A **distance–time** graph is a plot of distance on the y-axis versus time on the x-axis. The simplest type of distance–time graph is shown in Figure 18.8.

This graph illustrates that although the time increases steadily, the distance travelled is not changing. The body must be **stationary**.

> **A horizontal line on a distance–time graph means that the body is stationary.**

In contrast, Figure 18.9 shows that the distance is increasing by 5 m in every second, i.e. the body is travelling with uniform speed covering equal distances in equal units of time.

The slope of the graph $= \dfrac{AB}{OB}$

$$= \dfrac{20 - 0}{4 - 0}$$

$$= \dfrac{20}{4}$$

$$= \textbf{5 m/s}$$

The speed the body is travelling is 5 m/s.

> **The slope or gradient of a distance–time graph represents the speed.**

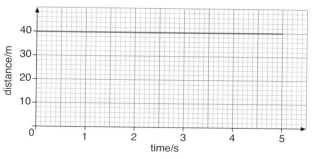

Figure 18.8 A simple distance–time graph of a stationary body

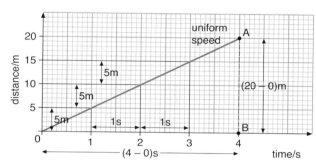

Figure 18.9 A distance–time graph of a body moving with uniform speed

---

6 Figure 18.10 shows a distance–time graph for a cyclist starting off from a set of traffic lights.
   a Between what times is the cyclist
      i travelling at her greatest speed
      ii stopped?
   b What distance has the cyclist travelled when she first stops?
   c Calculate the speed of the cyclist at time $t = 10$ seconds.

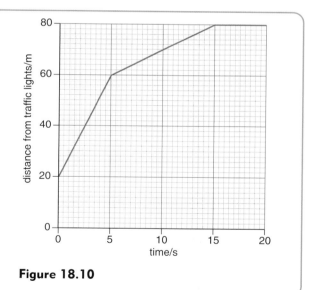

Figure 18.10

Measuring speed using a datalogger

We can measure the speed of a moving trolley using a datalogger and computer. The arrangement is as shown in Figure 18.11. A beam of light passes between the two position sensors; this is interrupted by the card on the trolley as the trolley passes through.

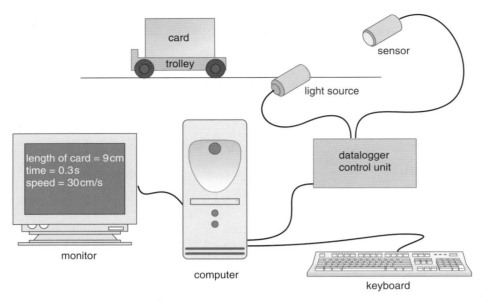

length of card = 9 cm
time = 0.3 s
speed = 30 cm/s

card

trolley

sensor

light source

datalogger
control unit

monitor

computer

keyboard

Figure 18.11 Measuring the speed of a trolley

The computer software first asks you to enter the length of the card attached to the trolley. As the card interrupts the light beam between the position sensors, one of the computer's internal clocks is switched on; as the card passes through and the light beam is again detected, the computer's internal clock switches off. The computer then does the arithmetic (speed = distance/time) to find the speed of the trolley. This is the trolley's average speed during the period of beam interruption. But because the trolley is moving quite fast this is roughly equal to the trolley's instantaneous speed.

ACTIVITY

Set up a runway with a slight slope so that a trolley will, when gently pushed, move at a steady speed down it. Measure the speed.
When the trolley has a constant speed down the runway, what can you conclude about the forces acting on it?
Now add weights on top of the trolley and once more give it a gentle push. Does it still move at a steady speed? Explain your findings.

This type of experiment can give convincing evidence for Newton's Law of Uniform Motion. Rather than tilting the runway to compensate for friction, a linear air track is used. The air from a pump passes through tiny holes in the track, so that there is very little resistance between the track and the 'trolley'. By using sensors at each end of the track, connected to timers, it can easily be shown that the 'trolley' travelled at the same speed at one end of the track as it did at the other. We can conclude that the 'trolley' was travelling at a constant speed, as predicted by Newton's Law.

Acceleration

We are all familiar with the accelerator pedal on a car. When the driver pushes this pedal with his/her foot, the car goes faster. When the foot is taken off the accelerator, the car's speed decreases. So we know that acceleration has to do with increasing or decreasing speed. In fact acceleration is the **rate of change of an object's speed**. In every case, the acceleration is caused by a resultant (unbalanced) force on the object.

Suppose a trolley is moving at 2 cm/s and that over a period of 4 seconds its speed increases to 14 cm/s. Then the speed increases by 12 cm/s over 4 seconds. So, every second, the speed increases by 3 cm/s. We can show this clearly in a table – see Table 18.2.

Table 18.2

Time in s	Speed in cm/s	Change in speed in cm/s
0	2	
1	5	3
2	8	3
3	11	3
4	14	3

Observe what is happening to the speed: every second the speed increases by 3 cm/s. We say that the trolley's acceleration is **3 cm/s²**. Note the unusual unit for acceleration.

What if the trolley is slowing down? Imagine the trolley moving up a runway. Its speed might change as shown in Table 18.3.

Table 18.3

Time in s	Speed in cm/s	Change in speed in cm/s
0	12.0	
1	10.5	−1.5
2	9.0	−1.5
3	7.5	−1.5
4	6.0	−1.5

Observe what is happening to the speed now. Every second the speed decreases by 1.5 cm/s. We say that the trolley's acceleration is **−1.5 cm/s²**. A negative acceleration is called a **deceleration** or a **retardation**.

To calculate the acceleration of an object we need to know:

- its starting speed, u
- its final speed, v
- the time, t, between starting speed and final speed.

The acceleration, a, can then be found from:

$$a = \frac{\textbf{change in speed}}{\textbf{time taken}} = \frac{(v - u)}{t}$$

Problem

Find the acceleration of a trolley if its speed increases from 2.5 m/s to 12.5 m/s in 5 s.

Solution

$$\text{Acceleration} = \frac{(v - u)}{t} = \frac{(12.5 - 2.5)}{5} = \frac{10}{5} = \textbf{2 m/s}^2$$

7 A lorry travelling at 27 m/s (60 mph) makes an emergency stop in 6 seconds.
  a Calculate the lorry's acceleration (assuming this to be uniform).
  b What does the negative sign in your answer indicate?

Measuring acceleration using a datalogger

To measure the acceleration of a trolley, say moving down a ramp, we need to use two sensors. One measures the **starting speed** of the trolley; the other measures the **final speed**. The computer's internal clock measures the time between one sensor and the other.

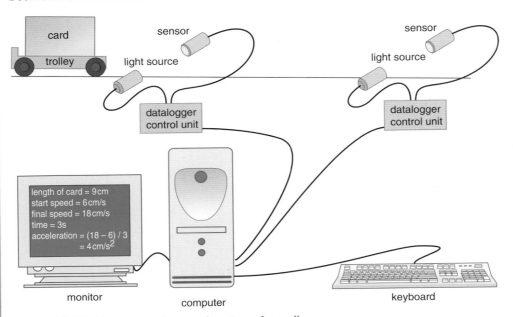

length of card = 9 cm
start speed = 6 cm/s
final speed = 18 cm/s
time = 3 s
acceleration = (18 − 6) / 3
            = 4 cm/s²

Figure 18.12 Measuring the acceleration of a trolley

ACTIVITY

Give a gentle push to a trolley on a horizontal runway and measure its acceleration as it nears the end of its motion. The acceleration will be negative – the trolley is slowing down.

ACTIVITY

Set up a runway with a slight slope so that a trolley will, when gently pushed, move at a steady speed down it. Now attach one end of a cord to the trolley and pass the other end over a pulley to a set of weights on a carrier. When the weights are released the trolley will accelerate. Measure the acceleration for different weights on the carrier.
  Is there is a relation between the weight on the carrier and the acceleration of the trolley?

8 How could you use a datalogger and computer to find the acceleration with which objects fall freely to the Earth?

Momentum

Figure 18.13 Moving objects have momentum

The **momentum** of a moving object is its mass multiplied by its velocity (speed). To avoid confusion we use the symbols m for mass and p for momentum. Then:

$$p = mv$$

where

    m is the object's **mass in kg**
    v is its **velocity in m/s**
    p is its **momentum** in **kg m/s**

Momentum, like velocity, has direction as well as size. The direction of the momentum and the direction of the velocity are the same.

Problem 1
Calculate the momentum of a car of mass 850 kg moving at 4 m/s.

Solution
Momentum = 850 kg × 4 m/s = **3400 kg m/s**

Problem 2
What is the velocity of a ball of mass 0.25 kg if its momentum is 3.5 kg m/s?

Solution
Momentum = mass × velocity

$$\text{Velocity} = \frac{\text{momentum}}{\text{mass}} = \frac{3.5}{0.25} = \textbf{14 m/s}$$

  9 Calculate the momentum of a car of mass 750 kg moving at 8 m/s.
10 What is the mass of a ball travelling at 70 cm/s if its momentum is 0.35 kg m/s?

Momentum and collisions

When two objects collide, the speed of each object generally changes. If the two objects are initially travelling in the same direction, the speed of one object will decrease while the speed of the other will increase. This means that some of the momentum of one object is transferred to the other.

Problem

A car has a mass of 550 kg and is moving along a straight line road with a steady speed of 3 m/s. Another car, of mass 450 kg, and travelling at a steady speed of 5 m/s, collides into the back of the first. After the collision each car moves at 3.9 m/s. Calculate:

a the momentum of each car before the collision
b the momentum gained by the 550 kg car as a result of the collision
c the momentum lost by the 450 kg car as a result of the collision.

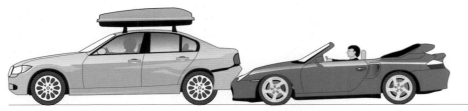

550 kg moving at 3 m/s   450 kg moving at 5 m/s

Figure 18.14

Solution

a Momentum of 550 kg car = mass × velocity
                   = 550 × 3
                   = 1650 kg m/s
momentum of 450 kg car = mass × velocity
                   = 450 × 5
                   = 2250 kg m/s

b Momentum of 550 kg car after collision = mass × velocity
                               = 550 × 3.9
                               = 2145 kg m/s

momentum gained by 550 kg car = 2145 − 1650
                                 = 495 kg m/s

c Momentum of 450 kg car after collision = mass × velocity
                               = 450 × 3.9
                               = 1755 kg m/s

momentum lost by 550 kg car = 2250 − 1755
                            = 495 kg m/s

Note that one car has gained additional momentum of 495 kg m/s, and the other has lost 495 kg m/s.

What happens when there is a momentum transfer in a collision? The answer is that **a transfer of momentum always means the presence of a force**. In this case, the car coming from behind exerts a forward force on the car in front, making it go faster. But the car coming from behind goes slower after the collision than it did before the collision. This is because the car at the front exerts a backward force on the car colliding with it. Now you might expect the sizes of these two forces to be equal. And you would be right!

The size of the force that acts in a momentum transfer depends on two factors:

- the amount of momentum transferred
- the time taken to transfer this momentum.

The more momentum transferred and the *shorter* the time it takes for it to be transferred, the greater the force that acts.

Now you can see why a fielder playing cricket or baseball pulls his hands inwards or downwards when catching a ball (Figure 18.15). The longer it takes to stop the ball, the smaller the force the ball exerts on his hands.

11 A car has a mass of 850 kg and is moving along a straight road with a steady speed of 4 m/s. Another car, of mass 1150 kg, and travelling in the opposite direction at a steady speed of 6 m/s, collides head on into the first. After the collision the cars stick together and initially move with a speed of 1.75 m/s. Calculate:

a the momentum of each car before the collision (one car will have a positive momentum and the other will have a negative momentum)

b the momentum of the combined cars after the collision (you will need to think about the direction of motion after the collision)

c the momentum lost by the 1150 kg car as a result of the collision

d the momentum gained by the 850 kg car as a result of the collision.

Comment on your answers to parts c and d.

Figure 18.15 Drawing back the hands when catching a ball

Find the mass of a heavy book (one between 0.75 kg and 1.5 kg would be suitable) using a balance. Drop the book from a known height (between 75 cm and 150 cm) on to electronic bathroom scales. Is there a link between the height from which the book falls and the maximum reading on the bathroom scales when the book hits it?

websites

www.bbc.co.uk/schools/gcsebitesize/physics/forces/speedvelocityaccelerationfhrev2.shtml
explanation of distance–time and other useful graphical methods

www.physicsclassroom.com/Class/momentum/u4l1a.html
introduction to the idea of momentum, with a few questions at the end

www.gcse.com/forces.htm
excellent pages on forces and motion, good for first-time learners or for revision

Questions

1 The sketch graph shows how the distance travelled by a cyclist changes with time.

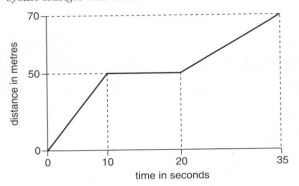

a i Describe what the cyclist was doing between times $t = 10$ seconds and $t = 20$ seconds. Choose from:
  stationary; going at a steady speed; going faster; going slower *(1 mark)*

  ii Calculate the average speed of the cyclist during her journey. Use the formula:

  $$\text{average speed} = \frac{\text{total distance}}{\text{total time}}$$

  You are advised to show clearly how you get your answer. *(3 marks)*

  CCEA GCSE Science: Single Award (Modular) Specimen Paper (Foundation Tier) 2006

b A motorist accelerates away from traffic lights at 3 m/s^2 as they turn from orange to green. Explain carefully what this means. *(2 marks)*

2 At the start of a tug-of-war competition Team A pulls with a force of 280 N and Team B also pulls with a force of 280 N.

team A
280N

team B
280N

a What is the resultant force on Team A? *(1 mark)*

b The force to the left from Team A remains 280 N, but the force from Team B to the right increases to 310 N. Calculate the size and direction of the resultant force in the rope. *(2 marks)*

CCEA GCSE Science: Single Award (Modular) Specimen Paper (Foundation Tier) 2006 (part question)

3 a What is friction? *(1 mark)*

b Two **identical** family cars travel down the same motorway at the same time.
Car A contains only the driver travelling to work. The boot is empty.
Car B contains the driver and four family members setting off on holiday. Car B is heavily loaded with lots of luggage in the boot.

  i Is the friction acting at the wheels on car B greater than, less than or equal to the friction acting at the wheels on car A? *(1 mark)*

  ii Give a reason for your answer to part **i**. *(1 mark)*

c A car of mass 1350 kg is travelling at 8 m/s. The mass of its passengers and their luggage is 650 kg. Use the equation:
  momentum = mass × speed
  to calculate the combined momentum of the car and its contents. *(3 marks)*

4 The graph shows how an athlete's distance from the finishing line changes in the last 35 seconds of a marathon race.

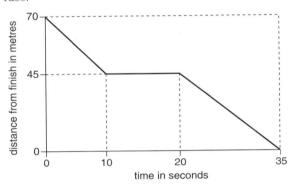

a How far was the athlete from the finish when she stopped? *(1 mark)*

b Between which times was the athlete moving fastest? *(1 mark)*

c Calculate the average speed of the athlete in the last 35 s of the race. *(3 marks)*

Radioactivity

The planetary model of the atom

All matter is made up of tiny particles called atoms. Inside every atom there are only three types of particles: protons and neutrons in the nucleus of the atom, and electrons in orbit around the nucleus. Turn back to Table 11.1, page 135, to remind yourself of the relative masses and charges of these particles.

A neutral atom must have the same number of protons (positively charged) as orbiting electrons (negatively charged). Figure 19.1 shows the structure of a helium atom. Since there are two protons inside the nucleus, the neutral atom must also have two orbiting electrons. Note that the diagram is not to scale: the diameter of the atom is about 100 000 times greater than that of the nucleus.

What makes one atom different from another?

Different atoms have different numbers of protons in their nucleus. Oxygen, for example, has 8 protons, while sodium has 11 and uranium has 92. This means that they have different numbers of electrons too, and it is the arrangement and behaviour of these electrons that makes the properties of different elements different – see Chapter 11. Here we are concerned with the nuclei of atoms. The relative numbers of protons and neutrons in the nucleus affects the **stability** of an atom.

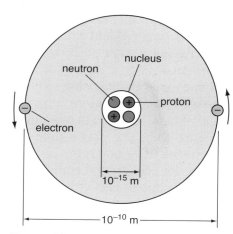

Figure 19.1 A helium atom

Radioactivity

In 1896 the French scientist Henri Becquerel discovered that certain rocks containing uranium gave out strange radiation that could penetrate paper and 'fog' a photographic film. He called the effect **radioactivity**. His students, Pierre and Marie Curie, were later to identify three separate types of radiation. Unsure of a suitable name, the Curies called them **alpha** (α), **beta** (β) and **gamma** (γ) radiation, after the first three letters of the Greek alphabet.

We now know that these radioactive emissions come from unstable nuclei. The nucleus **decays** or **disintegrates** to a more stable form, and in the process emits energetic radiation.

Radioactive material is found naturally all around us and even inside our bodies. One type of carbon found in the bodies of all living organisms, called carbon-14, is radioactive. Certain foods, such as strawberries, contain measurable traces of a radioactive form of potassium, potassium-40. Many rocks, particularly granites found in Cornwall and Aberdeen, emit a radioactive gas called radon. Other sources of such **background radiation** are:

Figure 19.2 Pierre and Marie Curie shared the Nobel Prize for Physics in 1903 with Henri Becquerel, for their extensive research on the radiation phenomena that he first discovered

- waste products from nuclear power stations
- radioactive materials used in medicine in hospitals
- cosmic rays striking the Earth from space.

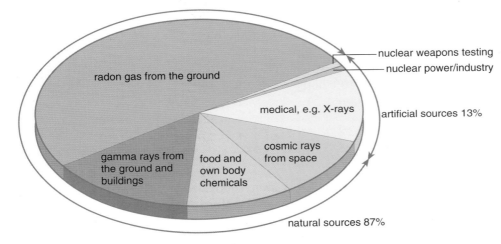

Figure 19.3 Typical sources of background radiation in the UK

Types of radiation

Table 19.1 opposite describes the nature of the three types of radiation, alpha (α), beta (β) and gamma (γ), and lists some of the properties. The **penetrating power** of the three types of radiation is illustrated in Figure 19.4.

Some experiments using radioactive sources can be done in the laboratory as teacher demonstrations, provided all safety regulations are followed. The range of beta particles in aluminium can be found using the apparatus shown in Figure 19.5. The Geiger tube detects the beta particles and the counter records the detection rate.

First the background count rate must be found and recorded. This is the count rate due to background radiation. All known sources of radiation should be removed from the laboratory, the counter attached to the Geiger tube and the reading on the counter recorded. Several such readings should be taken and an average calculated.

Table 19.1 Properties of alpha (α), beta (β) and gamma (γ) radiation

	Alpha (α)	**Beta (β)**	**Gamma (γ)**
Source	from an **unstable nucleus**		
What is it?	positively charged helium nuclei (2 protons plus 2 neutrons)	fast electrons	electromagnetic wave of high energy
Relative mass*	4	1/1840	0
Relative charge*	+2	−1	0
Range in air	2–4 cm	several metres	unlimited range, but gets weaker the further it travels
Penetrating power (what will stop it)	stopped by thin (tissue) paper	stopped by about 5 mm aluminium	thick lead can absorb much of it, but may not stop it completely

*Mass and charge in comparison with the proton

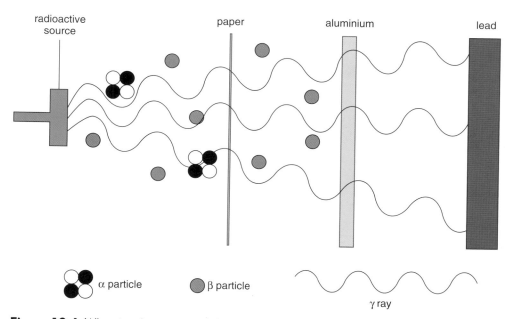

Figure 19.4 What it takes to stop (absorb) radioactive emissions

Figure 19.5 Apparatus for finding the range of beta particles in aluminium

Using tongs, the beta source should be placed a few centimetres from the Geiger tube and the count rate observed. All students should stand several metres away. Then sheets of aluminium are placed, one by one, between the source and the Geiger tube. The thicker the aluminium, the fewer the beta particles reaching the tube. To find the approximate range of beta particles in aluminium, the total thickness of aluminium between the source and the tube is measured when the count rate is reduced to the level of the background count rate.

The random nature of radioactivity

If you throw a fair dice, the chance of getting, say, a six is 1/6. But even if you throw the dice ten times, you cannot be sure of getting a six at all. It is similar with radioactivity. Alpha particles, beta particles and gamma radiation all come from the **random** decay of unstable nuclei. We cannot predict when a particular nucleus will disintegrate – we can only make predictions as to the probability (or chance) of a nucleus decaying in a particular time.

The half-life

For a particular radioactive material, a measurable quantity called the **half-life** is a useful indication of the level of radioactivity.

> **The half-life of a material, $T_{\frac{1}{2}}$, is the time taken for the radioactivity to fall by half.**

Figure 19.6 shows how the radioactivity, or **activity**, of a radioactive element falls off with time. The time for the activity to fall from a certain value to half that value is always the same – the half-life.

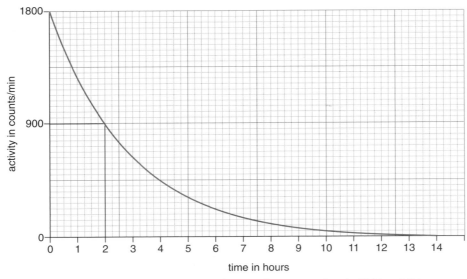

Figure 19.6 Radioactive decay curve for an element with a half-life of 2 hours

The half-lives of radioactive materials range from fractions of a second to millions of years. See Table 19.2. The half-life of any radioactive substance is fixed – we cannot do anything to increase or decrease it.

Table 19.2 Half-lives of some radioactive elements

Element	Half-life
uranium-238	4 500 000 000 years
carbon-14	5730 years
phosphorus-30	2.5 minutes
oxygen-15	2.06 minutes
barium-144	11.4 seconds
polonium-216	0.145 seconds

1   The activity of a radioactive source was measured at regular intervals.
The results are shown below.

Time in seconds	0	10	20	30	40
Activity	64	46	32	24	16

a   Plot the graph of activity (y-axis) against time (x-axis) and draw a smooth
curve through the data points.
b   Use the graph to find the time taken for the activity of the radioactive
source to fall to half of its original value.

The unit of radioactivity

The activity of a radioactive element is a measure of the rate of nuclear
disintegrations, or decays. The unit of activity is the **becquerel** (Bq). One
becquerel is equal to one disintegration per second.

ACTIVITY

**Simulate radioactive decay by throwing many 1 cm cubes, each with
one side painted red. Remove cubes falling with the red face
uppermost. Throw the remaining cubes again. The results of remaining
number of cubes and number of throws can be tabulated and plotted
on graph paper. Determine from the graph the number of throws
needed to reduce the number of cubes by 50%.**

Problems involving half-life

Problem 1
What mass of nitrogen-13 would remain if 80 g were allowed to decay for
30 minutes? Nitrogen-13 has a half-life of 10 minutes.

Solution

Mass of nitrogen-13 remaining	Time in half-lives	Time in minutes
80 g	0	0
40 g	1	10
20 g	2	20
10 g	3	30

10 g would remain after 30 minutes.

Problem 2

How long would it take for 20 g of cobalt-60 to decay to 5 g? The half-life of cobalt-60 is 5.26 years.

Solution

20 g to 10 g takes 5.26 years.
10 g to 5 g takes another 5.26 years.

Total time taken is **10.52 years**.

Problem 3

Strontium-93 takes 32 minutes to decay to 6.25% of its original mass. Calculate the value of its half-life.

Solution

% of strontium-93 remaining	Time in half-lives	Time in minutes
100	0	
50	1	
25	2	
12.5	3	
6.25	4	32

So 4 half-lives take 32 minutes.

Each half-life $= \frac{32}{4}$ minutes $=$ **8 minutes**.

Problem 4

When a radioactive material of half-life 24 hours arrives in a hospital its activity is 1000 Bq. Calculate its activity 24 hours before and 72 hours after its arrival.

Solution

Activity in Bq	Time in half-lives	Time in hours
2000	-1	-24
1000 (start from here)	0	0
500	1	24
250	2	48
125	3	72

Activity 24 hours before arrival is 2000 Bq.
Activity 72 hours after arrival is **125 Bq**.

2 A detector of radiation is placed close to a radioactive source of very long half-life. In four consecutive 10-second intervals the following numbers of counts were recorded:
100, 107, 99, 102
Why were the four counts different?

3 A certain material has a half-life of 12 minutes. What fraction of that original material would you expect still to be present an hour later?

Safety and radioactivity

All nuclear radiation is harmful and a potential cause of cancer. There is no generally accepted 'safe' level of radiation. We know that there is background radiation in the environment, which differs in level from one place to another. Radiation from laboratory/medical/industrial sources adds to this background count.

However, as we have seen in the section on half-life above, some radioactive sources decay much faster than others. In general, **the shorter the half-life, the quicker the emissions fall to an acceptable level** – 'acceptable' meaning that the source adds almost nothing to the level of the background radiation.

The following problem illustrates this general rule.

Problem

In a place where the background activity is 0.2 Bq, a radioactive source has an activity of 512 Bq and a half-life of 2 minutes. Estimate the combined activity (background plus source) after

a 8 minutes
b 32 minutes.

Why is the source activity only an estimate, rather than an exact numerical value? Comment on your answers.

Solution

The half-life is 2 minutes, so every 4 minutes the activity falls to $\frac{1}{4}$ of its previous value.

Time in s	0	4	8	12	16	20	24	28	32
Source activity in Bq	512	128	32	8	2	0.5	0.125	0.03	0.008
Combined activity of source and background in Bq	512.2	128.2	32.2	8.2	2.2	0.7	0.33	0.23	0.208

a After 8 minutes the combined activity is **32.2 Bq**.
b After 32 minutes the combined activity is **0.208 Bq**.

Source activity is only an estimate because radioactivity is a random event. Comment: After 8 minutes the combined activity (32.2 Bq) is still very much greater than background activity (0.2 Bq). After 32 minutes the combined activity (0.208 Bq) is only slightly above background.

Ionising radiation

What happens when alpha particles, beta particles and gamma waves collide with atoms as they pass through a material? The most likely collision is with one of the atom's orbiting electrons. When this occurs the electron is 'knocked out' of its orbit and removed from the atom (Figure 19.7). The atom, originally neutral, has now lost one of its negative charges (the electron), and becomes a positively charged **ion**. The process of changing a neutral atom into a positive ion is called **ionisation**. So we say that alpha particles, beta particles and gamma waves are **ionising radiations**.

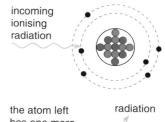
incoming ionising radiation

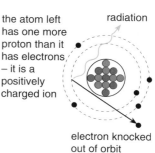
the atom left has one more proton than it has electrons – it is a positively charged ion

radiation

electron knocked out of orbit

Figure 19.7 Ionisation is the removal of an electron from an atom

Look back at Table 19.1 on page 257. Since alpha particles are the largest of the radiations emitted from a radioactive nucleus, they cause the greatest amount of ionisation in any material through which they pass. On the other hand, gamma waves pass straight through most matter causing very little ionisation. Beta particles have intermediate ionising ability – less than that of alpha particles, but greater than that of gamma waves.

Every time an alpha particle, beta particle or gamma wave causes ionisation, it loses energy. In fact alpha particles are so good at causing ionisation that they rapidly lose all their kinetic energy after travelling only a few centimetres in air. On the other hand, gamma waves have a very long range because they produce hardly any ionisation at all.

Ionisation kills

No one need get worried when a source of alpha particles is nearby. They have a range of only a few centimetres. Those that do get near us cannot get through our clothes. But suppose a person was to breathe in the dust of a material that emits alpha particles. Then the cells close to that dust are constantly being exposed to powerfully ionising alpha particles. And the ionisation produced can have two serious effects. It can:

- kill healthy cells
- damage the DNA of healthy cells, causing them to become cancerous.

These risks are posed by all ionising radiations – alpha, beta and gamma, and also X-rays – they can **kill healthy cells** and can **cause life-threatening cancers**.

Ionisation protects

Scientists quickly realised that they could put the ability of ionising radiation to kill cells to good use. If the radiation can kill healthy cells, then why not get it to kill cancer cells? This is exactly what is done in radiotherapy. **Radiotherapy** simply means using radiation to treat patients. Usually this is done using powerful X-rays, or gamma rays from a cobalt-60 radioactive source. The skill of the radiologist is to direct exactly the right dose of radiation at the tumour, killing the cancer cells while limiting the damage to the surrounding healthy cells (Figure 19.8).

Figure 19.8 Modern radiotherapy techniques allow accurate focusing of the ionising beam. This patient is being prepared for radiotherapy to destroy a brain tumour. The plastic mask holds his head in place once the beam is targeted, and also protects healthy cells from the radiation

ACTIVITY

Prepare a PowerPoint presentation showing how, and the reasons why, ionising radiation is used to treat cancer. A useful resource, which gives an introduction to what radiotherapy involves, is:

www.cancerresearchuk.org/

An example presentation can be found at:

www.northallertoncoll.org.uk/science/Salters /y11%20topics/sib/Radiotherapy.ppt

There are other applications for ionising radiations in hospitals. Most hospitals have a CSSD, a Central Sterile Supplies Department. This department arranges for the supply of sterile (germ-free) bandages, dressings, syringes, needles, delivery tubes, surgical instruments and so on. How are they sterilised? Years ago this was done using steam autoclaves, rather like large pressure cookers. Today, the most common sterilisation method is to use powerful gamma radiation. This destroys all bacteria, viruses and fungi present so that the hospital staff can be confident there is no risk of cross-infection.

Figure 19.9 Operating equipment is sterilised by gamma radiation

Extending the shelf-life of fruit and vegetables

Gamma radiation can be used to treat fresh food. By killing the bacteria and fungi on the food, the radiation helps the food to keep fresh for longer. This use is controversial, however, as many people are worried about the long-term effects on the human body of eating food that has been exposed to gamma radiation.

Figure 19.10 The strawberries on the left were exposed to gamma radiation just after they were picked

websites

http://lowdose.tricity.wsu.edu/images/Powerpoint_health.ppt
information about the health effects of radiation

www.cancerhelp.org.uk/help/default.asp?page=166
straightforward text-based material on cancer treatment using radiotherapy

www.bbc.co.uk/schools/gcsebitesize/
good for revision – follow the link to Radioactivity from Science: Physics

Questions

1 a The table below shows the particles that make up a neutral carbon atom. Copy and complete the table showing the mass, charge, number and location of the particles. Some information has already been added to the table.

Particle	Mass	Charge	Number	Location
electron		−1		
proton	1		6	in the nucleus
neutron			6	

(6 marks)

b Radon is a naturally occurring radioactive gas.
  i Explain what is meant by radioactive. *(1 mark)*
  ii Explain the danger of breathing radon gas into the lungs. *(1 mark)*
c **i** What is the range of beta radiation in aluminium? *(1 mark)*
  ii Draw a well-labelled diagram of the apparatus you would use to measure the range of beta particles in aluminium. *(3 marks)*

2 The following is part of a report on radon gas.

Radon-222 is a radioactive gas released during the natural decay of thorium and uranium, which are common, naturally occurring elements found in varying amounts in rock and soil. Radon is odourless, invisible, silent and without taste.

Radon-222 decays into radioactive elements, two of which – polonium-218 and polonium-214 – emit alpha particles, which are highly effective in damaging lung tissues. These alpha-emitting radon decay products are known to cause lung cancer in humans.

Each year in the USA exposure to indoor radon gas causes thousands of preventable lung cancer deaths. In fact, the Surgeon General has warned that radon is the second leading cause of lung cancer in the United States. Extensive evidence from studies of underground miners indicates that radon causes lung cancer in both smokers and non-smokers, although cancer is especially likely to occur in cigarette smokers. Exposure to both smoking and radon greatly enhances the risk of lung cancer.

The bar chart shows an estimate of the number of people in the USA who die every year from exposure to radon. Exact figures are not known, but it is thought that this lies in the range of 12 000 to 30 000. The numbers of deaths from other causes are taken from National Safety Council reports.

Radon does increase the risk of lung cancer, and physicians have the greatest responsibility to educate their patients about the health risk associated with radon.

Unless people become aware of the danger radon poses, they will not act. Millions of homes are estimated to have elevated radon levels.

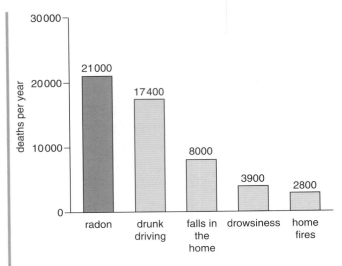

Fortunately, the solution to this problem is straightforward. Like the hazards from smoking, the health risks of radon can be reduced.

Radon levels tend to vary from day to day and from season to season. However, the quickest way to test for radon is with a short-term 'do-it-yourself' radon test kit, available by mail order. A short-term testing device remains in the home for 2 to 10 days, depending on the type of device. Long-term test devices remain in the home for more than 3 months. Afterwards both short- and long-term devices are sent to the laboratory for processing.

Radon test devices like the 'electret' ion detector contain a charged plastic disk. Alpha particles generated by the decay of radon strike the disk and reduce the charge on it. By measuring the charge reduction, the radon concentration can be calculated.

a By which one, if any, of the five senses (seeing, feeling, hearing, smell and taste) can radon gas be detected? *(1 mark)*
b How does radon mainly get into the body? *(1 mark)*
c Why are miners particularly exposed to radon gas? *(2 marks)*
d Which type of test device (long-term or short-term) is likely to give the best figure as to the amount of radon present in the home? Give a reason for your answer. *(2 marks)*
e What is the sign of the charge on the disk of a new 'electret' radon device? Give a reason for your answer. *(2 marks)*
f Suggest a reason why the author of the report showed, on the bar chart, 21 000 deaths from radon each year, when the exact number of deaths is unknown. *(1 mark)*
g In which paragraph in the passage are you told that doctors have the responsibility of educating others about the risks of cancer from radon? *(1 mark)*

CCEA GCSE Science: Single Award (Modular) Specimen Paper (Higher Tier) 2006

Chapter 20

Earth in space

By the end of this chapter you should know and understand:

➤ The names of the planets that make up our Solar System and their order of distance from the Sun

➤ That all the planets orbit the Sun in the same direction and in the same plane

➤ What is meant by the retrograde motion of Jupiter

➤ How the arguments about the geocentric model of our Solar System were resolved

➤ That there is a possibility of the Earth being struck by an asteroid

➤ That it is the gravitational pull of the Sun that keeps the planets in orbit

➤ How gravitational force varies on different planets and how this affects weight

➤ That planets have been detected orbiting other stars

➤ That stars are formed from clouds of hydrogen gas

➤ That galaxies are huge collection of stars and that our galaxy is called the Milky Way

➤ That the distances between the stars and the galaxies are enormous and are measured in light years

➤ That the galaxies are all moving away from one another

➤ The evidence for the Big Bang Theory

➤ The difficulties of space travel between the stars

The planets

The Earth is one of eight **planets** which travel around the Sun in an **elliptical** (squashed circular) path, or **orbit**. With the exception of Mercury and Venus, all of the planets have at least one moon. Other objects also orbit the Sun: these are the **comets** and the **asteroids**, and other smaller objects sometimes called **meteoroids**. All of these objects together make up the **Solar System**.

The orbits of the four inner planets are almost circular, with the Sun at the centre. The orbits of the other planets are much more elliptical (elongated, like a rugby ball). All the planets orbit the Sun **in the same plane**. Curiously, all the planets go round the Sun in the same direction, a fact which we will consider later when we look at the origin of the Solar System.

Until very recently, Pluto was considered to be the ninth planet. Its highly elliptical orbit, in a different plane from the other planets' orbits, suggests it was not formed at the same time in the same way as the other planets, and now it has been reclassified due to its very small size – no bigger than some asteroids.

Table 20.1 lists the planets, in order of their distance from the Sun, and gives some information on the planets' sizes and orbits.

Table 20.1 The planets

Planet	Planet diameter compared with Earth	Average distance of planet from Sun compared with Earth	Time to orbit the Sun compared with Earth year	Number of moons
Mercury	0.4	0.4	0.2	0
Venus	0.9	0.7	0.6	0
Earth	1	1	1	1
Mars	0.5	1.5	1.9	2
Jupiter	11.2	5.2	12.0	14
Saturn	9.4	9.5	29.0	24
Uranus	4.1	19.1	84.0	15
Neptune	3.9	30.1	165.0	3

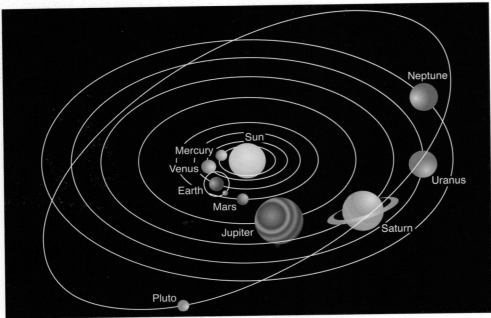

Figure 20.1 Our Solar System (not to scale). Note that Pluto is not considered to be a planet

The Sun itself is a **star**, continually producing heat and light mainly by nuclear fusion of hydrogen to form helium. We can get some idea as to the size of the Sun when we think that it is over 109 times the diameter of the Earth and contains over 99.8% of the mass of the Solar System.

Recent observations by astronomers suggest that there are many such planetary systems in the universe.

ACTIVITY

Find out more about the arguments for and against Pluto's status as a planet. What recent discovery finally made scientists decide to reclassify Pluto?

Planetary motion

Our common experience is that the Sun 'rises' in the east and 'sets' in the west. Based on such observations, Greek mathematicians like Pythagoras (around 500 BC) and Egyptian scholars like Ptolemy (around AD 120) taught that the Earth was the centre of the universe and that the other planets, the Sun and the stars all moved round the Earth. This was called the **geocentric model**. This Earth-centred model was upheld by the teachings of the Christian Church and widely believed until the 17th century.

However, careful observations of the motion of the planets puzzled some astronomers. As they looked into the sky they saw the planets move from east to west. However, some planets, in particular Jupiter and Mars, appeared at times to make strange loops as they travelled across the sky. This was called **retrograde motion**. Ptolemy explained these loops using a mathematical idea known as **epicycles**. Look carefully at Figure 20.2.

According to Ptolemy, Jupiter's orbit was the combination of its motion around point A and its motion around the Earth E. Arm EA rotates around the Earth every 12 years, but at the same time arm AJ rotates around A once a year. The position of Jupiter (J) is the result of the combined movement of EA and AJ. These spirals are called epicycles. If this was really what was happening, Jupiter would sometimes appear to loop backwards, as astronomers had observed.

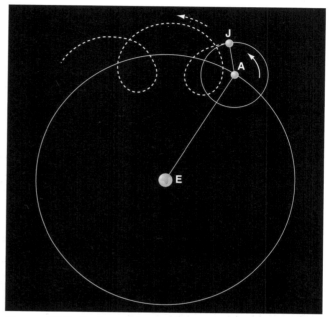

Figure 20.2 Ptolemy's epicycles

What is wrong with Ptolemy's theory? The main problem is that the theory was not based on experimental evidence, but was an attempt to justify the belief that the Earth was the centre of the universe. There was no scientific reason to believe that this strange idea was true. There were other problems that Ptolemy's theory could not explain:

- Why did the Moon show phases?
- Why did Venus sometimes look brighter than Mars, and Mars sometimes look brighter than Venus? If they orbited the Earth, would their brightness not remain constant?

All this changed when Nicolaus Copernicus put forward a revolutionary idea in the early part of the 16th century. Based on the observations of the planets, the Copernicus model placed the Sun at the centre of the Solar System, with the planets in circular orbits around it. This model, called the **heliocentric model**, put the planets in the same order as we know today to be correct.

With his model, Copernicus was able to:

- explain that the phases of the Moon occur because the Moon orbits the Earth while both orbit the Sun
- predict that Mercury and Venus should also show phases just like the Moon

● explain that since Venus and Mars both orbit the Sun, then there will be times when Earth is nearer Venus (and Venus is then brighter) and other times when Earth is nearer Mars (and Mars is then brighter).

Copernicus' greatest triumph was the explanation of retrograde motion. The apparent looping was due to the fact that Jupiter and the Earth were both in orbit about the Sun. The retrograde motion occurred because Jupiter's year was 12 times longer than that of the Earth.

In 1610, an Italian astronomer, Galileo Galilei, used a new invention, the telescope, to observe the planets. As Copernicus had predicted, he was able to observe the phases of Venus and Mercury, which, like the phases of the Moon, could not be explained by the geocentric model. And when he turned the telescope to Jupiter, he saw what he first took to be new stars. But if they were stars, their motion was very strange indeed, for they appeared to change position over just a few hours. Galileo knew he had made a mistake and realised that he was looking at some of Jupiter's many moons. This was final proof that not all objects in the sky orbited the Earth, but it took some time before everyone, including the Church, accepted the Sun-centred **heliocentric model** of planetary motion.

1 Using the information in Table 20.1, copy the table below and write in the names of the missing planets. Then write out a list of the planets in order of their distance from the Sun.

Planet	Average distance of planet from Sun compared with Earth
	5.2
Saturn	9.5
	19.1
Mars	1.5
	30.1
Earth	1
	0.4
Venus	0.7

2 What is the evidence that planets orbit the Sun?

3 Explain what is meant by retrograde motion, as applied to the planets.

Use your favourite search engine to find out about the Cassini-Huygens space probe. How long did the mission last? What did it tell us about the outer planets? Present your findings using PowerPoint.

Comets

Comets are large chunks of frozen rock covered by huge quantities of frozen water and gases. Like all objects in the Solar System, they orbit the Sun. But the orbit of a comet is much more elliptical (elongated) than that of the planets. Comets sweep in close to the Sun and then sweep out again, sometimes going beyond the planet Neptune. They can only be seen when their orbit passes close to the Sun, when solar energy causes some of the frozen gases and water to vaporise, giving the comet its spectacular, bright tail. As time passes comets lose more and more of their ice and gas each time they pass close to the Sun. Eventually, they lose their tail and it becomes increasingly difficult to see them from Earth.

One of the most famous comets was named after the English astronomer Edmund Halley. In 1682 he predicted that the comet would return in 1758. It did, and it has been seen every 76 years since. Halley's comet is next due in 2062. Unlike most comets, Halley's comet can be seen with the naked eye, without the need for binoculars or a telescope.

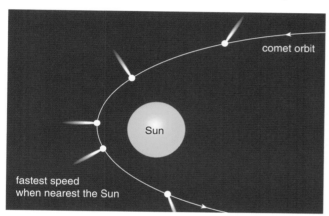

Figure 20.3 The path of a comet as it approaches the Sun

Figure 20.4 Halley's comet seen from Earth in 1986

Asteroids

Asteroids are large chunks of rock in orbit, ranging in size from about 1 km diameter to about 1000 km, and are sometimes called 'minor planets'. Most lie in the region between Mars and Jupiter (the Asteroid Belt) and all of them are much smaller than the planets. Only one (Ceres) has a diameter greater than 1000 km and only one (Vesta) is ever visible with the naked eye.

Very occasionally an asteroid is knocked out of orbit and comes close to the Earth, and there is always a chance of an Earth–asteroid collision. Large craters on the Earth's surface provide evidence of collisions in the past. Some scientists think that such a collision may have been responsible for the extinction of about 50% of the animal species on Earth, including the dinosaurs, about 65 million years ago. Such collisions are very rare, but possible at any time. The effect of a further large impact could be devastating. For that reason, the US Congress funded a team of scientists to consider how the path of an asteroid could be changed to prevent collision with the Earth. Their work led to an unmanned spacecraft landing on an asteroid in 2003. Data on the asteroid's composition was sent back by radio, in order to assess whether nuclear missiles would destroy it.

One of the closest 'near misses' was with an asteroid called 1989 FC – it flew past the Earth on 22 March 1989 at a distance of about 400 000 miles, which is only about $1\frac{1}{2}$ times further away than the Moon.

There are roughly 140 sites on the surface of the Earth where collisions with large objects from space are believed to have taken place. Not all such collisions are thought to have been with asteroids – some are thought to have been with large meteorites (the name for a meteoroid that reaches the Earth) and some are thought to have been with small comets. The effect of the weather on these impact sites has changed their appearance over time.

Figure 20.5 This crater in the Arizona desert, USA, is thought to have been formed by a meteor impact about 20 000 years ago

One example of an almost certain collision with an object from space is the 1219 metre-wide Meteor Crater in Arizona, Figure 20.5, thought to have been caused by a meteorite only 46 metres wide. Not all impacts leave deep craters. An example was the impact of a rocky object, about 30 metres in diameter, in Tunguska in Northern Siberia in 1908. It knocked down all the trees within a radius of 32 kilometres of the impact site.

What would happen if a large meteorite or asteroid hit the Earth today? Because the Earth's surface is largely sea water, it is most likely that the impact would be in the ocean. This would send a wall of sea water and steam high into our atmosphere, with possible changes to the local climate, and the subsequent tsunami (huge ocean wave) would probably cause widespread flooding and devastation. A land strike would be even more catastrophic. The impact would result in local devastation for many tens of kilometres and would send a dust cloud high into the atmosphere, reducing the amount of sunlight reaching the surface for months.

Gravitational forces in the Solar System

Gravity is the force of attraction between all objects, no matter how big or small they are. The bigger the mass of the objects, the bigger the gravity force between them. The force is only big enough to feel if one of the objects has a very large mass, such as that of a planet or a star.

The Sun is by far the biggest object in our Solar System. It is the gravitational pull of the Sun on the planets that keeps them in their orbits. In the same way, a planet's gravitational pull keeps its moons in orbit. Gravity is also the force that keeps satellites – for navigation, weather monitoring and communications – in orbit around the Earth.

Figure 20.6 The Aqua Earth observation satellite over a hurricane. The satellite monitors the water cycle and global temperature changes and will aid understanding of climate change and weather patterns

What does gravity mean on Earth? Gravity is the force that makes things fall to the surface of the Earth. **The force of gravity on any object is called its weight**.

If the weight of an object is simply the force of gravity on it, then weight must change from place to place in the universe. This is indeed what scientists have found to be so. See Table 20.2, which gives the weight of a 1 kg mass on the surface of the different planets.

When an object is far enough away from a star or a planet for there to be almost no gravitational force on it, then that object is said to be **weightless**.

Table 20.2 How weight varies on other planets

Planet	Weight in newtons of mass of 1 kg near the surface
Mercury	0.38
Venus	0.90
Earth	9.8
Mars	3.7
Jupiter	26
Saturn	12
Uranus	9.1
Neptune	12

The search for extra-terrestrial life

So far the quest for life beyond the Earth has consisted of manned spaceflights to the Moon, and unmanned probes to Mars, Venus, Jupiter and its moons, including robotic explorers on the surface of Mars. If life, similar to what we see on Earth, exists on other planets, then it will be **carbon-based** and will depend on the presence of **water** and **oxygen**. We would also expect to see the presence of **carbon dioxide**, the product of cell respiration. The atmosphere and where possible soil samples of other planets have therefore been examined for these chemicals, and a search made for any fossilised evidence that life existed in the past on the planet. So far, no life form has been observed on these missions.

Figure 20.7 A robotic explorer on the surface of Mars

However, it may be that the search has been too narrow. We may have been looking for the wrong evidence. We now know that life exists in places on Earth, where once we believed it could not. For example:

● microbes have been found in the sulphurous atmospheres of volcanoes and geysers
● deep-diving submarines have found microbes that get their energy from the heat produced by hot rocks and not from the Sun
● microbes have been found deep underground that use hydrogen for their energy source.

271

Data and images from the 1979 *Voyager* spacecraft mission to Jupiter and its neighbours showed that the surface of Europa, one of Jupiter's moons, was covered in water-ice. The later *Galileo* mission showed that Europa's ice could be between 9 and 16 kilometres thick. There is also evidence that the interior of Europa may be warm enough to melt some of this ice and maintain it as a liquid below the surface. It has also been confirmed that water-ice exists near the poles of planet Mars, and there has been speculation that there may be life beneath that ice. But so far, there is no proof that there is any life anywhere in the universe other than on Earth.

Some scientists believe that life is unlikely to be found in our Solar System and that certainly intelligent life is much more likely to be found elsewhere. Since the universe is so vast, much effort has been spent in trying to detect radio signals from intelligent life forms in space. This programme, called SETI (Search for Extra-Terrestrial Intelligence), has so far been unsuccessful.

The Goldilocks planet

Earth has sometimes been called the 'Goldilocks' planet. It is not too hot and not too cold. It is not too wet and not too dry. It gets some radiation from the Sun, but not too much. Its atmosphere contains breathable oxygen, but not too much. It has just the right conditions for intelligent life to flourish. Are there any other such planets in the universe? The answer is that we do not know. There are some questions to which science cannot yet give the answer.

However, astronomers have now observed Earth-like planets, orbiting very distant stars similar to our own and at a similar orbital distance. So perhaps there are other Goldilocks planets in the universe after all.

> **ACTIVITY**
>
> Suppose we were to find extra-terrestrial life on some distant planet. What are your arguments for and against trying to make contact? Prepare your arguments and then have a class debate.

How do stars form?

Stars begin to form when clouds of hydrogen atoms come together, because of gravity, to form a **stellar nebula**. As the clouds become more and more dense, they start to spiral inwards and the hydrogen atoms get faster and faster. Over millions of years gravity compresses the hydrogen so much that the temperature rises enormously. When the temperature reaches about 15 million °C, **nuclear fusion** reactions start. In these reactions, hydrogen nuclei join together to form helium nuclei with the release of enormous quantities of energy in the form of electromagnetic waves. At this stage the star is born – it begins to shine. The inward gravitational forces are balanced by the outward forces from nuclear fusion, keeping the star stable. This stable part of a star's life cycle usually lasts for billions (thousands of millions) of years. Our own Sun, which first began to shine about 5 billion years ago, is in this phase and is about half way through its life cycle.

The formation of our Solar System

The newborn Sun was still surrounded by its nebula, which was spread into a thin disk because the nebula was slowly spinning. Molecules within the nebula combined to form larger particles. The Sun determined what kinds of particles could exist. Close to the Sun, solar heat vaporised ices and prevented lightweight elements, like hydrogen and helium, from clumping together. This inner zone was dominated by rock and metal, which was pulled together by gravity into ever-larger bodies, called planetesimals, eventually forming the four rocky inner planets.

In the Solar System's outer region, though, it was chilly enough for ices to remain intact. They, too, merged into planetesimals, which in turn came together under gravity to form the cores of the four giant planets. Hydrogen and helium remained in this region far from the Sun. As the giant planets grew, their gravity swept up much of these leftovers, so they grew larger still. Most of the moons probably formed at the same time as their parent planets. Our Moon, though, probably formed later. One theory is that a body several times as massive as Mars collided with Earth. This collision blasted hot gas and molten rock into orbit around Earth. When this material cooled, gravity brought it together to form the Moon.

Now we can explain why the planets all travel around the Sun in the same direction and in the same orbital plane. They were all formed from the same spinning disc of matter, left over after the Sun's formation.

4 What is nuclear fusion and where does it occur in the universe?
5 Figure 20.8 shows a gas cloud far beyond the Solar System.
   a   Give another name for a gas cloud.
   b   What is the main gas within the cloud?
   c   What happens gradually to material within the cloud as time passes?
   d   What evidence for this can you see in the photo?

Figure 20.8 Visible light from a gas cloud in the constellation of Orion

Distances between stars

On looking at the night sky, it is important to remember just how very far away the stars are. The nearest star to Earth (after the Sun) is called Alpha Proximi. Light reaching Earth from this star started its journey 4.2 years ago! Physicists say the distance between Earth and Alpha Proximi is 4.2 **light years**.

So what is a light year?

A light year is the distance travelled by a beam of light in one year

Since light travels at a speed of 300 000 000 (or 3×10^8) m/s:

- in 1 minute light travels $3 \times 10^8 \times 60 = 1.8 \times 10^{10}$ m
- in 1 hour light travels $1.8 \times 10^{10} \times 60 = 1.08 \times 10^{12}$ m
- in 1 day light travels $1.08 \times 10^{12} \times 24 = 2.592 \times 10^{13}$ m
- in 1 year light travels $2.592 \times 10^{13} \times 365 = 9.46 \times 10^{15}$ m

So a light year is a staggering 9 460 000 000 000 000 metres, and since Alpha Proximi is 4.2 light years away, the distance between Earth and its nearest star is $9.46 \times 10^{15} \times 4.2$, or 3.97×10^{16} metres!

Galaxies

Our galaxy is called the **Milky Way**. It consists of about 100 000 million stars, all held together by the force of gravity. It is so huge that it takes a beam of light travelling at 300 000 000 metres per second about 100 000 years to travel from one side of it to the other. That makes the Milky Way 9.46×10^{20} metres (946 000 000 000 000 000 000 metres) across. Although it is so vast, it is only one of billions of galaxies in the universe, each of which may contain billions of stars.

The Milky Way viewed from above is a spiral-shaped galaxy with our Sun on one of the outer arms (see Figure 20.9). The nearest galaxy to us is the Andromeda galaxy. This is also a spiral galaxy.

a

position of our Sun

nucleus (centre of galaxy)

b

spiral arms

100 000 light years

Figure 20.9 The Milky Way galaxy, **a** from the side, **b** from above

6 Write the following objects in order of increasing size:
  star, planet, universe, galaxy, asteroid

The nature of the universe

When astronomers examine closely the components of the light from distant galaxies, they appear to have longer wavelengths than would be expected. Since red light has the longest wavelength in the visible spectrum, the effect is called **red shift**. The same sort of effect is obtained when a police car passes with its siren sounding. As the car approaches the sound appears to have a higher pitch than we would expect. But as soon as the car passes and travels away, the pitch falls. A falling pitch means an increasing wavelength, or red shift. Red shift is evidence that the source of the waves – light or sound – is moving away from us.

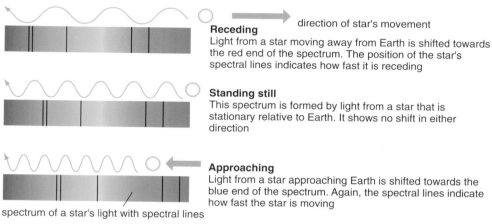

Receding
Light from a star moving away from Earth is shifted towards the red end of the spectrum. The position of the star's spectral lines indicates how fast it is receding

direction of star's movement

Standing still
This spectrum is formed by light from a star that is stationary relative to Earth. It shows no shift in either direction

Approaching
Light from a star approaching Earth is shifted towards the blue end of the spectrum. Again, the spectral lines indicate how fast the star is moving

spectrum of a star's light with spectral lines

Figure 20.10 How the motion of a star relative to Earth alters the spectrum of light from the star

The light from all observable galaxies beyond the Milky Way is red-shifted. This means that the galaxies are all moving away from the Earth.

What is more, the further a galaxy is away from the Earth, the greater is its red shift. This means that the most distant galaxies are moving away even faster than the nearer galaxies. The astronomer Edwin Hubble, after whom the Hubble Space Telescope was named, discovered this as long ago as the 1920s.

Red shift tells us that the galaxies are getting further apart. Since this is happening to all the galaxies, it means the whole universe is continually expanding. One way to picture this is to imagine a balloon being blown up. As the balloon inflates, points on its surface move further and further apart. Imagine that the points on the surface represent galaxies. As the balloon inflates, the 'galaxies' move away from each other.

ACTIVITY

Find out as much as you can about Edwin Hubble's career and discoveries.

7 a   What is 'red shift'?
  b   What does the red shift of light from distant stars tell us about neighbouring galaxies?

Figure 20.11 The universe is expanding like a growing balloon, carrying the galaxies further and further apart from one another

Continuous background radiation

Between the galaxies there is very little matter; perhaps only a single atom per cubic centimetre. If radio telescopes are directed at these areas of space, the atoms appear to give off microwave radiation. The wavelength of this radiation appears to be about the same, no matter where it occurs. Astonishingly, the wavelength corresponds to a temperature of about −270 °C, or 3 kelvin (3 K). It is therefore called the **3 K continuous background radiation**. But why is it there? To answer that question we must first ask how the universe came into being.

The origin of the universe

There are today two major scientific theories for the origin of the universe. These are the **Steady State Theory** and the **Big Bang Theory**.

Steady State Theory

The Steady State Theory suggests that **the universe had no beginning and it will never end**; it has always been in existence and it has always looked more or less as it does today. According to the theory, the universe is expanding but new matter is continually being created by processes that we do not understand. Many physicists are uncomfortable with the Steady State Theory because it suggests that our thoughts about energy conservation may not be correct. In addition, the theory provides no information as to *why* the universe is expanding, nor the origin of the 3 K continuous background radiation.

Big Bang Theory

In 1948 George Gamow, a Russian physicist, suggested that if all the galaxies are moving away from one another, then there must have been some moment in the past when they were very much closer together. Going back far enough in time, so Gamow argued, they must have come from the same place. This led to the idea that the universe originated with an enormous cosmic explosion – the **Big Bang**.

Most physicists today accept the Big Bang as the most likely explanation for the origin of the universe. Sometime around 10 to 15 billion years ago, there was an explosion, but it was not one of the conventional type that we are familiar with. Matter, energy, space and time only came into existence with the Big Bang.

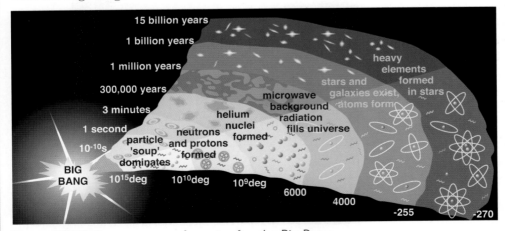

Figure 20.12 The sequence of events after the Big Bang

Not long after the Big Bang, the universe was made up of high-energy radiation and elementary particles like protons, neutrons and electrons (see Figure 20.12). After millions of years gravity started to pull this matter together into larger clumps which eventually were to form stars and galaxies. Today this process continues and astronomers can observe certain parts of the sky where new stars and galaxies are slowly being created (see Figure 20.8, page 273).

So what explanations does the Big Bang Theory offer for the expanding universe and the 3 K background radiation? The theory suggests that matter has been flying outwards ever since that first explosion. If gravity is strong enough to pull the matter back again, the universe will eventually start to get smaller and after some billions of years it may end in a **Big Crunch**. If gravity is not strong enough, the expansion will continue forever which looks more likely according to current observations. As for the 3 K background radiation, that is believed to be a distant 'echo' or remnant of the electromagnetic radiation created in the Big Bang.

> 8 What are the main differences between Steady State Theory and Big Bang Theory?

The prospect of deep space exploration

In 1969 Neil Armstrong and Buzz Aldrin made history by being the first people to step on the Moon, following a journey of about 400 000 km which took about four days. Although several manned space flights have been made to the Moon since then, there have been no manned flights to any of the planets. The USA has recently announced its intention to make a manned space flight to Mars by 2020, but at the moment manned flight to the outer planets like Jupiter or Saturn is only a dream. And beyond the planets remains, for now, strictly in the area of science fiction.

The reasons why space exploration outside the Solar System is so difficult have to do with the huge distances involved. The nearest star is about 4×10^{16} metres away. With present technology a journey of that distance would take tens of thousands of years! The problems facing such explorers would include:

- **logistics** – how to carry enough food, fuel, oxygen and water?
- **leaving Earth forever** – those setting out from Earth would know that they would certainly die in space, since the journey time would last many generations
- **cost** – space travel is very, very expensive. The Russians have placed people in Earth orbit for a few hours for a price of about 14 million dollars. What would be the cost of a flight to the stars?

websites

www.crystalinks.com/plutonews.html
links to recent news articles about the downgrading of Pluto

www.ifa.hawaii.edu/users/lin/ast110-6/ast110-04.ppt
includes an explanation of the retrograde motion of planets

www.turtletreeseed.com/legend.html
a Creation Story legend

http://phobos.physics.uiowa.edu/~kaaret/sgu_f04/L4_extrasolarplanets.ppt
information about the search for planets beyond the Solar System

www.innovations-report.com/html/reports/physics_astronomy
/report-54379.html
a report on the discovery of an Earth-like planet beyond the Solar System

www.telescope.org/btl/lc1.html
an account of the origin of stars (like our Sun) and their eventual decline

www.bbc.co.uk/schools/gcsebitesize/
follow the link to Earth and Beyond from Science: Physics

www.bbc.co.uk/science/space/origins/index.shtml
answers almost every question you might ask about the structure of the universe,
its origins and probable end; with useful links and an A–Z index

Questions

1 a The Solar System has many parts. Which items in the following list are part of our Solar System?

Sun   galaxy   moons   nebulae   asteroids
(1 mark)

b The Moon is a natural satellite of the Earth. What does this statement mean? *(1 mark)*

c State **one** use for an artificial satellite. *(1 mark)*

2 The diagram shows our Solar System. The Earth has been marked for you.

a Name the **two** planets indicated by the arrows. *(2 marks)*

b Some of the planets have moons. Explain the difference between a planet and a moon. *(1 mark)*

c Apart from our own Sun and its system of planets, scientists have evidence for the existence of other stars with a system of planets. The stars are easy to see, but the planets cannot be seen even with the most powerful telescopes. Explain why the stars are easy to see but the planets are not. *(2 marks)*

d What is meant by a **light year**? *(1 mark)*

3 Look at the table below.

Planet	Diameter in km	Gravitational pull in N/kg	Distance from the sun in km
Mercury	4678	3.7	57 910 000
Venus	12 103	9.1	108 200 000
Earth	12 756	10	149 600 000
Mars	6794	3.8	227 940 000
Jupiter	984 142	25	778 330 000

a What conclusion can you draw about the diameter of the planets and the gravitational pull? *(1 mark)*

b Jo has a mass of 70 kg on Earth. Calculate Jo's weight on the planet Mars.
You are advised to show clearly your working out. Remember to give the units with your answer. *(3 marks)*

c Which of the planets in the table above will take longest to circle the Sun? *(1 mark)*

CCEA GCSE Science: Single Award (Modular) Specimen Paper (Foundation Tier) 2006

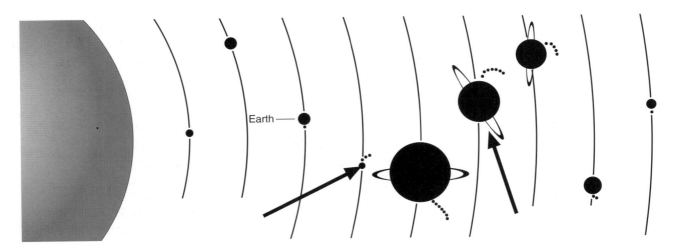

Earth

Index

Acknowledgements

The publisher is grateful to CCEA for their kind permission to reproduce past exam questions and specimen questions.

Photo credits

The following have supplied photographs or have given permission for photographs to be reproduced.

p.3 Cordelia Molloy/Science Photo Library; **p.5** *l, c* Martyn F. Chillmaid, *r* Rosenfeld/Mauritius Die Bildagentur Gmbh/photolibrary.com; **p.8** St. Mary's Hospital Medical School/Science Photo Library; **p.9** Andrew McClenaghan/Science Photo Library; **p.10** *both* Science Photo Library; **p.13** *l* PhotoStockFile/Alamy, *r* Philip Brittan/Alamy; **p.20** *t* A. Barrington Brown/Science Photo Library, *b* National Library of Medicine/Science Photo Library; **p.23** PhotoStockFile/Alamy; **p.34** Steve Gschmeissner/Science Photo Library; **p.37** Saturn Stills/Science Photo Library; **p.38** Sue Ford/Science Photo Library; **p.43** Edelmann/Science Photo Library; **p.44** *l* Janine Wiedel Photolibrary/Alamy, *r* Tom Kidd/Alamy; **p.45** *l* Tek Image/Science Photo Library, *r* Adam Hart-Davis/Science Photo Library; **p.52** *l* L. Willatt, East Anglian Regional Genetics Service/Science Photo Library, *r* CNRI/Science Photo Library; **p.53** *t* James Stevenson/Science Photo Library, *b* Richard Milner/Handout/epa/Corbis; **p.55** *r* John Mason/ardea.com, *l* Stephen Dalton/NHPA; **p.57** *l* popperfoto.com, *r* www.PurestockX.com; **p.58** akg-images; **p.68** John Durham/Science Photo Library; **p.71** *t* St. Mary's Hospital Medical School/Science Photo Library, *b* www.PurestockX.com; **p.72** Alex Macnaughton/Rex Features; **p.74** *t* Bubbles Photolibrary/Alamy, *c* Matt Cardy/Getty Images; **p.75** Science Photo Library; **p.77** George McCarthy/Corbis; **p.79** 42pix/Alamy; **p.80** Lester Lefkowitz/Corbis; **p.81** James Leynse/Corbis; **p.82** Gautam Singh/AP Photo/Empics; **p.86** *l* Rui Vieira/PA/Empics, *r* Marc Serota/Reuters/Corbis; **p.87** *lc* Terry Whittaker/Alamy, *rc* Eric Woods/OSF/photolibrary.com, *b* James Osmond/Alamy; **p.88** Wildscape/Alamy; **p.89** Michael Callan/Frank Lane Picture Agency/Corbis; **p.92** Paul Lindsay/Alamy; **p.96** *both* Martyn F. Chillmaid; **p.98** The Anthony Blake Photo Library/Alamy; **p.100** *t* imagebroker/Alamy, *b* Martyn F. Chillmaid/Photographers Direct; **p.101** *both*, **p.111**, **p.112** *both* Martyn F. Chillmaid; **p.119** *l* Robert Harding Picture Library Ltd/Alamy, *r* David Nixon/Alamy; **p.120** *tl* Chris Fairclough/Chris Fairclough Worldwide Ltd, *tr* John Lennon/Fotolibra, *bl* Tom Bean/Corbis, *br* nagelstock.com/Alamy; **p.128** Sipa Press/Rex Features; **p.129** WEDA/epa/Corbis; **p.131** Stringer/Malaysia/Reuters/Corbis; **p.135** *t* Science Photo Library, *b* Mary Evans Picture Library/Alamy; **p.136** *both* Bettmann/Corbis; **p.140** Science Photo Library; **p.143** *all* sciencephotos/Alamy; **p.151** Kaj R. Svensson/Science Photo Library; **p.155** *l* Elizabeth Whiting & Associates/Alamy, *r* Emma Lee/Life File Photographic Library Ltd; **p.159** *l* www.PurestockX.com, *r* Andrew Lambert Photography/Science Photo Library; **p.160** *l* Duomo/Corbis, *r* Larry Kasperek/NewSport/Corbis; **p.163** *t* © 2006 Smith & Nephew, *c* Pascal Goetgheluck/Science Photo Library; **p.165** Martyn F. Chillmaid/Science Photo Library; **p.166** Sheila Terry/Science Photo Library; **p.169** *l* Geoscience Features Picture Library, *r* Marble Arch Caves European Geopark; **p.170** *l* Martin Bond/Science Photo Library, *r* James Holmes/Zedcor/Science Photo Library; **p.171** Klaus Guldbrandsen/Science Photo Library; **p.178** Michael Donne/Science Photo Library; **p.180**, **p.182** Mauro Fermariello/Science Photo Library; **p.184** *l* Andrew Syred/Science Photo Library, *r* Eye of Science/Science Photo Library; **p.185** Alec Jeffreys/The Wellcome Trust; **p.187** Jim Varney/Science Photo Library; **p.192** Leslie Garland Picture Library/Alamy; **p.198** Donald Pye/Alamy; **p.200**, **p.201** Sheila Terry/Science Photo Library; **p.207** John Lennon/Fotolibra; **p.215** Phototake Inc./Alamy; **p.217** Medical-on-Line/Alamy; **p.218** Olivier Digoit/Alamy; **p.219** Steve Nichols/Alamy; **p.221** Lawrence Lawry/Science Photo Library; **p.222** David M. Martin, MD/Science Photo Library; **p.230** *l* Alex Bartel/Science Photo Library, *r* Motoring Picture Library/Alamy; **p.232** *l* Andriy Doriy/Alamy, *r* Franc Hormann/AP photo/Empics; **p.238** David Crausby/Alamy; **p.248** Martyn F. Chillmaid; **p.251** www.PurestockX.com; **p.253** *both* Neil Tingle/Action Plus; **p.256** Lebrecht Music and Arts Photo Library/Alamy; **p.262** Simon Fraser/Science Photo Library; **p.263** *t* Wellcome Photo Library, *b* Cordelia Molloy/Science Photo Library; **p.269** Royal Observatory, Edinburgh/Science Photo Library; **p.270** *t* Francois Gohier/Science Photo Library, *b* Science Photo Library; **p.271** NASA/Science Photo Library; **p.273** NASA, ESA, M. Robberto (Space Telescope Science Institute/ESA) and the Hubble Space Telescope Orion Treasury Project Team; **p.274** David A. Hardy, Futures: 50 Years in Space/Science Photo Library; **p.275** Mark Garlick/Science Photo Library

t = top, *b* = bottom, *l* = left, *c* = centre, *r* = right

Every effort has been made to contact copyright holders but if any have been inadvertently overlooked the publisher will be pleased to make the necessary arrangements at the earliest opportunity.